FAITH AND CHALLENGES
TO THE FAMILY

Contributors to this Volume

Carl A. Anderson, J.D.
Dean, John Paul II Institute for Studies
on Marriage and Family
Washington, DC

Hadley Arkes, Ph.D.
Edward Ney Professor of Jurisprudence
and American Institutions
Amherst College
Amherst, MA

**John J. Billings, M.D. and Evelyn L.
Billings, M.D.**
Founders and Leaders of the Ovulation
Method of Natural Family Planning
Melbourne, Australia

Monsignor Cormac Burke, J.C.D.
Judge of Roman Rota and Visiting
Professor of Canon Law
Holy Cross University, Rome

Allan C. Carlson, Ph.D.
President, The Rockford Institute
Rockford, IL

Msgr. Daniel N. DiNardo
Assistant Secretary for Education
Diocese of Pittsburgh
Pittsburgh, PA

Rev. Augustine DiNoia, O.P., Ph.D.
Executive Director, Secretariat for Doctrine
and Pastoral Practices
National Conference of Catholic Bishops
Washington, DC

Arthur J. Dyck, Ph.D.
Saltonstall Professor of Population Ethics
The Divinity School
Harvard University
Cambridge, MA

Jean Bethke Elshtain, Ph.D.
Centennial Professor of Political Science
and Professor of Philosophy
Vanderbilt University
Nashville, TN

Thomas Murphy Goodwin, M.D.
Assistant Professor, Division of Maternal-
Fetal Medicine
University of Southern California
Los Angeles, CA

Msgr. George P. Graham, J.C.D., Ph.D.
Pastor, St. Bernard's Church
Diocese of Rockville Centre
Levittown, NY

Sr. Margaret John Kelly, D.C., Ph.D.
Former Provincial of the Northeast
Province of the Daughters of Charity
St. John's University
Jamaica, NY

Joyce A. Little, Ph.D.
Associate Professor of Theology
University of St. Thomas
Houston, TX

Ralph Martin
President, Renewal Ministries
Ann Arbor, MI

Michael Medved
Film Critic for *The New York Post*
Co-Host "Sneak Previews," PBS-TV
Santa Monica, CA

John E. Murray, Jr., J.D., S.J.D.
President, Duquesne University
Pittsburgh, PA

Rev. Richard John Neuhaus
President, The Institute on Religion and
Public Life
New York, NY

Janet E. Smith, Ph.D.
Associate Professor of Philosophy
University of Dallas
Dallas, TX

Msgr. John G. Woolsey, M.A., M.Div.
Director, Family Life/Respect Life Office
Archdiocese of New York
New York, NY

FAITH AND CHALLENGES
TO THE FAMILY

Proceedings of the
Thirteenth Workshop for Bishops
Dallas, Texas

Russell E. Smith
Editor

The Pope John Center

© 1994 by The Pope John XXIII Medical-Ethics Research and Education Center, Braintree, Massachusetts

Library of Congress Cataloging-in-Publication Data

Workshop for Bishops of the United States and Canada (13th: 1994: Dallas, Tex.)
    Faith and challenges to the family : proceedings of the Thirteenth Workshop for Bishops, Dallas, Texas / Russell E. Smith, editor.
    p. cm.
    "The Pope John Center presented its Thirteenth Workshop for Bishops from 31 January to 4 February 1994"—Pref.
    Includes bibliographical references.
    ISBN 0-935372-38-5
    1. Family—Religious Life—Congresses. 2. Family—United States—Congresses. 3. Family—Canada—Congresses. 4. Catholic Church—United States—Membership—Congresses. 5. Catholic Church—Canada—Membership—Congresses. 6. Catholic Church—Doctrines—Congresses.
    I. Smith, Russell E. (Russell Edward) II. Pope John XXIII Medical-Moral Research and Education Center. III. Title.
BX2351.W67   1994   94-38298
261.8'3585—dc20   CIP

Contents

The Pope John Center presented its thirteenth workshop for Bishops from 31 January to 4 February, 1994, by means of a generous grant from the Knights of Columbus. The general theme for the conference was "Faith and Challenges to the Family." This Workshop, held during the "Year of the Family," focussed its attention first on the present state of the family, and then on ways in which the Church, assisted by medical and other professional leaders, may assist the family. Strong homes are essential if elemental human values are to be securely guarded. Only when homes are flourishing are the streets of the city safe, and the hopes of children and parents alike protected.

But the family faces countless challenges today. Moral revolutions have bruised the home, and social revolutions have undermined its defenses. Economic problems overwhelm families. Technological revolutions have shaken the home, in abusive uses of electronic media and in forms of medical technologies that undermine family responsibilities and ideals.

Yet, the family has not failed, and it need not fail. The Church is the bearer of "Good News" for the family, and of gifts of Christ strong enough to restore its energy.

* * *

In the keynote address on Monday evening, Father Richard John Neuhaus presented the foundational vision of what the family cries out to be, and the role that it is called to serve in this challenging time. Each of the following sessions treated important general themes which concern the family from complementary vantage points.

On Tuesday morning, the first full day of the symposium, Professor Jean Bethke Elshtain provided a factual analysis of the state of the family today: its weakness and its surprising strengths. Dr. Allan Carlson then spoke of the many sorts of causes that have tended to weaken the family in recent decades. Film critic Michael Medved then spoke of the profound ways in which the entertainment media affect the home.

The distinctive values that the family is called to serve, and the special contemporary challenges to each of these values were treated by Monsignor Cormac Burke. He addressed the inner nature of authentic marital love, and of the flawed and far less effective kinds of love that today are often called upon to replace it. Professor Janet Smith then explained why the saying "the child is the supreme gift of marriage" needs such thoughtful reflection today. Reasons why larger societies must not—as they too often seek to do—take over the rights and responsibilities of families was then explored by Professor Joyce Little.

Concerning the responsibilities of the Church toward the family, Monsignor John Woolsey spoke of the vision the Church must bring to families and the kinds of help that the Church owes to contemporary families. Ralph Martin then spoke of the profound improvements needed in marriage preparation tasks in the changed circumstances of our time. Dr. John Murray spoke of what Church leaders must do to stir Catholic physicians, lawyers and intellectuals to become once more defenders of family values.

The "break-out sessions" covered a variety of topics. Professor Hadley Arkes explored the depth of the homosexual revolution of our times, and showed how severely it affects the family. Dr. Murphy Goodwin discussed the moral, pastoral and medical problems created by the astonishing recent increases in infertility among people and the issue of "uterine isolation."

Professor Arthur Dyck spoke about how to face issues that arise when population and environmental concerns seem to confront the rights and duties of families. Doctors John and Evelyn Billings, who have done magnificent creative work in making effective natural family planning accessible, spoke of the many blessings that families everywhere can find in the pastoral care Natural Family Planning (NFP) makes possible. Sister Margaret John Kelly analyzed and gave suggestions on how to face the new problems that arise with current health care reform (or evolution).

The Workshop's finale was a discussion of *Veritatis splendor* and the *Catechism of the Catholic Church*. Father Augustine DiNoia reflected on the encyclical's "Christian anthropology." Monsignor George Graham explored a major blessing rightly hoped from the new catechism: it should provide a changed faith context, radically facilitating improvements in family education. Professor Carl Anderson traced ways in which the new catechism can assist pastoral leaders in providing more realistic education in family values, after decades of weak family education on the grass roots level. Finally, Monsignor Daniel DiNardo spoke of a practical plan for making serious systematic catechisms of all of our adults more manageable for pastoral leaders.

All in all, it was a very full and most productive week. The Pope John Center is proud to offer this collection of proceedings to all those who would wish to share in this educational process about one of the most important topics of our times. *Tolle, lege...fruere*!

* * *

Many people contributed generously to the successful execution of the 1994 Workshop for Bishops. The planning, content and hospitality necessary for an international event of this magnitude depend on many hard-working, self-sacrificing individuals who obviously love the Church very much. We are very grateful to everyone who made this Workshop such a success.

We are very grateful to the Supreme Knight, Mr. Virgil C. Dechant, and to the Knights of Columbus for their generous sponsorship of this workshop. We are also very grateful to the faculty of this year's workshop, for their patience with the many deadlines and for their scholarly competence and presentations.

Special thanks go to the Most Reverend Charles V. Grahmann, Bishop of Dallas, for his gracious hospitality. Thanks also to the seminarians of the Diocese of Dallas who are home on their "pastoral year" for serving the Masses, singing, and acting as sacristans. In this regard, special thanks go to Father Thomas Cloherty for overseeing all the liturgical arrangements. We are also very grateful to the local councils of the Knights of Columbus and the Catholic Women's Guilds of the Diocese of Dallas for their kind assistance. Thanks also to the Spanish translators—Fathers Rutilio J. del Riego, Fidel Cervantes and Rolando Fonseca from Texas, and Sister M. Nieves, P.D.D.M., from the Archdiocese of Boston.

We are also grateful to the staff of the Harvey Hotel in Dallas for their graciousness and service. A very special word of thanks goes to the Nuns of the Poor Clare Federation of Mary Immaculate, the Daughters of St. Paul and the Religious Sisters of Mercy of Alma, Michigan, who prayed for the success and for the participants of the conference. Finally, we are deeply grateful to Mrs. Jeanne Burke and Mr. Donald Powers for their indefatigable effort and diligent assistance from the beginning of this workshop's conception to the moment this book was delivered to your hands.

The Reverend Russell E. Smith, S.T.D.
President
Feast of St. Bonaventure, 1994
Boston, Massachusetts

**To my Brother Bishops
taking part in the Thirteenth Workshop organized by the
Pope John XXIII Medical-Moral Research and Education Center.**

I greet you all with affection in the Lord on the occasion of
your annual meeting devoted to reflection on significant contemporary moral issues in the light of the rich patrimony of Catholic
teaching. It is my hope that these days of prayer and study will
help you to carry out with ever greater competence the mission
you have received as shepherds and teachers of God's People in
North and Central America, the Caribbean and the Philippines.
Once again I express my gratitude to the Knights of Columbus for
their generosity, inspired by authentic ecclesial concern, in making this gathering possible.

The theme of your Workshop, "Faith and Challenges to the
Family," is especially appropriate in view of the International Year
of the Family being sponsored by the United Nations. The Church's
celebration of the Year of the Family seeks to promote among the
faithful a renewed appreciation of the family's unique place in the
divine plan of creation and redemption. God calls families to the
service of life and love. In responding to this vocation, families
provide for the personal growth and fulfillment of their members,
and contribute immeasurably to the good of society as a whole. As
the Second Vatican Council teaches, "the well-being of the indi-

vidual person and of human and Christian society is intimately connected with the healthy state of the community of marriage and the family" (*Gaudium et spes*, 47).

An unambiguous proclamation of the truth about the nature, dignity and vocation of the family must be considered an essential part of the Church's witness to the Gospel. From the first chapter of Genesis to the last pages of the Book of Revelation, the Scriptures evoke the marriage covenant as an expression of the faithful love which unites God with his people. The "great mystery" of Christ's redemptive love for the Church (Eph 5:32; cf. *Catechism of the Catholic Church*, No. 1602) is manifested in a unique and irreplaceable way by married couples whose love is made fruitful in openness to life and in generous sacrifice on behalf of their children. "As servants of Christ and stewards of the mysteries of God" (1 Cor 4:1), we must not fail in our task of upholding the dignity and true nature of the marriage bond, and of proclaiming the moral demands of authentic conjugal love and family life.

But ensuring sound teaching about the family, important as it is, is not enough. Every effort must be made to assist Christian couples to live this Sacrament with unfailing fidelity, conscious of the demands it makes and the graces it promises. In the face of a general crisis of values in society, a crisis which makes evident the need for a deep spiritual renewal in the Church herself, we Bishops must seek to respond effectively to the tragic breakdown of family life. We should not be silent out of a misguided concern not to offend; nor should the need to address certain specific questions and situations detract from the pastoral care due to the majority of families striving to live their vocation with fidelity. Certainly "pastoral charity requires that Church agencies be particularly concerned with families in difficulty, broken families, one parent families, but it also demands that the central object of the Church's pastoral attention should be the traditional stable family where education, socialization and transmission of Catholic faith and values is accomplished" (*Ad Limina Address* to a group of United States Bishops, June 8, 1993, No. 4).

As experienced pastors, you realize that there is an urgent need to encourage a positive and full presentation of the Church's authoritative teaching on human sexuality and its relationship to the transmission of life. The crisis caused in the Church by the spread of certain unacceptable tendencies in moral theology (cf. *Veritatis splendor*, 4-5) calls you to make every effort to ensure that the faithful are trained in a correct understanding of the relationship of human freedom to the demands of truth, as they seek to live in a way pleasing to God and worthy of their calling.

In catechisms and preaching and in the preparation of young couples for marriage, particular attention must be paid to the family's irreplaceable mission as the true foundation of society (cf. *Gaudium et spes*, 52). As the first school of love, the family is the place where children learn the importance of respect for the dignity of others, and the need for a generous and self-giving love which reaches out to those less fortunate. For this reason, "the family which lives this love, even though imperfectly, and opens itself generously to the rest of society, is the primary agent of a future of peace" (*Message for the 1994 World Day of Peace*, 2). In this regard, efforts to re-define the family and to grant other forms of cohabitation the same legal privileges as those accorded to the family should be clearly opposed as not corresponding to God's revealed will for the family, and consequently as harmful to the stability and well-being of society as a whole.

Dear Brothers, may the Holy Spirit sustain you as you strive, in conformity with the Lord's command (cf. Mt 28:19-20), to guide and accompany the faithful by your teaching, and to find "ever new ways of speaking with love and mercy not only to believers but to all people of good will" (*Veritatis splendor*, 3). Commending you to the prayers of Mary, Mother of the Church, I cordially impart my Apostolic Blessing as a pledge of grace and peace in Christ her Son.

From the Vatican, January 14, 1994

Joannes Paulus pp. II

Virgil C. Dechant
Supreme Knight

Your Eminences, Your Excellencies, Reverend Monsignors and Fathers, Revered Sisters, Speakers and Guests at this thirteenth Dallas Workshop:

On behalf of our more than 1.5 million members of the Order of the Knights of Columbus—plus our families—throughout the world, it is my privilege to express our warm and cordial greetings to you as we gather once again for the "Dallas Experience."

The Officers and Directors of our Order have been pleased to collaborate with the Pope John Center over the span of 12 previous Workshops, going back to the first one in 1980. Our relationship with the Center and with its Board, under the leadership of its Chairman, currently Archbishop William Levada, and its President, Father Russell Smith, has always been most cordial and beneficial to the purpose of this gathering.

As you, our shepherds and teachers, confront the various medical-moral issues that come so frequently to your desk either directly or through inquiries from the media, you may sometimes find you are in need of up-to-date and relevant information with which you can respond. With almost daily advances in science and in technology, a bishop needs all the help he can get in simply "keeping up," and this Workshop accomplishes this by making available to you the experts in these various fields. Thus the theme of this gathering, "Faith and Challenges to the Family," is most timely and beneficial. By means of this Workshop, we hope to provide you with at least some of the necessary means you need to fulfill your roles as pastors and teachers.

At the same time, this gathering also affords the opportunity for bishops of various lands and cultures to get to know one another, to form friendships and to share experiences. This is not the least of the benefits to be derived from this week.

Further it affords the Knights of Columbus yet another vehicle for expressing to our bishops, priests and deacons that we strongly affirm your mission of ministry not only to God's people in general, but to the Knights of Columbus members and families in particular. Our sponsorship is a special expression of the theme of our annual Convention last year, that the Knights of Columbus stand, first and foursquare, "In Solidarity with our Priests." We know full well that we cannot continue to prosper and to perform good works as a society of Catholic men and families without your blessing and involvement. At the same time, *you* must know that we love and appreciate you. We hope that this thought will stay in your minds during this week as the days of the Workshop unfold.

Even as the International Year of the Family begins, and even as the Church's participation in it as announced by our Holy Father takes shape, it is good that Brother Bishops can gather in union to discuss challenges to the modern day family in light of that faith which we share. May the Holy Spirit guide these deliberations and may Our Blessed Mother also look over each and every one of us.

FAITH AND CHALLENGES
TO THE FAMILY

The Reverend Richard John Neuhaus

As honored as I am by the invitation to address this assembly, it may seem presumptuous for one on whose hands the oils of ordination have hardly dried to be lecturing bishops on "Faith and Challenges to the Family"—or on anything else, for that matter. By way of excuse, I can only say that my temerity in accepting this invitation is matched by the dubious judgment of those who extended it. Whether they made a mistake will be for you to judge.

Seven years ago I published a book, *The Catholic Moment*, in which I contended that the premier responsibility for the Chris-

1

tian mission rests with the Catholic Church—the premier opportunity, and therefore responsibility, for evangelization and cultural transformation in America and the world. I am regularly asked whether I think The Catholic Moment has been missed, whether The Catholic Moment is now past. The answer is emphatically No. In part because, if the Catholic Church is what she claims to be, every moment, from Pentecost until Our Lord returns in glory, is The Catholic Moment. In part because my "reading of the signs of the times" suggests that the world is newly open to, newly hungry for, a sure word of truth and hope, a word that is most certainly possessed and most convincingly presented by the Catholic Church.

The Catholic Church offers the word of truth and hope also for the future of the family. *Familiaris consortio*, the 1981 apostolic exhortation on the family in the modern world, declares that "Humanity's passage to the future is through the family." As reiterated in this year's World Day of Peace Message, the Holy Father's argument is that to care about the human project is to care about the family. And the Church cares—lovingly, intensively, passionately—about the human project. The planners of this conference have chosen as our theme, "Faith and Challenges to the Family." The family today is challenged on many fronts. Indeed it may seem that the family is overwhelmed by challenges. Distinguished experts gathered here will be addressing economics, work, gender roles, law, education, popular culture, and how each of these poses a challenge to the family. But it all begins with, and ever comes back to, faith and challenges to the family.

The Church has a doctrine of the faith, a truth divinely inspired and humanly informed, regarding marriage and the family. With this truth she challenges the Catholic faithful and the world. Families that meet the challenge of faith are equipped to meet the many other challenges that will surely come their way. With faith, everything is possible; without it, all foundations rest upon shifting sand. In reflecting on family life and so much else, we are haunted by the question of Our Lord, "When the Son of man returns, will he find faith on earth?" (Lk 18:8). It is no secret that the Church's teaching on sexuality, marriage and family is ignored by many Catholics and is derided by the world. This is not to say that the teaching is rejected, for to be rejected it must be understood, and to be understood it must be taught. I trust you will not disagree if I say that all too frequently the Church's truth about marriage and the family is not taught—not confidently, not persistently, not winsomely, not with conviction.

It is not taught, in part, because in our culture it is frequently derided and distorted. The Archbishop of Baltimore has recently addressed with refreshing candor the ways in which the communications media are captive to a twisted version of "the Catholic story." A central component of that story is the claim that most Catholics dissent from the Church's teaching on sexuality and family life. But of course that claim is false. In order to dissent one must know what one is dissenting from. Yet that claim of the media, repeated often enough, has an intimidating and inhibiting effect upon the Catholic people, upon catechists, upon priests, and, dare I say, even upon some bishops. Repeated often enough—and it is repeated incessantly—it insinuates the suspicion that, in this vital area of human life, the effective teaching of Catholic doctrine is a losing cause, perhaps an already lost cause.

Again, I believe our situation is best described not in terms of dissent but of widespread ignorance and confusion. Admittedly, the problem is compounded by the fact that there are some who do dissent—theologians and others who are not above employing ignorance and confusion in an effort to advance their own views. One speaks of this with sorrow and hesitation, and yet speak of it we must in the context of this meeting. It is not a matter of making allegations, for those responsible could hardly be more public in identifying their views and declaring their purposes. Theirs is not the quiet and conscientious dissent of scholarly service to the Church, helping her to articulate the truth ever more fully and persuasively. Rather, it is all too often a dissent of bitter opposition and angry alienation. It is a dissent that confuses opinion research with the *sensus fidelium* and attributes magisterial authority to "the spirit of the times" as authoritatively expressed by academic guilds and the prestige media.

This is the phenomenon addressed, no doubt with a heavy heart, by the Holy Father in his recent encyclical, *Veritatis splendor*. "Dissent, in the form of carefully orchestrated protests and polemics carried on in the media, is opposed to ecclesial communion and to a correct understanding of the hierarchical constitution of the people of God." As this Pope has affirmed again and again, revealed moral doctrine is truly doctrine of the faith. What is at stake is infinitely more than intramural squabbles between liberals and conservatives, progressives and traditionalists. What is at stake is whether people understand that they are invited to the high moral drama of Christian discipleship, of living in the truth. Souls are at stake. And if we do not believe that souls are at stake, we must seriously ask ourselves what business we think we are in.

But I tell you nothing that you do not know better than I. Having mentioned the doleful realities of widespread ignorance, confusion and subversion of faith, I would now leave it behind. I leave it behind because you as the bishops of the Church well understand that it is your responsibility, in communion with Peter, to protect the right of the Catholic people to be taught the truth in its fullness and clarity. Please God, we will soon have behind us those long years of celebrity dissent, of bitter acrimony, of tediously publicized irascibility. It is time to move on; it is past time. The Church has not the time, the world has not the time, countless men and women eager to live the adventure to holiness have not the time for interminable intramural disputes that obscure the splendor of Christian truth about marriage and the family. It is time to move on.

If we have the will and the wit for it, if we have the faith for it, a world that has lost its way is waiting to receive the gift of the Church, which is the good news of the One who is the Way. A world that has come to doubt the very existence of truth waits to hear from the One who is the Truth. A world falling headlong into the culture of death looks with desperate hope to the One who said, "I am the way, and the truth, and the life" (Jn 14:6). If we have the will and the wit for it, if we have the faith for it, this is our moment in The Catholic Moment which is every moment in time, and is most certainly this moment in time.

At the edge of the Third Millennium we stand amidst the rubble of the collapsed delusions of a modernity that sought freedom and life by liberating itself from the author and end of life. Many of the best and the brightest announced the death of God; what appeared, as is now abundantly evident, is the death of man.

It is for man—for the *humanum*, for men and women in their personal dignity and vocation to community—that the Church contends. The Holy Father has tirelessly reiterated that the revelation of God in Christ is both the revelation of God to man and the revelation of man to himself. Father Avery Dulles has aptly said that the teaching of John Paul II should be described as "prophetic humanism." This is the prophetic humanism that the Church proposes to a world that is wearied and wasted by false humanisms that deny both man's nature and his transcendent glory. The Church neither can nor wants to impose this authentic humanism on the contemporary world. In the words of the encyclical *Redemptoris missio*, "The Church imposes nothing, she only proposes." But, if we understand the crisis and opportunity of our historical moment, we will propose the truth—urgently, winsomely, persuasively, persistently, "in season and out of season" (2 Tim 4:2).

I am convinced that there is reason to hope that, after the long winter of its jaded discontent, the modern world may be entering a season of greater receptivity to the truth that the Church has to offer. The great British novelist Anthony Burgess sometimes described himself as an apostate Catholic. Shortly before he died, he wrote, "My apostasy had never been perfect. I am still capable of moaning and breast-beating at my defection from, as I recognize it, the only system that makes spiritual and intellectual sense." Like the apostasy of Mr. Burgess, the apostasy of our world from Christian truth is by no means perfect. The Holy Father speaks frequently of the Third Millennium as a "springtime"—a springtime of evangelization, a springtime of ecumenism, a springtime of faith. He cannot know and we cannot know what is in store for us, but we can be prepared. We can be prepared to be surprised by a time in which thoughtful men and women will give a new hearing to the only truth that "makes spiritual and intellectual sense."

With respect to the family or anything else, one runs a risk by suggesting that the world needs to hear, whether it knows it or not, the truth that the Church has to offer. One runs the risk of, among other things, being accused of triumphalism. If the alternative to triumphalism is defeatism, we should not fear to be known as triumphalists. But the only triumph that we seek is the triumph already secured by the One who came "not to be served but to serve" (Mt 20:28). Springtime may not produce immediate results, indeed the result may seem like failure. But we know that "unless a grain of wheat falls into the earth and dies, it remains alone; but if it dies, it bears much fruit" (Jn 12:24). And there were seeds sown long ago in cultures once called Christian, seeds that may again be breaking through the earth that has for so long been hard frozen under the ice of indifference and unbelief. I take it that this is what the Holy Father means when he so earnestly calls us to the tasks of "reevangelization." To evangelize and to reevangelize—to sow anew, and to nurture to new life what is already there but has for so long been stifled and stunted by neglect and faithless distraction.

The Church is always and relentlessly the "sower who went out to sow." Some seeds fall on rocky ground and some among the thorns, but others fall on good soil and bring forth grain, some a hundredfold, some sixty, some thirty. At the end of the parable Our Lord says, "He who has ears to hear, let him hear" (Mt 13:3f.). I take it that the purpose of this gathering is that we should hear again, and understand more fully, and embrace more firmly the splendor of Christian truth regarding marriage and the family. We go out to sow that truth, knowing full well that it will frequently encounter the rocks and thorns of resistance and derision. We will sometimes be discouraged, but we have not the right to despair, and finally we have not the reason to despair. The words of the psalmist we make our own: "He that goes forth weeping, bearing the seed, shall come home rejoicing, bringing in the sheaves" (Ps 126: 5f.).

If, in anticipating the springtime of the Third Millennium, we are to sow more confidently and effectively, if our sowing is to transform the world (and we are called to nothing less than that!), we ourselves must be transformed. Permit me to suggest five transformations of pressing urgency. First, we need to cultivate the courage to be counter-cultural. Second, we need to appropriate more fully the gift of Peter among us, a gift luminously exemplified by this pontificate. Third, we need to recognize that the Church's teaching about sexuality, marriage and family has a coherent structure, it is all of a piece. Fourth, we need more fully to honor marriage as a Christian vocation. Fifth, we need an intensified commitment to what *Familiaris consortio* calls the "politics of the family." I will, however briefly and inadequately, touch on each of these five needed transformations.

Whether "in season or out of season," those who propose Christian truth must always cultivate the courage to be counter-cultural. Until Our Lord returns in glory, we will be wrestling with what it means to be in the world but not of the world. The truth that the Church proposes is for the world, but the Church will inevitably appear to be against the world when the world resists the truth about itself. The necessary posture of prophetic humanism, therefore, is one of being against the world for the world. Moreover, cultural resistance to the truth has more formidable sources. With St Paul, we never forget that "We are not contending against flesh and blood, but against the principalities, against the powers, against the world rulers of this present darkness, against the spiritual hosts of wickedness in the heavenly places" (Eph 6:12).

Especially in North America, some fear that the call to counter-cultural courage is an invitation to return to the "ghetto Catholicism" of an earlier era, but that is not the case. Sociologically speaking, immigrant Catholicism was not so much counter-cultural as subcultural. The progression is to move from subcultural striving to cultural success to counter-cultural challenge and transformation. The remarkable cultural success of American Catholics in the last half century is a tragic failure if its means that now Catholics are just like everybody else. Real success is marked by the confidence and courage to challenge the culture of which we are securely part. Or we might put it this way: there is a crucial difference between being American Catholics and being Catholic Americans. We are constantly told that there is a distinctively American way of being Catholic. The course of counter-cultural courage is to demonstrate that there is a distinctively Catholic way of being American. The Catholic Moment happens when American Catholics dare to be Catholic Americans.

An earlier generation prided itself on being accepted by American culture and we should honor what was honorable in that achievement. But surely our task is to prepare a generation that will dare to transform American culture. Catholicism is no longer a suppliant, standing hat in hand before our cultural betters. We are full participants who unhesitatingly accept our responsibility to remedy a culture that is descending into decadence and disarray. The remedy begins with each person who hears and responds to the radical call to holiness in accord with moral truth. This is the message of *Familiaris consortio*: "In a particular way the Church addresses the young, who are beginning their journey towards marriage and family life, for the purpose of presenting them with new horizons, helping them to discover the beauty and grandeur of the vocation to love and the service of life."

This is the message of *Veritatis splendor*, that we are called to nothing less than moral greatness—"to be perfect as your Father is perfect." This is the drama, this is the adventure, this is the audacious hope of Christian discipleship. We must settle for nothing less, and persuade the Catholic people to settle for nothing less. We are told that young people today, immersed as they are in hedonistic self-gratification and consumerism, are deaf to the call to moral greatness. Tell that to the hundreds of thousands of young people who gathered in Denver last August. Tell that to millions of television viewers who witnessed in Denver a spiritual explosion in response to the culture-transforming call to live in the splendor of truth.

The second needed transformation is for Catholics in America to more fully appropriate the gift of Peter among us as exemplified by this pontificate. For more than fifteen years now, we have been graced with one of the most determined and vigorous teaching pontificates in the two thousand year history of the Church. We have witnessed before our eyes the vibrant, Spirit-guided development of doctrine that John Henry Cardinal Newman celebrated as a unique strength of the Catholic Church. And yet I believe we must confess that this gift has not been truly received among us. The teaching of this pontificate, it seems to me, has hardly begun to penetrate the institutions and practices of American Catholicism. Dare I say it? In large sectors of the theological, administrative, educational, and catechetical establishments, this pontificate is viewed not as a gift but as an aberration—as a temporary interruption of the "progressive" march of intellectual and moral accommodation to the spirit of the times.

But this, too, may be changing. A younger generation is little interested in the tired ecclesiastical politics of the last quarter century, the endless wrangling of conservative vs. liberal, progressive vs. traditionalist, liberationist vs. magisterial. They want to get on with the bracing adventure of being authentically and distinctively Catholic. As for future priests, we are told that seminarians today are timorous, dull and conformist; and no doubt there are some who fit that description. There is reason to hope, however, that there are many more who are eager to be enlisted in a great cause, to serve the greatest of causes—the salvation of souls, the daring of discipleship, the anticipation of the coming of the Kingdom of God. Pray that we will be worthy of a new generation of priests who will settle for nothing less.

Moreover, we will soon have, at long last, the *Catechism of the Catholic Church*. While it is addressed specifically to bishops, I hope that every bishop will make this a motto of his ministry: A copy of the *Catholic Catechism* in every Catholic home. Catholic families cannot be faithful to the teaching of the Church if they do not know the teaching of the Church. Now at last, after a long season of uncertainty, the Catholic people will have in hand a reliable, lucid and persuasive guide for living the life to which, at their best, they intuitively aspire.

To cultivate the courage to be counter-cultural, to appropriate the gift of this pontificate, and then a third needed transformation: To recognize that the Church's teaching on sexuality, marriage and family is all of a piece. Here, although we may wish otherwise, it is necessary to speak of *Humanae vitae*. Much of the theological energy of a generation has been dissipated in rancorous dispute over that encyclical. Surely it is past time to move on. That every conjugal act should be open to the gift of new life is the consistent and emphatic teaching of at least five pontificates. Surely it is past time to acknowledge—clearly, unambiguously, and, yes, gratefully—that this is an essential part of the truth proposed by the Catholic Church. It is of a piece with all that the Church teaches about the human person in marriage and family life. That teaching is, if I may borrow a phrase, a seamless garment. A few academics may continue to fret about what is "infallible" and "irreformable," but the Catholic people cannot live well the lives to which they are called if they live with a sense of uncertainty, contingency and conditionality about the moral truth that claims their allegiance.

Maybe, people are led to think, the Church will change its position on this or that or the other thing. The "maybes" of conditionality produce conditional Catholics, and conditional Catholics are deprived of the joy of unqualified discipleship. We are not dealing here with inconvenient rules of the Church that can be changed at will. Again, *Familiaris consortio*: "The Church is in no way the author or the arbiter of this norm. In obedience to the truth which is Christ, whose image is reflected in the nature and dignity of the human person, the Church interprets the moral norm and proposes it to all people of good will, without concealing its demands of radicality and perfection." The teaching of *Humanae vitae*, especially as it is illuminated by the more comprehensive argument of *Veritatis splendor*, displays an ensemble of mutually dependent insights that constitute the structure of faith regarding sexuality, marriage and the family.

Of course there are pastoral problems, very difficult problems, in connection with this truth. The Church is infinitely patient and understanding toward those who struggle with the demands of the truth; but the Church's love is never the love that deceives by disguising the truth. The readiness to forgive is ever greater than the capacity to sin; and no one has fallen away who, having fallen, seeks the grace to rise and walk again. The People of God look more often like a bedraggled band of stumblers than a spit-and-polish company on parade, but the way of discipleship is no less splendid for that. It is the splendor of truth that calls us, and truth will not let us go.

Here, too, the teaching of the recent encyclical applies: "Commandments must not be understood as a minimum limit not to be gone beyond, but rather as a path involving a moral and spiritual journey toward perfection, at the heart of which is love." It is pitifully inadequate simply to teach that artificial contraception is wrong. In the Church's teaching, every "no" is premised upon a prior and greater "yes." All too often that "yes" has not been heard, and it has not been heard because it has not been taught. The Church's teaching is to be presented not as a prohibition but as an invitation, an invitation to what St Paul proposed as the "more excellent way" (I Cor 12:31)—the way of love. Only in the light of that more excellent way does the prohibition make sense. Only those who know what they are called to be can understand the commandments about what they are to do, and not to do.

The way of love is openness to the other, and openness to life. It is the uncompromised gift of the self to the other and, ultimately, to God. Against a widespread dualism that views the body as instrumental to the self, the way of love knows that the body is integral to the self. Against a sexuality in which women become objects for the satisfaction of desire, the way of love joins two persons in mutual respect and mutual duty, in which sacred bond respect turns to reverence and duty to delight. Against a culture in which sex is trivialized and degraded, the way of love invites eros to participate in nothing less than the drama of salvation.

There are many, also in the Church, who dismiss this way of love as an impossible ideal. Married couples beyond numbering who live this way of love tell us otherwise. They testify that it is ideal and it is possible. We need more effectively to enlist their testimony in advancing the authentic sexual revolution, which is the liberation of sexuality from bondage to fear of life and bondage to the self. This, too, may be part of the springtime that we are called to anticipate: that a world exhausted and disillusioned by the frenzied demands of disordered desire may be ready, even eager, to hear the truth about love. But ready or not, it is the truth that we are commissioned to propose.

The fourth transformation: We need more convincingly to honor marriage and family as Christian vocation. In popular teaching and piety, it seems to me, we have yet to overcome the false pitting of celibacy against marriage. We speak of "vocations" to the priestly and religious life in a way that can obscure the truth that every Christian has a radical vocation to holiness. In agreement with a venerable tradition, we may want to say that celibacy is a "superior" calling, but we must never do so in a way that suggests that married Christians have settled for the second best. For all Christians, the greatest vocation is the vocation that is truly theirs. I expect that this truth would be more convincingly communicated were the Church to raise to the altars more Christians who exem-

11

plified outstanding holiness in their vocation as mothers, fathers, husbands, and wives. The Catholic Church has a gift for eliciting and celebrating the extraordinary in the ordinary. With respect to marriage and the family, we might do that more effectively if we had more married saints, formally acknowledged as such.

For compelling reasons—reasons freshly articulated in this pontificate—celibacy will, I believe, continue to be the norm for priests of the Latin Rite. A renewed accent on marriage as a vocation to holiness is not in tension with the vocation to priestly celibacy. On the contrary, as every Catholic is challenged to discern the radical call to live in the splendor of truth, I believe that we will experience a great increase both in vocations to the priesthood and in families that will settle for nothing less than the adventure that St Paul describes as "being changed into his likeness from glory to glory" (2 Cor 3:18).

Fifth and finally, we need a renewed commitment to what *Familiaris consortio* calls "the politics of the family." Years before "pro-family policy" became a popular phrase in our political culture, the Holy Father pleaded with Catholics to become "protagonists" in "family politics." He directed our attention to the Church's "Charter of Family Rights," and urged upon us the rich doctrine of "subsidiarity" which underscores the importance of mediating structures in society and, above all, the irreplaceable role of the family. No state, no party, no academic institution, no other community of faith has proposed such a comprehensive and compelling vision of the family in the modern world. The Church's teaching is a bold proposal for family justice that can inform public thought and action on everything from welfare policy and employment practices to the right of parents to choose the education they want for their children. School choice is not a matter of preference but a matter of justice. For the poor among us, it is increasingly a matter of survival.

And, of course, family rights presuppose the most primordial of rights, the right to life. To strike at the transmission of life is to strike at the heart of the family. Here, however inadequately, the Catholic Church has already had a transformative influence on American culture. Although today, thank God, we have many allies, especially among Evangelical Protestants, for a long time Catholics stood almost alone in the witness for life. Without the Catholic Church there would be no prolife movement in America or the world today. The proponents of abortion, euthanasia, population control, and genetic engineering are right to view the Catholic Church as the chief obstacle to their ambitions. We earnestly pray that one day they may be persuaded to be our friends, but until then we wear their enmity as a badge of honor.

Let these days in Dallas make clear that we will not rest, nor will we give others rest, until every unborn child is a child protected in law and welcomed in life. We do not deceive ourselves about the encircling gloom of the culture of death. Perhaps the darkness will grow still deeper, but we will not despair. We have not the right to despair, and, finally, we have not the reason to despair. For we know that the light of life shines in the darkness "and the darkness has not overcome it" (Jn 1:5). The darkness shall never overcome it. Never. Never.

"Humanity's passage to the future is through the family." The prophetic humanism of this Pope and this Church proposes to the Catholic people and to the world how that future can be lived with moral dignity and grandeur. We do not know how this proposal will be received, but we will persist in proposing it "in season and out of season." At the edge of the Third Millennium maybe the springtime is at hand; maybe the long dark winter has just begun. We do not know. We do not need to know. God knows.

We do know this: Now is the time of our testing. And it is the time of our splendor in contending for the splendor of the truth. If we have the will and the wit for it. If we have the faith for it.

PART ONE: THE FAMILY TODAY

Chapter 2

THE FAMILY TODAY: A STATUS REPORT

Jean Bethke Elshtain, Ph.D.

In their November 17, 1993, pastoral message, "Follow the Way of Love," the Catholic Bishops reminded us that: "The family exists at the heart of all societies. It is the first and most basic community to which every person belongs. There is nothing more fundamental to our vitality as a society and as a church for, in the words of Pope John Paul II, 'the future of humanity passes by way of the family.'"[1] Agreeing as I do with the Bishops in this matter, it is my solemn duty to report that the status of the family is very troubled indeed. On *every* index of well-being, the quality of life for America's children is declining. Indeed, it must be said that American children are more and more in peril because they are less and less assured of the sustained care, support and safety that comes only with order and nurturance in their immediate environments. Children are bearing the brunt of a profound cultural shift whose negative features we are now in a position to observe and whose continuing costs will last much longer than our own lifetimes. It is my hope that renewed attention to the declining status of the family, perhaps because the evidence of wreckage is visible to even the most insouciant among us, will help to forestall further destruction.

I have been in the front lines of the family debate, as it is sometimes called, for nearly two decades. I can assure you that it has not been easy. A defense of the two-parent family and the need for children to be reared in a situation of trust, intimacy, fidelity, and security was regarded by many, and called by some, a reactionary position, retrograde with reference to possibilities for dramatic social transformation in favor of ties that are less binding. I submit to you that the experiment in loosening up the ties that bind has been tried and that it has failed. It has failed our children; it has failed our parents; and it has failed our society.

There is a high correlation between broken homes and a whole range of troubles for children. Three out of four teenage suicides occur in households where a parent has been absent. Eighty percent of adolescents in psychiatric hospitals come from broken homes. Tracking studies report that five out of six adolescents caught up in the criminal justice system come from families where a parent (usually the father) is absent. A 1988 government survey of 17,000 children found that children living apart from a biological parent are twenty to forty percent more vulnerable to sickness. Out-of-wedlock births are nearing eighty percent in some inner city neighborhoods where family disintegration is most severe. Recent reports indicate that every day in America over five hundred children, ages ten to fourteen, begin using illegal drugs and over one thousand start drinking alcohol. Among fifteen to nineteen year olds, homicide by firearms is the third leading cause of death after motor vehicle accidents and suicide. Murder is the leading cause of death for young African Americans, and those who kill them are themselves young black men. This is just one small snippet of the overall and increasingly grim picture.

Let me lift up for your consideration just one additional statistic, this from a document called the "Kids Count Data Book" issued by the Casey Foundation. What researchers learned was startling. But, before I report the dramatic data, let me suggest that these findings help to support the call for a dramatic change in the way in which we think about the family and its troubles. One view, widely held, is that poverty is the leading cause of family disintegration, breakdown and troubles for children. It has seemed to many of us for a long time that this is too simple a picture of what is going on. In fact, we have suggested that cultural transformation itself fuels poverty and other social and economic problems. Now to the figures.

Two groups were compared. In one group, the couple, a young man and woman, completed high school; got married; and waited until age twenty to have a child. In the second group, none of those things happened. The biological mother and father did not marry; neither completed high school; and a child was born before the mother was twenty years old. In the first group, with high school completion and marriage, only eight percent of the children are in poverty. In the second group, where high school was not completed and marriage was eschewed, fully 79% of these children are in poverty. What these figures suggest is that the best antipoverty program for children is a stable, intact, two-parent family. Changes in family structure over the past generation are strongly correlated with rising rates of poverty among children.

Consider another example. We have known for a long time that divorce under current laws often spells economic hardship, even disaster, for custodial parents and their minor children. A widespread "culture of divorce" does precious little to sustain couples through periods of marital turmoil. The current slight decline in the divorce rate is one small ray of hope. But what most needs attention is the post-divorce situation in child-rearing households and, perhaps even more importantly, rebuilding and reweaving the threads of community in order to encourage young people to marry before they have children.

My status report to you begins, then, with an insistence on the importance of mothers and fathers to the life of child, the church and the community. In light of the undeniable evidence of family breakdown and deinstitutionalization, especially the severing of basic parental ties, it is enormously disturbing to read and listen to those who, despite all the evidence, continue to paint a rosy picture of "change" and "readjustment" and who refuse to confront the actual situation in which America's parents and children find themselves. The decline in the well-being of America's children is directly traceable to the stresses and strains which undermine the family as an ethical entity that, in the words of a political philosopher, William Galston, "transmits or fails to transmit the beliefs and dispositions needed to support oneself and to contribute to one's community."[2]

The status of the family matters because there are a range of tasks that families undertake that cannot be delegated satisfactorily to other institutions. Stable, intact families make a vital contribution to the nurturing of communities and citizens. More and more teachers, for example, complain that they cannot do their job as teachers because frustrated, angry, lonely children "act out," behaving violently towards classmates and teachers or, alternately, are "clingy" because they lack parental guidance and comfort. This prevents children from working on reading, writing, and arithmetic. We see, once again, that family breakdown fuels other troubles.

This assessment received powerful confirmation recently as a result of a study comparing parents' and teachers' ratings of more than two thousand children from ages seven to sixteen. The study showed that emotional and behavioral problems have been increasing since the mid-1970s for American children. As *The New York Times* reported, of 118 specific problems and abilities assessed, there was a significant worsening in 45. That significant worsening was primarily in the area of behavioral problems, including withdrawal, immaturity and overdependency, inability to concentrate or being too nervous to concentrate, aggressivity, including lying, cheating, meanness to others, destroying other people's things, disobedience, temperamental outbursts and incessant demands for attention, anxiety and depression, many fears and worries, feeling unloved, nervous, sad, and depressed.

This is terrible. Dr. Thomas Achenbach, Director of the Center for Children, Youth and Families at the University of Vermont, comments, "It's not the magnitude of the changes, but the consistency that is so significant." He goes on to aver that there are "probably multiple factors behind such a widespread increase in problems." But he cites especially "less parental monitoring of what kids are doing, less time with parents because there are more single-parent families and families with both parents working, and schools are having to cope with noneducational issues, like discipline, making it harder for them to fulfill their basic mission."[3] We come back, again, to the underlying problem that fuels other difficulties, the breakdown of the family.

This enables us to see quite clearly that, although the family is the locus of private life, it is also critical to public life, to the life of community and civic associations. Here the testimony of parents and experts converges. When parents are asked to tell their own version of our current discontents, they lament the fact that it is harder to do a decent job raising children in a culture that is unfriendly to families and family attachments. A culture that mocks those who raise questions about the wisdom of celebrating single-parent households is scarcely a culture prepared to look at the Smith family in Fremont, Nebraska, and say to Betty and Bob, "Well done. Keep at it. We're with you. We are supporting you in your effort." The overwhelming majority of Americans, between 80-88%, believe that being a parent is much more difficult than it used to be. Pessimism about the decline of family values is increasing, especially among women and Hispanic and African American citizens.

While the debate of experts and advocates over the past several decades has tended to focus on how to get both parents into full-time work or to fund child care given the fact that both parents are in full-time work, the grassroots conversation revolves around cultural values. Parents express a pervasive fear that they have less time to spend in the ethical task of child-rearing and, as a result, that their children are succumbing to the values of a culture parents view as excessively individualistic and materialistic.

Let me offer one other piece of testimony, this from a taxicab ride I took recently in Washington, D.C., heading from the Capitol to National Airport. My taxi driver was a Nigerian woman who had come here with her family some eight years ago. She told me that she was hoping to return to Nigeria because American culture was destroying her family. She said to me, as I took notes in the back of the cab, "If they don't tidy that mess up, you can forget it. Where there is no family structure, kids don't have to answer to anybody. America has to tidy this up! All this lack of discipline. The kids get dumped. We can't even salvage our own kids." She went on to tell me that her thirteen-year-old son had been caught using drugs and that her eleven-year-old daughter had taunted her recently, during the course of a disagreement with her mother, "When I'm twelve years old, I'll have a baby and I'll be on my own." My taxi driver witness, shaking her head, said angrily: "The baby becomes the job, then a second baby becomes a promotion. Things now are so terrible. I'm sure all this was set up in good faith, but now everything seems to be going wrong."

The time is surely right to bring together the concerns of parents and of witnesses on the street with the evidence and analyses of experts. Both scholarly and public opinion now converge on the conclusion that our children are in trouble and, according to the National Commission on Children, those growing up in single-parent households are at greater risk than those in two-parent households for poverty, substance abuse, adolescent childbearing, criminality, suicide, mental illness, and dropping out of school. Why should this surprise us? Families teach us our first lessons in responsibility and reciprocity. Writes Ernie Cortez, Jr., head of the Texas Industrial Areas Foundation Network, in a piece on the Catholic tradition of family rights:

> Families teach the first lessons of relationships among persons, some of which are essential not only to private life but to public life as well. Within the family, one learns to act upon others and to be acted upon. It is in the family that we learn to identify ourselves with others or fail to learn to love. It is in the family that we learn to give and take with others—or fail to learn to be reciprocal. It is in the family that we learn to trust others as we depend on them or learn to distrust them. We learn to form expectations of the others and to hold

them accountable. We also learn to hold ourselves accountable. These lessons of reciprocity, trust, discipline, and self-restraint are important to the forming of relationships in public life.[4]

This family is not an isolated unit but very much a social institution, nested in a wider surround, that either helps to sustain parental commitment and accomplishments or puts negative pressure on mothers and fathers. That pressure obviously takes many forms and I have mentioned just a few. Being a parent isn't just another lifestyle choice. It is an ethical vocation of the weightiest sort. Communities, including churches, should lighten the burden and smooth the path for parents in order that the complex joys of family life might rise to the surface and in order that the undeniable burdens of family responsibility might be more openheartedly borne.

Children lost to society in increasing numbers may be a growing phenomenon but it is one we must name for what it is: a loss, a crying shame. Protecting, preserving and strengthening family autonomy and the well-being of mothers and fathers is a way of affirming our commitment to the individual and to that democratic society that best speaks to the aspirations of individuals. The rights of persons are fundamentally social. What is at stake in the family debate and our response to it, is nothing less than our capacity for human sociality.

To mutter blithe nostrums about "choice" and "independent motherhood" when our eyes should be on the fourteen-year-old crack-addicted, undereducated, pregnant girl living in a disintegrating and violent neighborhood rather than the glamorous "Murphy Brown," is both cruel and contemptuous, although in the American academy today this sometimes gets presented as the liberal thing to do or to say. It is not. It is illiberal in the extreme, if by liberal we mean generous, open-handed and not bound by prefabricated tenets. Only the most rigid of individualistic orthodoxies can celebrate single-motherhood as good for either women or children. Creating a norm out of what is a tremendous burden and, in the vast majority of cases, an unwelcome reality is a strategy of evasion, indeed, of repudiating what a preferential option for the child requires.

Taking this latter tack, we are well advised to begin with a covenanted view of marital commitment in which we all have a stake, as parents, as citizens, and, undeniably, as Christians. Given the dismal status of the family, I would hope that over the next decade in American society we could set aside sterile disputes and get down to the business of confronting the wider crisis of values. For make no mistake about it, the problem of values lies at the heart of the matter—not poverty, not crime, not the lack of day care, but values. That fuels all the other issues and all the other problems.

Let me conclude by lifting up for our consideration an ethical ethnography on interfamilial relations. Thirteen years ago, Dr. Arthur Kornhaber and Kenneth L. Woodward published a book called *Grandparents, Grandchildren.*[5] The story the authors tell is gripping, alternately tender and dismal. They point out that every time a child is born a grandparent comes into being. Their book is "about the emotional attachments between grandparents and grandchildren. More precisely, it is about the loss of these attachments and the effects of this loss on children, on older people, and, to a more limited extent, on the generation in between."[6] Children, who are astute about such matters, know that they are grandchildren. Grandparents, similarly astute, know they are grandparents. How does our society help or hinder, sustain or sever this vital connection? For in the long view of history, cutting the connection between grandparents and grandchildren is a relatively recent event. Perhaps that is progress. Perhaps it represents a salutary advance in individual freedom. Perhaps children are better off if they don't have to negotiate lots of complex, intense relationships.

Not so, claim our authors and they empty a bushel basketful of evidence on the table drawn from in depth interviews from three different groups of grandparents and grandchildren: those with close contact; those with sporadic contact; and those with no contact. These groups encompassed three hundred grandchildren/ grandparents pairings. With the sporadic and no contact grandchildren, they found a sense of "loss, deprivation, abandonment." Children in these two groups were more likely to express bitterness and cynicism about old people in general. The "no contact"

24

grandchildren were especially troubled and troubling. "All we found," the authors write, "was a wound where, the children felt, a grandparent ought to be."[7] Such children drew grandparents as shadowy figures or ugly caricatures. These children did represent a grandparent—but as a malign and wizened untrustworthy "old person." Not a happy situation.

By contrast, the grandchildren with close contact with grandparents told a variety of specific, concrete stories about their particular grandparents. They, unlike the "no contact" group, could muster a sense of a future as older people; they had some inkling of a life cycle. For the children who had known grandparents well and lost them through death, "their grandparents lived on as constant objects, fixed forever as large and compelling, almost 'heroic' figures in their minds."[8] Of course, many of these grandchildren did some complaining about a grandparent's eccentricities, but they were quite specific complaints about a quite specific individual human being, not hazy images of disgusting old people. Alas, our authors continue, the pressures of contemporary American culture encourage grandparents to sever ties with grandchildren, whether voluntarily and in the name of "not interfering" with their children's lives, or involuntarily and often bitterly when their child divorces his or her mate and the grandchildren are taken away.

Our current individualistic social contract mandates detachment. Old and young alike pay the price. This is something we must recognize and to which we must give explicit articulation. I have no time here today to tell you about the forms that recognition might take as an alternative to contemporary American individualism, but I think I can summarize it in this way, using an old Celtic saying: "We all warm ourselves on fires we did not build, we all drink from wells we did not dig." That is the recognition that familial nurturance helps to provide for children. Without such forms of recognition, we will enter the nightmarish world of Hobbes' social contract where life is nasty, brutish and short. We will enter a world of pathos captured in the words of one young boy, shuttled about from one foster care situation to another, who said to a friendly counselor who was trying to comfort him, "I am nobody's nothing."

In this society today, more American children, every day, realize they are nobody's nothing. That is where we are at, to our shame and to our peril.

Notes

1. U.S. Bishops, "Follow the Way of Love," *Origins,* (December 2, 1993) V. 23, No. 25, p. 433.

2. Cited in Jean Bethke Elshtain, "Family Matters," *Christian Century,* (July 14-21, 1993) pp. 710-711.

3. Daniel Goleman, "New Study Portrays the Young as More Troubled," *The New York Times,* (Wednesday, December 8, 1993) p. B9.

4. Cited in Elshtain, "Family Matters," p. 711.

5. Arthur Kornhaber and Kenneth L. Woodward, *Grandparents, Grandchildren,* (New York: Doubleday, 1980).

6. *Ibid.,* p. xii.

7. *Ibid.,* p. 35.

8. *Ibid.,* p. 44.

Chapter 3

WHY THINGS WENT WRONG: THE DECLINE OF THE FAMILY

Allan C. Carlson, Ph.D.

The "decline of the family"—a phrase dismissed not so long ago as a canard of the political right or as a uniquely "black problem"— now has the statistical validation which passes as the modern version of revealed truth. The bipartisan National Commission on Children concluded in its 1991 *Final Report* that the declining well-being of children in the United States could be traced to adult irresponsibility toward marriage vows and parenthood. More recently, Rutgers University sociologist David Popenoe has shown that the family in America is in serious decline in three areas:

27

—As a *demographic* reality, with family households decreasing in size and as a percentage of all households and surviving as groups for shorter times and for a shorter portion of the average life span;

—As an *institutional* presence, with the average family unit turning its last few functions (such as food preparation and early child care) over to corporate or state interests;

—And as a *cultural* force, with the claims of family life holding diminishing value relative to the claims of "the self" and of "the greater welfare."[1]

A comparative look at family decline in the United States, Canada, and Mexico shows both common themes and revealing differences. Any effort to understand "family decline," though, must logically begin with a definition of "family." The one suggested by both the anthropological record and the natural order becomes: a family is a man and a woman bonded together through a covenant of marriage to bear and rear children, to regulate sexuality, to provide mutual care, to create a small home economy of shared production and consumption, and to maintain continuity across the generations.

Particularly in the United States, popular perceptions of family strength and decline have been strongly influenced by the peculiar social record of the 1950s, the "Baby Boom" era. As we start, it becomes important to separate this mid-20th century anomaly from long term trends.

The latter reveal that the family finds a natural home in a culturally agrarian society, organized on a householding economy embracing subsistence agricultural and small-scale production. In this environment, production in the household binds each family together as a "community of work."[2] Gender roles are not in dispute, for wives stand alongside husbands as co-workers in the family enterprise. Children are welcomed into the family circle as potential co-workers, as heirs to the family enterprise, and as a source of security in illness and old age.

As late as the 1840s (and in some regions much later), the United States claimed such a social-economic structure defined by: the primacy of the household economy;[3] the sustained influence of kinship ties and ethnic and religious communities over economic life;[4] the "child-centered use of land" to perpetuate families on the soil;[5] the continuing power of intergenerational bonds, where "the line was more important than the individual and the patrimony was to be conserved for lineal reasons;"[6] and an abundance of children, with the average U.S. woman bearing seven live children, and with *half* of the U.S. population age 15 or younger.

This agrarian, householding social order also predominated in Canada until the late 19th century, with particular strength in Quebec.

But modern industrialization and the rise of the modern state worked jointly to undermine this family-centered social order, beginning in the United States. The rise of the factory, the office, and the impersonal employer severed the place of work from the home, with vast consequences. Relative to the sweep of human social history, philosopher Karl Polanyi labeled this one change "the Great Transformation."[7] In historian John Demos' words, "Family life was wrenched apart from the world of work—a veritable sea change in social history."[8] Concerning gender roles, this shift leveled the reciprocal, complementary tasks of husbands and wives in household production, and threw men and women into competition with each other in the sale of their labor. Older children, as well, could forego obedience to family and sell their labor to third parties. In short, the autonomous, cooperative family changed into a collection of competitive individuals. Infants, small children, and the infirm had no immediate prospects for individual gain; the spreading industrial system left their fate uncertain.

Judged even in secular terms, Pope Leo XIII's 1891 encyclical *Rerum Novarum* (*On the Condition of Workers*) was among the most insightful early diagnoses of this change, and the most creative blueprint for response. The encyclical rejected the wage theories of both classical liberalism and socialism, arguing instead for a third way, resting on "the natural and primeval right of marriage" and "the society of the household." Appealing to the natural law, the document concluded that the principle behind all valid employer-worker contracts was a wage payment "sufficiently large to enable the father to provide comfortably for himself, his wife, and his children."[9] Virtually alone among social observers of that era, Leo understood that a firm boundary must be built between the *authentic* "socialist" economy of families rooted in altruism, *and* the *inevitable* competitive world of corporations and states, and that *defining* and *defending* that boundary from intrusion either way was a critical moral, intellectual, and social task.

Rerum Novarum termed the payment of a living family wage to male heads-of-households a personal moral obligation, which Christian employers should fulfill. Writing for an American audience fifteen years later, Father John Ryan shifted toward *state coercion* as the means to this goal. As he explained in his book, *A Living Wage*: "The laborer has a right to a family Living Wage...because it is an essential condition of normal life." Since Nature and Reason had decreed that the family should be supported by its head, "the State has both the right and the duty to compel all employers to pay a Living Wage."[10] This implicit cession of both individual and institutional Christian responsibility to the state marked a striking departure from the older Catholic tradition that emphasized the twin powers of Church and state, each bearing its own particular duties.[11]

State authority, moreover, was a two-edged sword. Summoned to save the family, it stood also as a threat to family authority and to the family economy, with a practical interest in family decline. In the United States, the expansion of the state into hitherto private family matters also began near 1840, with Catholic families as a distinctive common target.

The "child saving" or "reform school" movement, as example, took root in New England at this time. Behind its official purposes of "preventing vice and immorality" and "saving neglected and abused children" lay another agenda: an effort by the Unitarian Yankee elite to break the hold of newly arrived Irish Catholic parents over their children, by restricting the moral and educational claims of families. So-called "child protection" laws gave birth, in turn, to the legal concept of *parens patriae*, or "the parenthood of the state," through which poor, immigrant children were commonly taken from their parents without just cause for incarceration in reform schools.[12]

The "common" or "public school" movement, as it took shape in Massachusetts under the tutelage of Horace Mann, also sought implicitly to release newly arrived Irish Catholic children from the moral influence of "parents and priests."[13]

After 1900, the modern welfare state grew only as it effectively displaced the family in fulfilling the dependency functions: namely, the care of the young, the old, the sick, and the infirm. While the social dislocations caused by industrialization were used, in the beginning, to justify the institutions of social security as a "support" to families, the process soon gained its own, perverse momentum. Indeed, the welfare state as an institution clearly held an interest in family turmoil: the more that families failed, the greater the demand for state services. As Popenoe has concluded, the *very existence* of the welfare state has compromised and weakened the institution of the family and has seriously damaged religiously-grounded volunteerism and charity as well.[14]

This joint and mutually reinforcing advance of corporate industrialism and state authority came at the expense of families, and the signs of stress were soon evident. The birth rate tumbled by two-thirds. This was a time, I might add, well before the introduction of modern contraceptive methods or widespread birth control propaganda. Nonetheless, U.S. citizens still found ways to avoid bearing children, and to reduce average family size from seven to near two children. During the same period, the U.S. divorce rate began a measurable advance, while the propensity to marry declined. In short, family decline in the U.S. actually began near 1840, and continued at an uninterrupted pace for a century.

The same developments occurred in Canada, albeit with a time lag of about forty years. As late as the 1880s, Canadian fertility was at a high, pre-Transformation level, and population growth rapid. But a process of family deterioration had set in by 1900, as the same forces affecting the U.S.—large-scale industrialization and state centralization—moved north.

In Mexico, a strikingly different pattern could be found: from independence in the early 19th century through the revolution of 1910-17 up to 1940, this nation was locked in a pattern of high fertility tied to a high mortality rate, a situation linked in turn to economic stagnation. Yet during the 1940-65 period, something quite extraordinary occurred: economic output in Mexico grew by 7.4 percent annually from the mid-1940s to the mid-1950s, and by

4.3 percent annually from the mid-1950s to the mid-1960s, figures *exceeding* the growth rates of both the U.S. and Canada. More remarkably, this sustained economic expansion was linked not only to *a decline* in mortality but also to *an increase* in fertility, with the average number of children born per woman increasing *15 percent*, to 6.7.

This decidedly different course of development rested on a far more family-supportive set of institutional developments and policy choices. First, agrarian reform after 1940 distributed nearly 10 million hectares of land to Mexican peasants. While stimulating spectacular gains in productivity and production, the program also resulted in the resettlement of the majority of the rural population subsistence farms, where the family was the unit of both production and consumption, and where the natural family economy thrived. Extended rural families also served as the base from which individuals were sent out in search of temporary employment in urban centers or in the United States (through the *bracero* program), meaning that economic mobility could be *better achieved* through larger families.[15]

Second, even in the cities, economic growth occurred in a context of positive family integration. As two development economists have explained this phenomena: "foremost was the continuing importance of the family as a unit of production and consumption. The family served as a base from which to pool the fortunes of several potential earners seeking temporary, low-wage jobs."[16] At the same time, much of the new urban economic activity occurred in small firms that were family owned or operated. Job allocation at large firms also gave preference to family ties.

Third, Mexican public policy was unusually supportive. The General Law of Population, adopted in 1947, contained measures to promote marriage and fertility. This pronatalism drew further reinforcement from health regulations prohibiting the sale and use of contraceptives and a criminal code banning abortion.

Under this family-centered economic and political regime, the Mexican population climbed from 19.7 million in 1940 to 48.3 million in 1970, a 150 percent increase in the context of: a *growing* agrarian sector; an *expanding*, family-oriented urban-industrial complex; a *rising* per-capita income; a family-centered system of dependency and security; a *stable currency*; high tariffs; and *low levels* of public debt and foreign borrowing. In many respects, Mexico in this quarter century had found a reasonably successful "third way" of economic organization, avoiding the anti-family extremes of both statist socialism and centralized capitalism.

In the United States, meanwhile, the century-old unraveling of family life also came to a temporary end, with a startling shift in all the indicators during the 1940-60 period:

—the marriage rate *climbed* by 40 percent between 1940 and 1946, and remained high another half-dozen years;

—the divorce rate *fell* by over 50 percent between 1946 and 1960;

—the birth rate *surged* 60 percent, while the average completed family size rose from 2.3 children in 1940 to nearly 4 children in 1957.

What caused this dramatic break in U.S. social history, where the negative family trends of a century's duration reversed and the unique "Fifties family" emerged in their stead?

The first factor I would cite was *the militarization of society*. It was the permanent military mobilization of the Cold War, not World War II, that helped to change America. Instead of demobilization after victory in 1945, as had happened after all other U.S. wars, the U.S. sustained a large peacetime standing military force throughout the 1950s and early '60s, an unprecedented development. For a majority of American males, military service became a common experience, and the conformity and obedience learned there seems to have passed over into conformity in the civilian domain, as so-called "organization men" settled into family life.[17]

Another factor was *the renewal of "familistic" religion*. The "fertility rise" in the late 1940s was largely the consequence of new marriages and a "catching up" on babies deferred by the war. But something else occurred in the period after 1950: a deliberate return of *large families* of four or more children. This was particularly true among American Catholics. In 1953, only 10 percent of Catholic adults under age 40 reported having 4 or more children, virtually identical to the 9 percent for U.S. Protestants. By 1958, the Protestant figure was still 9 percent, but the Catholic figure had more than doubled, to 22 percent. More amazingly, these new large families defied a reputed law of sociology: they were concentrated among the *better* educated, with the greatest increase among Catholic women with college degrees. The fertility increase among Catholics also was positively associated with weekly attendance at Mass. In short, it could be fair to label this *real* U.S. "Baby Boom" a "Catholic phenomenon."[18]

Also sustaining the "Fifties family" was *a strengthened "family wage" culture*. Since the 1840s, as noted before, the labor unions, progressive reformers, and Catholic theorists had sought to construct a "family wage" economy, delivering a wage to male heads-of-households that would, by itself, sustain a family. Their proudest achievement was the liberation of married women from toil in the factories, so that they might care for the home and children and so *prevent* the full industrialization of human life. To be sure, such a system did rest on intentional job and wage discrimination against women: the accepted argument was that women workers deserved only an "individual" wage, since they usually had no dependents or worked only to supplement a husband's wage.

However, U.S. wartime regulations in 1942 ended direct wage discrimination against women: Equal pay for equal work was basically achieved by 1945. But for another 25 years, "job segregation by gender" more than compensated for this. Women workers crowded into "women's jobs" that invariably paid less than "men's jobs," and the so-called "wage gap" between men and women actually grew.[19] As Nobel-prize winning economist Gary Becker has shown, this sort of change should be associated with more marriages and more births, which is just what occurred.

Tax reforms in 1944 and 1948 also created a strongly pro-family U.S. tax code. While marginal tax rates were high, the personal exemption was set at $600 per person, roughly 18% of median household income. In effect, the progressivity of the Federal income tax was being offset by family size. Congress also introduced "income splitting" in 1948, giving a strong incentive to marriage and placing a real financial penalty on divorce.[20]

Meanwhile, *housing subsidies* for families grew dramatically. Tax benefits included the exemption of both imputed rent and mortgage interest from taxation. Subsidized VA and FHA loans were restricted by custom and regulation almost exclusively to married-couple families.

Intellectuals lent their support to the "Fifties family," as well. Harvard University's Talcott Parsons, the era's most influential sociologist, celebrated the "upgraded" family system of the 1950s, which he called the "companionate family," focused on the "personality adjustment" of adults in the suburbs.[21] In the field of psychology, John Bowlby set the tone by stressing the importance of a full-time mother for children, particularly infants.[22] And the discipline of Home Economics reached the peak of its influence, in the effort to give content to the title, "household engineer."[23]

Finally, this family system generally enjoyed *popular reinforcement*, in film and television, and in mass magazines such as *Life*, *The Saturday Evening Post*, and *Ladies Home Journal*.

In Canada, related external developments—supplemented by the creation of a universal child allowance—did *not* produce exactly similar results. For example, the fall in the overall Canadian birthrate did *not* reverse in the 1950s: it simply held steady for about ten years, before continuing its downward course. Meanwhile, the fertility of Catholics in Quebec actually fell. By 1962, Quebec's average completed family size was 3.6 children, *lower* than that of all Canada (3.8) or even of Anglo-Protestant Ontario (3.7).[24] These developments in Canada point to the peculiarity of the U.S. "Baby Boom" experience, and its linkage to special circumstances not capable of reproduction in other times and places.

Indeed, the critical point here is that *the reorganized U.S. family of the 1950s—whether* in the sociologists' image of "an organization man" married to "a household engineer" in a "companionate marriage" focused on "personality adjustment" in the suburbs *or* in the *alternate* image of the modern large Catholic family—was a special, and partially successful effort to restore family living in a modern, industrial environment. But it was also *fragile* and *time dependent*, resting on an unusual ideological mix that cannot be recreated. Indeed, virtually all of the forces behind the restored U.S. family *collapsed* in *the 1960s*, and what we now call the "traditional family" dissolved, like a sand castle caught in a rising tide.

Statistics from the Sixties and early Seventies tell this tale:

— The marriage rate for women, ages 20-24, fell a stunning 55 percent;

— the divorce rate soared by 125 percent;

— meanwhile, the U.S. birth rate tumbled 46 percent;

— even among those births which still occurred, a steadily rising proportion were "out-of-wedlock" by 1993, over 30 percent.

What lay behind this rapid collapse of the *"traditional family" of the 1950s*? (or, viewed another way, this return *with a vengeance* of the long term trends?):

To begin with, the conformist America, rooted in a patriotic militarization of society, was a casualty on the rice paddies of Vietnam.

More importantly, Christianity failed in its family-sustaining tasks. Not only did sermons on "chastity" and "fidelity" disappear from Protestant pulpits, but "Mainline" Protestant leadership also went on the attack, with a National Council of Churches panel in 1961 labelling marriage an "idolatry" and embracing the "sexual modernist" agenda of opposition to population growth, readily available abortion, and the promotion of contraception.[25] The Roman Catholic laity, meanwhile, grew disoriented after Vatican II, opening fissures on family and sexual issues that have still to be closed. Given the widely publicized divisions among theologians over sexual issues, it appears that the laity simply followed the easiest of several disputed paths of obedience.[26] In their detailed study of Catholic reproductive behavior in the state of Rhode Island, demographers Leon Bouvier and S. L. N. Rao have traced the collapse of the unique "Catholic Fertility" to the years between 1967 and 1973. Average *expected* family size among Catholics fell from 3.3 to 2.8 children in that short period. Among Catholic women with some college education, the decline was even more dramatic: from 3.7 to 2.7 children. Moreover, frequency of attendance at Mass no longer proved to be related to fertility. Even the large family ideal vanished. In 1967, 28 percent of "devout" Rhode Island Catholics planned to have five or more children; by 1971, less than 7 percent did.[27]

For a time, American Mormons—or Latter-Day-Saints— seemed to be an exception here. While fertility tumbled elsewhere

36

in the U.S. during the "baby bust" of 1965-80, the birth rate actually *rose* in Mormon-dominated Utah, along with average completed family size. Doctrinal constancy relative to procreation and the desirability of large families appears to have been the cause of this divergence from the U.S. norm. However, after 1980, Mormon fertility began to fall, a shift apparently linked to the flow of wives and mothers into the paid labor force. Large families could no longer be sustained on one income, while the two-career family could scarcely accommodate a large number of children.[28]

Public policy changes further eroded the "Fifties family." The addition, as an afterthought, of the word "sex" to Title VII of the Civil Rights Act of 1964, became by 1970 the chief tool in eliminating job segregation by gender, so ending the nation's informal "family wage" system.[29] Viewed philosophically, this development marked the nearly complete victory of liberal feminists, who emphasized the radical *equality* of men and women, over the social feminists, who emphasized women's *distinctions* and unique gifts.

From the Tax Reform Act of 1963 through the Tax Reform Act of 1986, Congress and the Presidency dismantled the pro-family/pro-marriage tax code created in the late 1940s, sharply increasing the relative tax burden of married-couple families with children. Government welfare programs, in effect, also transferred income from families based on marriage to families created through "out-of-wedlock births." Meanwhile, regulatory changes stripped federal housing subsidies of their pro-marriage/pro-family biases, in favor of "non-discrimination." By the early 1980s, there was even evidence suggesting that Federal housing subsidies now *encouraged* divorce and discouraged children.[30]

A legal revolution also commenced in the U.S. Courts, where the "rights" of individuals triumphed almost completely over duties toward family and community, a change summarized by labels such as "no fault divorce," "children's rights," and "abortion on demand."

During the 1960s, the leading intellectuals turned on the suburban "companionate" family, labelling it "narrow, distorted," even "fascist." As fear of global overpopulation increased, U.S. political leaders mobilized support for restrictions on fertility. The 1972 Presidential Commission on Population Growth and the American

Future, in effect, declared war on the U.S. "three child family," with a tacit anti-Catholic undertone.[31]

Finally, television began to explore new avenues of comedy, starting with the widowed father of "My Three Sons," quickly reaching complex cohabitation in "Three's Company," moving to "Murphy Brown," and then well beyond. It is now conventional for the U.S. networks to depict girls in their early teens with the sort of carnal knowledge once confined to prostitutes.

Similar developments affected Canada, this time with the *same* results: mounting family instability; fewer marriages and more divorces; dramatically fewer children; and rising levels of social disorder.[32] Signs of decline were particularly sharp in Quebec, where, according to one study, "the influence of the Catholic church declined drastically and strict adherence to Catholic prescriptions was no longer the norm." At the same time, the structure of French Canadian education shifted from "a traditionally classical one" to "a professionally oriented one," a change directly linked to family decline.[33]

In Mexico, meanwhile, the political class brought an arbitrary end to that nation's unique family-centered economic order, leaving unresolved the question of whether it could have continued. Starting in the late 1960s, the government sharply cut back land distribution to family farmers, and restructured land sales, subsidies, and regulations in favor of industrialized farms. Under pressure from the World Bank and other external authorities, the Mexican government rejiggled incentives elsewhere in favor of large, multinational corporations. As a result, "small, family-based enterprises lost ground to the extending reach of large modern businesses."[34] Again under internationalist pressures, a Constitutional amendment and revisions of Mexico's Law of Population took effect in 1973. They aimed at limiting population growth through state birth control propaganda and expanded contraceptive usage. The construction of thousands of state health clinics proved to be the Mexican government's principle weapon in this quasi-war against rural fertility. Sterilization emerged by 1982 as the leading form of Mexican contraception, with 70 percent of sterilizations being performed in state clinics or hospitals. At the same time, authorities extended government old-age pensions to rural communities, consciously aware that this action would reduce "the extended-family, multigenerational character of the household unit:" and so "encourage fragmentation of the extended family."[35]

The results of these changes were dramatic. The nation's crude birth rate tumbled from 46 (per 1000) in 1970 to 33 in 1981 and 29 in 1988. The proportion of married Mexican women using contraception climbed from 29 percent in 1976 to 48 percent a mere six years later. Evidence also showed that the introduction of state old-age pensions in rural Mexico had "a significant negative effect on fertility."[36] Massive permanent emigration to the United States began in the late 1960s, further disrupting extended family bonds. In the end, Mexico followed the lead of the United States and Canada in favoring the expansion of the international corporate sector and the state, at the expense of a family-based economy, community and national. In a sense, the recent ratification of the NAFTA Treaty sealed this common rejection of a family-centered "third way" on the North American continent.

What, then, are the common lessons from these tales?

The first is that the family unit can never be "at home" in an individualist, industrialized society. Tension between the "corporate state" and the "family state" will always exist. As G. K. Chesterton put the matter, earlier in this century: "From its first days in the forest (the family) had to fight against wild monsters; and so it is now fighting against these wild machines. It only managed to survive then, and it will only manage to survive now, by a strong internal sanctity."[37]

The second lesson is that governmental policy, particularly through differential taxation, can have a positive influence on family living. More common, though, are efforts by the "abstract" state to suppress its principal rival, the family, and the negative consequences—unintended or not—of state intervention to "save the family."

The third lesson is that religious and cultural structures are the most effective tools in crafting "shelter" for family living in a competitive, industrial sea. In its adoration of a "Holy Family" of child, mother, and father, Christianity offers a unique power and meaning to the human family of father, mother, and child. Religious devotion, however, cannot serve as a substitute economy.

The family's survival depends as well on a rightly ordered economic sphere, a "third way" where the autonomous family unit is protected from the misapplication of both market-driven individualism and coercive statist collectivism.

The fourth lesson is that a "third way" in a modern, progressive environment is possible. The Mexican record between 1940 and 1965 suggests that a family-centered system resting on agrarianism, small-scale enterprise, private forms of security, and an openness to children, can be successfully reconciled with a market system based on free exchange and real per-capita economic growth. On a much more limited scale, the successful expansion of the Amish community in the United States (from 5000 members in 1900 to 150,000 members in 1990) and of Hutterite communities in the U.S., Canada, and Mexico offers a similar lesson: we are not the captives of blind economic forces; we do have real *alternatives* to the centralized "corporate state" that are compatible with liberty and family life.

In this disordered time, it falls to the larger religious bodies to take up the task of rebuilding family-centered communities, where the natural human economy can operate again. Means include: parish-level support for family-scale enterprises; the creation of Christian communities linking faith, work, and residence; new emphasis on defending and expanding Christian rural life; and a recommitment by councils of Christian employers to their personal, moral obligation to pay a living family wage.

Relative to individuals, lay men and women are both called home to rebuild families with an inner sanctity, to relearn the authentic meanings of the ancient words *husbandry* and *housewifery*, and to exercise the natural family functions of education, the care of the weak, charity, and a common economic life.

Notes

1. *Beyond Rhetoric: A New American Agenda for Children and Families. The Final Report of the National Commission on Children*, (Washington, DC: U.S. Government Printing Office, 1991); and David Popenoe, "American Family Decline, 1960-1990: A Review and Appraisal," *Journal of Marriage and Family* 55 (August 1993): 527-55.

2. John Demos, *Past, Present, and Personal: The Family and the Life Course in American History*, (New York: Oxford University Press, 1986), p. 28.

3. See James A. Henretta, "Families and Farms: *Mentalite* in Pre-Industrial America," *William and Mary Quarterly*, 35 (Jan. 1978): 9-30.

4. As example, see: Daniel Snydacker, "Kinship and Community in Rural Pennsylvania," *Journal of Interdisciplinary History*, 13 (Summer 1982): 41-61.

5. Philip J. Greven, Jr., *Four Generations: Population, Land and Family and Family in Colonial Andover, Massachusetts*, (Ithaca, NY: Cornell University Press, 1970), p. 251; and Barry Levy, "'Tender Plants'" Quaker Farmers and Children in the Delaware Valley, 1681-1735," *Journal of Family History*, 3 (Summer 1978): 116-29.

6. Henretta, "Families and Farms," pp. 26, 30.

7. Karl Polanyi, *The Great Transformation*, (Boston: Beacon Press, 1944).

8. Demos, *Past, Present and Personal*, p. 32.

9. Pope Leo XIII, *Rerum Novarum*; in *Two Basic Social Encyclicals*, (Washington, DC: The Catholic University of America Press, 1943), pp. 15, 55-59.

10. John A Ryan, S.T.D., *A Living Wage: Its Ethical and Economic Aspects*, (New York: MacMillan, 1910); and Ryan, *Distributive Justice: The Right and Wrong of our Present Distribution of Wealth*, (New York: MacMillan, 1916), pp. 374-76.

11. See Thomas Molnar, *Twin Powers: Politics and the Sacred*, (Grand Rapids: William B. Eerdman's, 1988).

12. Anthony Platt, *The Child Savers: The Invention of Delinquency*, (Chicago: University of Chicago Press, 1969), pp. 45-74.

13. As Princeton University demographer Normal Ryder has described the process, in more universal terms: Mass state education has served as modern society's agent in freeing individuals from obligations to family and faith. "Education of the junior generation is a subversive influence.... Political organizations, like economic organizations, demand loyalty and attempt to neutralize family particularism. There is a struggle between the family and the State for the minds of the young," where the state school serves as "the chief instrument for teaching citizenship, in a direct appeal to the children over the heads of their parents." (Norman Ryder, "Fertility and Family Structure," *Population Bulletin of the United Nations* 15 (1983): 20-32.)

14. David Popenoe, *Disburbing the Nest: Family Change and Decline in Modern Societies*, (New York: Aldine de Gruyter, 1988), pp 205-06, 221, 238-41.

15. Francisco Alba and Joseph E. Potter, "Population and Development in Mexico Since 1940: An Interpretation," *Population and Development Review* 12 (March 1986): 49-51, 56.

16. Alba and Potter, "Population and Development in Mexico Since 1940," p. 57.

17. See: Walt W. Rostow, "The National Style," in *The American Style: Essays in Value and Performance*, ed. Elting E. Morrison (New York: Harper Collins, 1958), pp. 246-313.

18. William D. Mosher, David P. Johnson, and Marjorie C. Horn, "Religion and Fertility in the United States: The Importance of Marriage Patterns and Hispanic Origin," *Demography* 23 (Aug. 1986): 367-69; Judith Blake, "Catholicism and Fertility: On Attitudes of Young Americans," *Population and Development Review* 10 (June 1984): 39-40; Gerhard Lenski, *The Religious Factor: A*

Sociologist's Inquiry, (New York: Doubleday, 1961), pp. 203, 215-18; and Lincoln H. Day, "Natality and Ethnocentrism: Some Relationships Suggested by an Analysis of Catholic-Protestant Differentials," *Population Studies* 22 (1968): 27-30.

19. In 1939, the median woman's wage was 60 percent of a man's; by 1966, only 53 percent. See: Allan Carlson, *From Cottage to Work Station: The Family's Search for Social Harmony in the Industrial Age*, (San Francisco: Ignatius, 1993), pp. 51-56.

20. See: Allan Carlson, "A Pro-Family Income Tax," *The Public Interest* 94 (Winter 1989): 69-76.

21. Talcott Parsons, "The Normal American Family," in *Man and Civilization: The Family's Search for Survival*, ed. Seymour M. Farber (New York: McGraw Hill, 1965), pp. 31-49; and Parsons, *Social Structure and Personality*, (New York: The Free Press of Glencoe, 1964).

22. John Bowlby, *Maternal Care and Mental Health*, (New York: Schocken Books, 1950).

23. Carlson, *From Cottage to Work Station*, pp. 139-57.

24. Larry H. Long, "Fertility Patterns Among Religious Groups in Canada," *Demography* 7 (1970): 139-42; Thomas K. Burck, "The Fertility of North American Catholics: A Comparative Overview," *Demography* 3 (1966): 174-87; and Jacques Legare, "Demographic Highlights of Fertility Decline in Canadian Marriage Cohorts," *Canadian Review of Sociology and Anthropology* 11 (1974): 287-307.

25. See, in particular: Elizabeth Stell Genne and William Henry Genne, eds., *Foundations for Christian Family Policy: The Proceedings of the North American Conference on Church and Family, April 30 May 5, 1961*, (New York: National Council of The Churches of Christ in the U.S.A., 1961).

26. See: Charles F. Westoff and Elsie T. Jones, "The End of 'Catholic Fertility,'" *Demograpy* 16 (May 1979): 290-11; and Gerhard Lenski, "The Religious Factor in Detroit: Revisited," *American Sociological Review* 36 (1971): 48-50.

27. Leon Bouvier and S. L. N. Rao, *Socio-Religious Factors in Fertility Decline*, (Cambridge, MA: Ballinger, 1975), pp. 1-4, 84-91, 156-58; Charles Westoff and Larry Bumpass, "The Revolution in U.S. Catholic Birth Control Practices," *Family Planning Perspectives* 9 (Sept.-Oct. 1977): 203-07.

28. James E. Smith, "A Familistic Religion in a Modern Society," in *Contemporary Marriage: Comparative Perspectives and a Changing Institution*, ed. Kingsley Davis (New York: Russell Sage Foundation, 1985), pp. 276-96; and Tim Heaton and Sadra Calkins, "Family Size and Contraceptive Use Among Mormons, 1965-75," *Review of Religious Research* 25 (Dec. 1983): 102-13.

29. Andrea Beller, "Title VII and the Male/Female Earnings Gap: An Economic Analysis," reprint 297 (Madison: Institute for Research on Poverty Research Series, University of Wisconsin, 1979).

30. George Sternlieb and James W. Hughes, *America's Housing: Prospects and Problems*, (New Brunswick, NJ: Center for Urban Policy Research—Rutgers University, 1980), pp. 58-66.

31. See: *Population Growth and the American Future: The Report of the Commission on Population Growth and the American Future*, (Washington, DC: U.S. Government Printing Office, 1972), pp. 12-15, 98, 103-04.

32. See: William Gairdner, *The War Against the Family*, (Toronto: Stoddart Publishing Co., 1992).

33. From: Natalie Kryiazis and J. Henripin, "Women's Employment and Fertility in Quebec," *Population Studies* 36 (Nov. 1982): 432; J. Henripin and E. Lapierre-Adamcyk, *La Fin de la Revanche des Berceaux: Qu'en Pensent les Quebecoises*, (Montreal: Les Presses de l'Universite de Montreal, 1974); and Evelyne Lapierre-Adamcyk, "Les aspirations des Quebecois en matiere de fecondite en 1980," *Cahiers Quebecois de Demographie* 10 (Aug. 1981): 171-88.

34. Alba and Potter, "Population and Development in Mexico Since 1940," pp. 62-64.

35. Jeffrey B. Nugent and R. Thomas Gillaspy, "Old Age Pensions and Fertility in Rural Areas of Less Developed Countries: Some Evidence from Mexico," *Economic Development and Cultural Change* 31 (July 1983): 809-29.

36. Nugent and Gillaspy, "Old Age Pensions and Fertility in Rural Areas," p. 824.

37. G. K. Chesterton, *Collected Works*, Vol. IV (San Francisco: Ignatius Press, 1987), p. 260.

Chapter 4

MEDIA AND THE FAMILY

Michael Medved

Introduction

Sitting down at breakfast this morning, I was asked one of the questions that I'm fairly regularly asked when people recognize me from television, which is, "Have you become *persona non grata* in Hollywood? Have you been frozen out of the industry in some way?" The answer is, I still manage to do my job, but I *have* been surprised by the intensity of the reaction that my book has provoked.

After all, I'm not unique in saying that popular culture today is in a miserable state. How many people do you know who think that television is wonderful at the moment? That it enriches our lives? That movies are better than ever?

Do you know how many people in America think that movies today are better than ever? One. His name is Jack Valenti. He gets paid to draw that conclusion. He's head of the Motion Picture Association of America, and as *Variety* reveals, he gets paid $850,000 a year to think publicly that movies are better than ever.

Given the general acceptance of the notion that things aren't great with our popular culture, what was it about my book that provoked such, shall we say, an enthusiastic response? I'll give you a little bit of an idea of some of the flavor of that response. Michael Winner, who is the creator of such worthwhile contributions to Western civilization as the movies *Death Wish, Death Wish 2, Death Wish 3* and, yes, *Death Wish 4*, said in his review of my book that, "The decade is still young, but I think it's safe to say that Michael Medved's *Hollywood vs. America* will emerge as the worst book of the decade."

I was also thrilled that Paul Verhoeven—who has given the world such films as *Robo Cop, Total Recall,* and *Basic Instinct,* which I had previously reviewed under the title *Basically It Stinks*—called me a Nazi on television. I took particular umbrage to that, since my mother and her parents fled Nazi Germany in 1935.

And then my favorite of all the responses to my book was the front-page editorial in *Variety* by its editor, Peter Bart, denouncing me under the headline, "The Hills are Alive with the Sound of Medved." And there was a little caricature of me—not a flattering one, I should tell you. Peter Bart in his review said *Hollywood vs. America* is "not so much a book as it is a nervous breakdown set in type." At the very end of his review he said, "As much as I detest blacklists, a good case can now be made that Medved should be banned from all future screenings." This is in print. It exists.

What's astonishing about this is that these people who are such stalwart defenders of the First Amendment, believe in absolute freedom of speech—just so long as you don't use that freedom of speech to criticize them.

The question remains: What is it that's so different in my work from general, everyday complaints about Hollywood that arouses people to this degree? Thinking about it, I've realized that the most sensitive thing about this book is the fact that it strips away the three basic lies—the big frauds that Hollywood perpetrates in order to justify its own stupidities and excesses and irresponsibilities. What I want to do with you this morning is actually look at those three lies, and to prepare you for rebutting them whenever these subjects come up.

They are three lies you hear all the time. Lie Number One: "It's just entertainment. It never really hurt anybody." Lie Number Two: "We're just great capitalists. We give the public what it wants. Don't blame us; blame yourselves." And Lie Number Three: "If you don't like this material, it's always easy to just turn it off."

Lie Number One

The first point—the common line that, "Hey, lighten up, it's just entertainment; it has no impact on the real world"—is a fundamental contradiction that is at the very core of Hollywood's view of reality. That contradiction emerged recently from a major studio head, who made the rather remarkable claim that the film *Lethal Weapon 3* deserved credit and praise because it had saved thousands of lives. Now, I wasn't immediately able to discern the life-giving messages in *Lethal Weapon 3*. But eventually it was explained that there's a crucial scene in which Danny Glover and Mel Gibson are preparing to zoom off on a high-speed chase, but before they do, they fasten their seat belts.

Now think about the logic here. There's an assumption that when people see two popular stars up there on the screen fastening seat belts, everybody's going to imitate what they see. But when they see the other 99.9 percent of the movie—which is eye gouging, eviscerations, falling from high buildings, shootings and dismemberment of all kinds—nobody will imitate *that*.

This is very typical of Hollywood's approach. They want you to believe that they are capable of all kinds of positive influence. But when it comes to any influence that might be questionable—oh, that never happens, of course.

This is an industry that breaks its elbow patting itself on the back whenever it sends out messages about designated drivers, or recycling or condom consciousness. (Condoms, of course, are the talisman of the moment. It's absolutely magical. All you have to do is use the word condom in a film and you're going to get some kind of an award, some kind of praise for the responsibility of your message.) The idea is that people can be influenced by this rather subtle material, but the rest of the movie or TV show is not going to influence them. No, not at all.

Do you know where you see this? The practice of product placement. That's where in a motion picture a large corporation has paid very good money in order to display its corporate logo, whether it be Pepsi or Budweiser or Nike. That logo is sort of flashed on the screen, as in those moments when somebody hoists a beer can and holds it up to the screen. Businesses pay for that. The average film today is taking in just under a million dollars per film in product placement costs.

Now, why do the corporations do it? Are they eleemosynary institutions? Are they trying to offer some charitable support for Hollywood? Nonsense. There are studies—abundant studies—that show that even a few seconds of a corporate logo associated with a glamorous star can have a measurable impact on sales and the way the public responds to that product and to that brand name. Yet, the industry wants you to believe that everybody's focused on that corporate logo, that nobody is looking at what's going on in the rest of the screen. It's insanity.

Imagine that there's a little bottle of Scope on the bed stand in a bedroom scene. And there's a bed with two beautiful, nude, writhing bodies in ecstasy. And the only thing the public is watching is the bottle of Scope? This is nonsense. Complete and utter nonsense.

And you see the same sort of illogic regarding television. I'm always struck by the fact that otherwise well-educated people say, "Well you know this idea that televised imagery impacts real life, it's scientifically unproven. There are studies that say different things." This is garbage. The only major studies that deny a link between prolonged exposure to televised violence and more hostile and aggressive attitudes in real life are those studies which were paid for by the networks. And there are many of them, which should be accorded the same kind of moral dignity as all those studies by the tobacco industry which show that smoking is good for you.

In 1982, the Surgeon General of the United States released a report about the role of TV violence in creating a more violent society around us. It was a report accompanied by five full volumes of documentation and hundreds of studies. ABC-TV turned around and issued a statement that said, and I quote, "There is no conclusive proof that televised imagery impacts real-world behavior in any way." To which my response is: Oh yeah? If ABC-TV really believes that, then it should start refunding several billion dollars in advertising revenues, because if televised imagery doesn't impact real world behavior, what is it doing charging for ad time? The idea is that people are going to be sold on everything from canned goods to candidates with 30 seconds of a commercial, but that the surrounding 30 *minutes* have no impact. Isn't that absurd?

And the advertising model is very important to keep in mind, because it not only demonstrates that there is impact from the mass media on real world behavior, but it shows the way that impact works. For instance, people always say, "Well, if you believe that Hollywood has an impact on America and that televised or motion picture violence helps make people and society more violent in real life—encourages irresponsible behavior—then why is it that film critics, people like yourself who see five and six movies a week, aren't especially well represented among ax murderers?"

Now, I can't speak for all of my colleagues, but I will say that the answer to that is very simple. Let me just try a little show of hands. How many people here have ever seen an ad for the Lexus automobile on television? Virtually all of us, right? How many people here have gone out and bought a Lexus? Okay, a few of us. Now, we've just proved that Lexus ads have no impact, right, because lots of people see them and they don't go out and buy the car? That's the same logic that people use to deny television's influence.

Of course it's absurd. Lexus is not a dumb company. It's part of Toyota—they know what they're doing. Their ads don't have to change behavior on the part of *everyone* who sees them in order to have an impact. They need to only change behavior on the part of a relatively small number of people to have a profound effect on the corporation and its sales.

By the same token, violent material on TV doesn't need to impact everyone who sees it. If it impacts only a small proportion of vulnerable viewers, then that in itself will have a profound effect on society. And the impact on the rest of us is also significant, just as it is with the Lexus ad. Because for all those people who see the Lexus ad, even those who don't run out and buy the car and don't have the money to buy it, the ad redefines our attitude toward this particular product. If it weren't for advertising campaigns—if we see just a Lexus driving by on the street—most people probably wouldn't associate it as a status symbol of any kind. We'd be unaware of it. But what television advertising does is make us aware of something as a desirable goal. "Maybe I can't buy the car, but maybe someday it would be nice. Maybe this car is hip, it's chic, it's glamorous, it's desirable."

That's exactly the long-term impact of television portrayals of sexual behavior and violence. Those portrayals redefine normal behavior. They redefine what is chic, glamorous and desirable. And even for those people who don't immediately run out and imitate that behavior—who don't go out and buy the car—it changes our evaluation of not only what is accepted in our society but what is expected. So, the argument that "It's just TV, it's just movies, it has no impact on anybody, it's just entertainment" is nonsense. It shows Hollywood's fundamental contradiction in its approach to the world: "We can influence people when we want to, when we want to take credit for it, for the purpose of selling advertising or anything else. But other than that, we deny all influence."

Lie Number Two

That brings me to the second line of denial—the second big lie—that people in the entertainment industry love to promulgate: "Don't blame us; blame society. If what we have up there on screen is ugly and disgusting and nauseating and horrific, it's because that's the kind of horrible country we live in. That's what people want. After all, we're good capitalists. We just give the public what it wants. We're just like a big capitalist candy machine. You put in the money and then you get the brand that you choose."

One of the fundamentals of the idea that they're just giving the public what it wants is the fact that over 60 percent of all movies released in the United States are rated R—are drenched in violence, graphic sexuality and rather unpleasant language—and that that's the only kind of movie that does business. Hollywood has been saying for years that you have to put this material into even innocuous movies, otherwise you're dead in the water at the box office.

This was conventional wisdom in Hollywood for a long time. It was such strongly held conventional wisdom that it was almost in passing that I decided to do something which I don't think anyone had ever done before, which was check it out, to see if it was true. What I was hoping to find was that the bias in favor of R-rated films in terms of box office performance wouldn't be that great— that PG films might do almost as well as R films, showing that Hollywood wasn't simply following the market. I did my initial computer study, based on every movie released in 1991—and 600 of them were released that year—and their domestic box office gross.

When the statistics came back, my jaw dropped. I couldn't believe what I had found. According to my numbers, in 1991, when 61 percent of all movies were rated R, PG movies, which are aimed at family audiences, did *three times better* at the box office than R-rated films.

I was so stunned by this that I needed to check myself. I actually submitted this entire project to the research director for the Screen Actors Guild, who is a very skilled Hollywood researcher. I said, "Will you check this, because it doesn't sound right?" He came back and said "It's exactly right. I'm fascinated with this right now. Do you mind if I work with you and we go ahead and check it out in previous years to see what has happened?" So we went back 10 years and analyzed movies released in the United States.

Do you know what's incredible? What's incredible is that there isn't a single year—not one—since 1983 in which PG movies haven't done substantially better on average than R-rated films. In fact, they averaged more than 2-to-1 larger domestic box office grosses. And during that time period the percentage of R-rated films, which were doing worse at the box office during the whole 10-year period, went up from 46 percent of all films released to 61 percent in 1991 and, by some estimates, to 65 percent last year, 1992.

Ladies and gentlemen, this is nuts. It suggests not that Hollywood is evil, but that it's radically dysfunctional. And I must tell you that since my book came out, all of a sudden, there have been a bunch of different studies that have confirmed exactly what I found. And the conventional wisdom seems to have shifted.

Mark Canton, the president of Sony Columbia Studios, gave a speech at ShoWest to all motion picture exhibitors in which he said, "We must now do what any smart business person knows we must do, make more PG movies." Now, this is March 9, 1993, that he made that speech. What took him so long? It's been so obvious for a long time. If anyone doubts that Hollywood is motivated by its own dark obsessions, rather than some kind of intelligent response to the public, all you need to do is look at these statistics and then you need to break the statistics down.

Why are most movies rated R? Is it because of violence? No, it's because of language. I will acknowledge that there is an audience, and always will be an audience, for hyper-violent films. There are people who love to see heads blown up and limbs chopped off. That exists in America. That audience is composed primarily of drooling, sub-literate, hormone-addled, violence-prone, adolescent boys. And you know who you are.

So there may be an audience for violence. But what's the audience for language? Who says, "Let's go spend $15 at the local Bijou or Multiplex in order to hear our favorite stars talking dirty?" Have you ever heard of anyone who left a theater complaining

—feeling cheated—because the language in the movie he just saw was too clean? Who thinks like that, except people in Hollywood?

Recently, one of the more unpleasant films I saw was a film called "Hoffa," which is about everybody's favorite dead labor leader. In this particular film, they used the F-word 268 times. I don't count these words. I'm too busy trying to watch the film. I subscribe to a service that I think is manned by little gnomes who go out with little counters to the theater and count them.

They counted 268 F-words in *Hoffa*. It's so extraordinary. Do you know how easy that makes it for the screen writer? You just have to hit the same key on the word processor again and again and again. I recently was on a flight, I was astonished that they were offering an airline version of *Hoffa*. It must be about 10 minutes long.

The fact is it's not just movies like *Hoffa*. If you're going to see a movie about Jimmy Hoffa and Bobby Kennedy, you've got to expect to hear a certain amount of harsh language, especially between the two of them. But the fact is, it has crept into children's movies. Unbelievably, 46 percent of PG movies—PG *movies*—now contain the F- or the S- word at least once. Seventy-three percent of PG-13 movies contain those words. Who would miss them if they were taken out?

This is not a response to the marketplace. There is not a single market study that suggests that the American people respond better to foul language in movies. In fact, there was a major opinion survey, with 1,604 respondents, that was about motion pictures. That study found that 82 percent felt that there was too much foul language in movies. Do you know how many of the 1,604 respondents felt there was too little foul language in movies? Not one. They couldn't find one out of 1,604 people.

This obsession with foul language is not a market-driven phenomenon. This is not an industry responding to America.

Look at the portrayal of religious believers. This is a profoundly religious country—something Hollywood doesn't seem to understand. One of the points I love to make is that on Super Bowl Sundays, when we seem to celebrate our big national religion and everybody watches the Super Bowl, what do more people do on those Sundays together than watch the Super Bowl? Do you know?

They go to church. About 100 million people watch the Super Bowl, and around 110 million go to church. Forty to 45 percent of Americans go to church or synagogue every single week.

It's a reality you don't see on screen and, moreover, when you do see anyone religious, he's invariably portrayed as a crook or a crazy or very often both. Is that a response to market forces?

Every single one of these movies about crooked clergy has failed at the box office. You can't find one in the last 20 years that's made a dime, and yet they keep getting made. Is that a question of giving America what it wants?

Finally, and most dramatically, look at the portrayal of this country—of our past, of our future, of our institutions. They did three major bio films this year. They were about Hoffa, Malcolm X and Charlie Chaplin. Each of these films was hugely expensive, and each of them lost very big money. Very big money. *Malcolm X* lost less money than the other two, but still lost. Chaplin was such a big money loser, it put Carolco into Chapter 11. Chaplin was such a flop with the public they had to subpoena people to go to see it.

But what do all these three figures have in common? What they have in common is that they all lived the American nightmare. They all had fundamentally unhappy, embittered experiences with American life and American society. That is not the experience of most people who live here, who still believe in the American Dream, who are profoundly grateful for this country, who are instinctively patriotic. Yet, Hollywood doesn't get it, and doesn't respond.

Right now they are simultaneously developing five different films about the Black Panther Party. When those five films are in production at the same time, they will probably employ more people than were ever *members* of the Black Panther Party. But I would submit to you that there's no market study that says, "Let's do Black Panther films right now," especially after the performance at the box office of *Malcolm X*, which was certainly well-made.

The point is, nobody thinks, "We're going to make a movie about Black Panthers and it's going to be a sweet little money machine." That's not the thinking. These people are consumed with the desire to make some serious statement, to be taken seriously as artists. They've bought into the absurd idea that the only kind of artistic statement worth making is one that shakes people up, that assaults convention, that shows the creator is some kind of alienated artist.

They don't want to be known as a member of the establishment, even though they may ride in a chauffeur-driven limousine and get $5 million per picture. They think of themselves as some kind of sensitive spirit, just like they were in the old days in Greenwich village, when they were struggling actors, wearing black turtlenecks and drinking espresso and talking about existentialism. That's all these people want to keep faith with.

Just a few weeks ago, we were celebrating the anniversary of Lexington and Concord, the beginning of the American Revolution. Hollywood took a swipe at the American Revolution six years ago. It was a movie called *Revolution,* which cost $37 million for Warner Brothers to make. It starred Al Pacino as a member of the Continental Army. He apparently was the only member of the Continental Army with a Bronx accent.

Aside from its ludicrous aesthetic quality, what was really notable about it was that they made a decision to do a revisionist view of the American Revolution. They took this inspiring struggle for American independence and made the colonists into the bad guys. It's unbelievable. You know what? Not only did this $37 million movie fall on its face *here*—it earned less than $3 million at the box office—it was even a flop in England.

So I would submit to you, when people say that Hollywood is just following the famous bottom line—"It's the fault of the capitalist system; it's the fault of the profit motive"—they're not telling the truth. That's the second of Hollywood's big lies. These are terrible businessmen, who are not responding intelligently to the public.

Lie Number Three

That brings me to the third and final lie, which is, "Well, if you don't like this stuff, who's forcing you to watch it? Just turn it off and, meanwhile, please shut up." Let me give you a personal account of why that is such an utterly misleading and irresponsible lie.

My wife is a clinical psychologist. One afternoon while I was home, she had patients and I was supposed to watch my older daughter, Sarah, who is now six years old. Sarah was home with one of her little friends from first grade, and they were playing. They were basically self-sufficient, so it was not a very big job to watch them. So, I was at the word processor, and all of a sudden I hear from downstairs these rather blood curdling screams. It's my daughter. I think, "Oh my God, this little boy she brought home from school has chopped her head off or done something horrible."

I ran downstairs and my daughter had tears running down her chubby little cheeks. She was very upset. I asked, "Sarah, baby, what's wrong? What's upsetting you so much?" She just pointed and said, "It's that, Daddy, it's that." And then I looked over to see what "that" was. And "that" was something that this little boy had taken out of his book bag and brought home with him from school. You know what it was? It was a Terminator doll.

Have any of you seen a Terminator doll? It's a big seller for Mattel Toys. It obviously is in the image of Arnold Schwarzenegger. It has various arms that you can take off. You can actually take out its heart and remove its head. It has bombs and grenades and buzz saws and submachine guns. Most strikingly, it has a little ring behind the neck that you pull so that the thing talks. And it says things like, "I vill blow you away" and "I vill kill you now," and "Hasta la vista, baby." Actually, I think it speaks more clearly than the real life Mr. Schwarzenegger.

I think it was the talking that scared my daughter, who is, admittedly, an incurable and terrible wimp, which I'm glad for, actually. She recovered from having seen the Terminator doll. I'm not saying that this was a wound on her soul. By no means. But it did bring home to me one very important point. I would no more take my daughter to see the *Terminator*, or have her watch the *Terminator* on TV or on video, than I would drag her over broken glass. It's just not something I want to do. I would have been perfectly happy if my six year old had been able to lead a Terminator-free childhood. But that option is not available today. It's not available because the popular culture is so ubiquitous. It is everywhere. You cannot escape it.

Let me try a little demonstration here. How many people in this room have been to a Madonna concert? Don't be ashamed. Okay, I think we had one. How many people here, when you go home this evening, are going to find Madonna CDs or tapes in your personal collection? Two or three. How many people here know who Madonna is? Absolutely everyone!

Ladies and gentlemen, you never made a conscious choice to place Madonna into your imagination. They tell us we lose 10,000 or so brain cells every day that we're alive after the age of 30. Who would want to use precious brain cells for focusing on Madonna? If I had a choice, I'd just as soon that this lady weren't in my imagination, weren't in my consciousness. I never chose to put her there. But there she is. She is inescapable. It doesn't matter whether you choose to buy her product or to watch her on MTV. She's there. I guarantee you there are Amish kids in Pennsylvania, there are Hasidic Kids in Brooklyn, who know who Madonna is.

That illustrates the fundamental truth: saying, "If you don't like the popular culture, you can just turn it off" is like saying, "If you don't like the smog, you can always stop breathing." The fact is, as the late, great Joe Louis said, "You can run, but you can't hide." This stuff is everywhere.

Maybe it doesn't impact you, or through some super-human effort you protect your children. But it's the other children in school who come home with the Ninja Turtles material or the Terminator material. It's everybody else's kids and your neighbors, and it's everywhere around you. It's part of the very environment that we all breathe, and this is why this is such a passionate, cutting-edge issue for so many people. The most fundamental thing that we all want is to be able to pass on values to our own children, to be able to transmit our approaches to the world to the next generation.

People today increasingly—and I think appropriately—view Hollywood, view the popular culture, view the entertainment industry as a force that interferes with, undermines, and works against precisely those values that we want most to pass on to our own kids. That's why people are so upset. That's why they should be upset. That's why what we need in this country is what could be described as a cultural environmental movement. It would be a movement in the same sense that we are asking big corporations to take more responsibility for their pollution of our air and water. These gigantic entertainment conglomerates have to be held more accountable for their pollution of the cultural atmosphere that we all breathe.

We have to be able to be more discerning consumers, to recognize that entertainment isn't necessarily harmless, to cut down our own TV consumption. Everybody in this room can watch less TV. That would send a powerful message. But beyond our own consumption decisions and our own willingness to take charge of this issue in our own lives, we need to work together with some of the established organizations that are trying to address this issue.

For example, we need to write letters, which is easy. It's like writing a letter to Santa Claus in care of the North Pole. All you have to do is write "The President, Warner Brothers Pictures, Hollywood, California." It gets delivered.

Ultimately—particularly at this time, when the business is in crisis, when their profits are so low, when audiences have been declining, when they recognize they have a problem—there is a possibility of making a difference.

I believe that we're at a very, very interesting moment in this struggle. There are people in the entertainment industry who are hearing the dissatisfaction in a way they have never heard it in the past. It's going to be a long-term effort, and I will conclude by saying that it is an effort that could be described in the same way that Winston Churchill described a rather more serious, more heroic situation many years ago, when he said, "This is not the end, nor is it even the beginning of the end, but it is perhaps the end of the beginning."

Chapter 5

THE GAY LIBERATION AGENDA

Hadley Arkes, Ph.D.

I cannot make a return to the Bishops' workshop without re-cording my thanks again for the warmth of your reception two years ago when I appeared before this group for the first time. Bishop Charles caught me after my talk, and he earnestly enjoined me—as though I needed any enjoining—to keep cultivating what he called my "art form" in merging philosophy with comedy. But I've been arguing explicitly in recent years there is indeed a con-nection between comedy and philosophy; that the comedians are really in the same business as the philosophers: The comedians make their living by playing on the shades of meaning, or the logic, contained in our language. You can take, as an example, Henny Youngman's line: "My wife will buy anything that's marked down. She brought home an escalator." I used to say that my favorite epistemologist was Lou Costello. In one notable instance, his partner, Bud Abbott, came up with a fine idea, and Costello said, "That's an excellent thought; I was just going to think of it myself." A colleague of mine in philosophy can go for two weeks on that line. The laugh is the telling sign that the point was understood, and at times, the laugh marks the recognition that we might not acknowledge if the point were offered to us in the form of an argument. In the arguments over homosexuality, this form of acknowledgment may turn out to be particularly telling; for with this subject, the laughs do indeed reveal recognitions, or they confirm premises, that people would be quite reluctant these days to acknowledge in public. And so I've suggested, in this vein, that the core of the argument against homosexuality may be conceded, instantly and unguardedly, in the laughs that people cannot hold back when they hear a certain line of Rodney Dangerfield's. And that line was Rodney Dangerfield's lament that "I was afraid the first time I had sex—I was afraid, because I was all alone."

There was no joke, and no laugh, without the underlying recognition that what he was offering was, of course, not really sex. Or, if this was sex, then as Roger Scruton would suggest, it is sex without courtship and without seduction. The recognition behind Dangerfield's line is that this is not sex, not only because there is no engagement with another person, but because the act is merely genital stimulation. It is an act dramatically removed from any prospect of addressing the real end that marks the nature of sex in the strictest sense—as the union of man and woman (a distinction of gender whose very logic and significance derives only from the purpose and meaning of sex); and the purpose of that union of course, the purpose that affects the engagement of sex at every point, is the creation of new life. But from that perspective, even sex between two persons may not strictly speaking be sexual, any more than Dangerfield's sex *da solo*. Two persons together may merely recapitulate, in tandem, the masturbation implied in Dangerfield's joke. In the case of a homosexual coupling, that significance may be plainer; but it may be present, also, in relations between a man and a woman who seek their sexual engagement as a kind of recreation—as they might perhaps go bowling—and be quite as detached, as they are when they are bowling, from any interest in the deeper meaning of sex, as an enduring bond between two souls embodied; a bond that may furnish the frame, or the setting, for welcoming and nurturing children.

We are simply reminded here that there is a truth we cannot evade, imprinted in our natures, as John Paul II would say, and marked in the "natural teleology" of the body. The decisive and inescapable quality of that truth has been implicitly acknowledged even by the spokesmen for gay rights, who have not seemed to grasp, however, the depth of the concession. And so I had the occasion to point up, last summer, a piece on "The Politics of Homosexuality," struck off by Andrew Sullivan, the young and professedly "gay" editor of the *New Republic*. The piece brought to mind that observation of John Courtney Murray, that the atheist and the theist essentially agree in their understanding of the problem: the atheist does not mean to reject the existence of God only in Staten Island; he means to reject God universally, as a necessary truth. He accepts the same framework of reference, and he makes the same move to a transcendent standard of judgment. In the same way, and without quite realizing it, Sullivan made a comparable concession for the advocates of "gay rights" ("The Politics of Homosexuality," *New Republic* [May 10]). For Sullivan had put into place, as the very ground and framework of his argument, a structure of understanding that immanently called into question any claims for the homosexual life as a rival "good."

Sullivan recalled the pain of awareness and reconciliation in his own family, with the recurring memory of his father weeping when Andrew declared, as he says, his sexuality. Sullivan sought then to ward off the promoters of a "queer politics," a politics of cultural subversion, which promised to deepen the separation between homosexuals and their families. Sullivan pleaded for a politics that would not break off relations with "heterosexual families," as he called them, "whose cooperation is needed in every generation, if gay children are to be accorded a modicum of dignity and hope."

But the delicacy barely concealed: That "cooperation" is needed in every generation precisely because "homosexual families" cannot produce "gay children." Gay children can come into being through the only kind of family that nature knows. We do not really find, then, two kinds of "families" carrying out transactions with one another. But rather, we come to recognize again the primacy of "sexuality" in the strictest sense, the only sexuality that can produce "another generation."

That literal meaning of sexuality, imprinted in our natures—in the very meaning of our genders—provides the ground of nature that makes traditional marriage intelligible. Only two people, only a heterosexual couple, can beget a child. Not more than two, and not two people of the same sex. The law that confines marriage to two people, and only two people, of opposite sexes, is a law rendered intelligible and compelling, as I say, by the natural teleology of the body. And yet, there seems to be a curious forgetting these days, especially in the circles of the educated, that there is an ensemble here woven tightly of logic and nature: that the rejection of one part is bound to render other parts less plausible or defensible. And so, Andrew Sullivan has made an impassioned appeal for allowing gay couples to enjoy "the apex of emotional life...in the marital bond." In this appeal, gay couples should be given the same standing, or legal recognition, for the commitment that joins them in their love.

But once marriage is detached from the natural teleology of the body, there is nothing that need confine marriage to the principle of monogamy. If we look at the ethic that describes the "gay life" we do not find an excruciating yearning for monogamy (if we can use that word) or the exclusive love of a single partner. We find a life characterized by a staggering multitude of partners; and indeed, that sense of liberation from the restraints of convention forms one of the deep appeals of the gay life. We should not be surprised, then, that the movement for gay rights, sprung from this same ethic, has not made monogamy central to its moral doctrines. Quite the opposite: The ethic of sexual liberation that attends "gay rights" is an ethic that bids us to recede from any moral judgment about the way in which people understand and practice their "sexuality." And that state of affairs presents us with this unavoidable predicament: Once marriage is detached from nature, or natural coupling; once we accept the notion of gay marriage; there is no clear ground on which to explain why marriage must be confined to two people. We would have no ground of principle on which to resist the gay people who claim that their love is not confined to one other person, but connected, in a network, to two or three others. And after all, why not? If we admit gay marriage, what is there in the notion of gay marriage that necessarily confines that alliance to the constraints of monogamy? At the moment, we could cite nothing other than mere convention or custom in explaining why we would reject a return to polygamy. And I do mean polygamy, not merely polyandry. For how could the law permit a marriage of multiple partners to people of the same sex and yet forbid that arrangement to heterosexual couples?[1]

Again, I have taken this path into the subject for the sake of recalling that the traditional understanding of marriage and sexuality is sustained by a formidable union of nature and logic; by facts that cannot be effaced; and by principles that cannot be evaded without falling into incoherence. Some of us would say that the "natural law" provides another ground of conviction here, to support the teachings of revelation and faith. But the teaching of the Church on marriage and homosexuality would be compelling even if the Church, for the sake simply of argument, said nothing at all about revelation and faith. And yet, in the face of understandings of this kind, accumulated over a tradition of moral reflection, we find now a class of leaders in the academy and in the courts of law, who look upon people bearing moral reservations about homosexuality, and they conclude that this aversion must spring from a primitive superstition. Or, they attribute this judgment to a personal bias so irrational that it cannot give a reasoned account of itself. And so, just a couple of months ago, in the District of Columbia, three seasoned judges, in a federal court of appeals, struck down the policy of the Navy to exclude, from the service and from the academy in Annapolis, people who have professed their homosexuality. In the course of rendering their judgment, this panel of judges strained their wit to consider the reasons that might lie behind the policies of the Navy. And by their own report, they could find nothing but an unaccountable prejudice, which could not supply, as they said, "any rational basis."

In this respect, the decision by the federal court offers a precise echo of the judgments pronounced by other judges, state and federal, in courts all over the country. Whether the courts are in Washington, D.C., or out West in Colorado, or removed to places even more exotic, like Hawaii, the variations in landscape and people and manners recede, and the judges speak in a remarkably uniform voice. It is the voice of "legal positivism," and the voice of legal positivism is still the voice of Justice Holmes. Holmes thought it would be a notable advance "if every word of moral significance could be banished from the law altogether." In that temper, or with that sense, the judges are proceeding in a striking concert to expunge from the law every trace of a moral understanding that would cast doubts on homosexuality or call it into moral question. The difference now is that the judges have a stridently moralistic sense as they go about the task of purging traditional morality from the Constitution. For the most part, they disclaim any pretension to know of moral truths. Their moral convictions are supplied by the "higher law of the Constitution," but unlike the first generation of our jurists, they no longer take seriously a moral law, even more fundamental, that stands behind the Constitution.

Nothing much has altered in this understanding in recent years, and yet things have taken a decided turn for the worse just within the past year. The judges have become more brazen; their attacks on traditional morality have become more explicit. The movement can be measured precisely in two notable cases, one from Colorado, the other from Hawaii. In both cases, the judges have advanced the project of sweeping from the law every provision that implies an adverse judgment on homosexuality, or which refuses to accord to homosexuality a standing or a legitimacy that is comparable to normal sexuality.

In the case from Colorado, as I will try to show, the reasoning of the judges is entirely implausible, and it cannot explain the decision. The most plausible account is a political account: The election of Mr. Clinton brought the prospect of new appointments to the Supreme court, and the appointment of Ruth Bader Ginsburg has changed the calculations of the judges. In my estimate, the judges have anticipated that Ruth Bader Ginsburg represents the fifth vote to overturn the decision of the court in *Bowers v. Hardwick.* That was the decision, in 1986, in which the Court refused to overturn the statute on sodomy in Georgia.[2] It refused, that is, to find in the logic of the Constitution a constitutional right to engage in homosexuality. And therefore the Court refused to overturn the laws in the separate States that condemn sodomy or withhold from homosexuals the stamp of legitimacy. Ruth Ginsburg replaces Justice Byron White, who wrote the opinion of the court in *Bowers v. Hardwick.* That decision was decided narrowly, with a margin of one vote, and there is every reason to expect that Justice Ginsburg will cast a vote in the other direction. The one thing needful is a case that will require the Supreme Court to revisit its judgment in *Bowers v. Hardwick.* With that end in mind, the judges, I think, are willing to send up virtually any case that will compel a review by the Court. The judges may produce that effect if they merely manage to strike down a statute, in one of the States, that refuses to recognize the rightness of homosexuality. And that, the judges are willing to do, even with the use of reasoning that the judges could not regard as plausible.

There is hardly a clearer case in point than the recent litigation in Colorado. The case arose over a referendum, a constitutional amendment, that was passed by the voters in the election of November, 1992. This was the celebrated "Amendment 2." The aim of the amendment was to brake the tendency, spreading through the State, to treat "gays" as a class of victims on the same plane as groups suffering discrimination on the basis of race, religion or gender. And so the Amendment sought to forbid governments and authorities at all levels—from the State to school districts—to enact and enforce

> any statute [or ordinance] whereby homosexual, lesbian or bisexual orientation, conduct, practices or relationships shall constitute or otherwise be the basis of, or entitle any person or class of persons to have or claim any minority status, quota preferences, protected status or claim of discrimination.[3]

It was plain, from the text, that the Amendment did not license an active regimen of criminal enforcement, to seek out and prosecute homosexual acts. It did not represent a return to statutes on sodomy. It merely forestalled legislation that would work in a sweeping way to forbid or punish all acts of "discrimination" against homosexuals. That kind of legislation could strike at domains of privacy and the free exercise of religion: It might deny people the right to discriminate in the sharing of their homes with people whose "sexual" engagements they find objectionable on religious or moral grounds. Amendment 2 merely established that these kinds of objections may still be plausible and legitimate in the eyes of the law. Or to put it another way, the Amendment merely preserved the right of people, in private settings, to cast an adverse judgment on homosexuality, and to respect their own moral judgments.

It was only to be expected, of course, that this Amendment would be challenged in the courts. But what could not have been expected, even in these times, was that a Supreme Court in Colorado should be willing to overturn a constitutional amendment on the basis of reasoning as empty and contrived as the reasoning that the judges brought forth in this case. Lest we forget, this Amendment was adopted by the people of Colorado as part of the constitution, or the fundamental law, of the State. And yet, the Supreme Court of Colorado was willing to credit the notion that this new part of the constitution was incompatible with principles that were even more fundamental yet in the Basic Law of the State—namely, a "right not to have the State endorse and give effect to private biases."

The "bias" is apparently a leaning away from homosexuality. But it would be necessary to remake the dictionaries in order to reduce this condemnation of homosexuality to the standing merely of a "private bias." If I reported that "I have a tooth-ache," I would be invoking a private knowledge, drawn from my own sensations. No one else may share those sensations; they are distinctly and exclusively mine. Others may trust my report on my own pain, but the direct knowledge of that pain is not accessible to anyone apart from myself. That is an irreducibly private knowledge. But the arguments about the rightness and wrongness of homosexuality are publicly accessible. The rejection of homosexuality has been part of a doctrine, publicly taught, publicly shared, by Christians and Jews, and by communities registering their understanding in the laws. None of that is to say that the traditional teaching here is unproblematic. Nor would it suggest that this teaching cannot be exposed to a serious, philosophic questioning—and a philosophic defense. But this traditional teaching could hardly be reduced to the standing of a "private bias" *without calling into question, for the same reason, almost all parts of our statutes.* For the opponents of the Amendment contend that all arguments about "morality" are merely expressions of private taste or religious belief. And of course, every law implies an understanding of right and wrong. We might as aptly say that the laws on civil rights, or the laws that confine marriage to human beings, rather than couplings of humans and animals, are all the reflection of merely "private biases."

That implication must be evident even to the men regarded in Colorado as supreme jurists. But they did not expend their jural genius on only one line of argument. They managed to produce, also, this striking novelty: that Amendment 2 violated a deep commitment to "equality" in the constitution of Colorado, because it deprived gays and lesbians of an equal standing to participate in the political process and advance their interests through the law.

What is so breathtakingly original in this construction is that the Court finds this subtle denial of political rights without the aid of any of those measures that used to awaken our sensitivities in the past: The Amendment disfranchises no one. It offers no literacy tests or contrivances to block voters from the rolls. It removes from no person the right to vote, to run for office, to contribute money or buy advertising to support any candidate or any proposition put before the voters in a referendum. In fact, this argument is persistently embarrassed by the fact that, by most measures—education, income, and even political involvement— gays usually stand among the higher ranks. In the county court in Denver, in the middle of December, Judge Bayless confirmed again the premises of the Supreme Court, but even Judge Bayless admitted that the gays in Colorado can hardly be described as a powerless, disfranchised group. Amendment 2 passed by a vote of 813,966 to 710,151. The percentage of homosexuals in the State was estimated at about 4 percent, and yet this 4 percent managed to attract to their side the support of 46 percent of the voters. As the judge remarked, "that is a demonstration of power, not powerlessness."[4] Yet, in Dr. Johnson's phrase, Judge Bayless thinks clearly but faintly: If no one has been disfranchised, and gays in Colorado can command a volume of support, five or ten times their own population, how can it possibly be the case that gays are being denied an "equal" right to participate in the political life of the State?

But the deeper inanity of the argument might be revealed if we took the words of the Court and put, in place of gays and lesbians, some "sexual orientations" that even gays are not willing to defend. Let us suppose that the voters of Colorado passed another amendment which bars any legislature from treating as a "victimized class" people who engage in sex with small children or with animals. And then, the court fills in the blanks and says:

> [The] right to participate equally in the political process is clearly affected by [the Amendment], because it bars [people who engage in pederasty and bestiality] from having an effective voice in governmental affairs insofar as those persons deem it beneficial to seek legislation that would protect them from discrimination based on their sexual orientation.[5]

In any courtroom outside of Colorado, the argument, cast in this form, would reveal its own vacuity. In Amendment 2, a judgment of constitutional gravity was registered by the people of Colorado: It was a judgment about the kinds of ends that were not legitimate for a legislature to incorporate in its policy and enforce with the powers of law. The voters of Colorado affirmed a decision to respect the rights of people, especially in private settings, to honor their own convictions about homosexuality. They sought to confirm this private right, against the willingness of local legislatures to invade these domains of privacy and moral judgment.

The judges in Colorado are as able to grasp these elementary points as well as jural primates anywhere else. It is not that they are deficient of wit, but overflowing with craftiness and daring. Now it is worth bearing in mind that the decision in Colorado was handed down in July, only a couple of months after a momentous decision in Hawaii, a decision that has been curiously muted, or underreported, by the press. The Supreme Court in Hawaii used the equivalent of a Hawaii Equal Rights Amendment in order to challenge the refusal, under the current laws, to issue marriage licenses to couples of the same sex. The issue has been muted so far, I suspect, because the court professed to take only a small step, and remand the issue to the lower courts. But those lower courts will soon be drawing out the full significance of this decision. The Equal Rights Amendment in Hawaii forbids discrimination based on sex or gender. Yet, the law makes a discrimination based on gender when it grants a marriage license to a heterosexual couple and denies it to another couple, composed of two persons of the same sex. One couple is given a right denied to the other, and the difference turns entirely on the gender of the people constituting the couples.

This same argument had been made over 20 years ago, in an article in the *Yale Law Journal*: The authors had contended that the logic of the Equal Rights Amendment (ERA) would have to remove the barriers to homosexual marriage. That implication was vigorously denied at the time by the proponents of the ERA, but now, 20 years later, the Supreme Court in Hawaii was drawing precisely that implication, and drawing precisely that result—or nearly. The Court deftly held back from drawing the conclusion fully. It simply recorded the judgment that discriminations based on sex were now suspect classifications, and that the State would have to bring forth an overriding, or compelling, interest in order to justify this discrimination against homosexual couples.[6] The matter was returned then to the lower courts.

But the Supreme Court has already framed the problem in a way that makes the outcome virtually predictable. The premises have been shaped, the burdens of argument have been assigned, and the rest is mainly a matter of waiting for an opportune moment to spring the decision. The supposedly limited step of the Court seems mainly to be a bit of judicial statecraft, as the judges try to prepare the public mind by letting the decision unfold in stages and soften the shocks of surprise.

But if the State of Hawaii establishes the legality of marriage for homosexuals, the question enters a new phase. For the judgment in Hawaii would then connect with the "Full Faith and Credit" clause of the Constitution (Art. IV, Sec. 1). That is the Clause that sustains the expectation that the driver's license secured in Massachusetts will be honored even if the driver moves to Illinois; or that the marriage legally performed in Tennessee will be honored in Massachusetts. A question would have to arise then as to whether the other states would be obliged to honor the gay marriage sanctioned by the laws of Hawaii. It is an arguable question, but the burden of proof would have to shift to those who claim that the marriage need not be honored. The presumption has been that the contract of marriage would be honored, but there have been some signal exceptions in the past. Those exceptions have touched a layer of some of the deeper, moral presuppositions tucked away in the notion of marriage. Judges might bite their lips and honor the marriage of a 15-year-old from Kentucky, but when it came to the matter of incestuous marriages, the states would draw the line. We may forget that the issue of mixed racial marriages had to be contested in the courts because, on this issue as well, some of the states thought they were dealing with a moral groundwork of marriage. They thought, at any rate, that they were reaching a question of their most fundamental public policy, which placed limits on their obligation to honor just any marriage contracted in another state. But as I say, the burden of proof would have to fall on those who contend that the state need not honor a homosexual marriage sanctioned by the laws of Hawaii. In making their case, the people resisting this obligation would have to place their main reliance on the argument that it is legitimate for a state to incorporate, in its laws, a moral understanding that there is something undesirable or wrong about homosexuality, or something at least that deserves not to be promoted. And yet, that is precisely the premise that the judges have made it their object to discredit, and indeed, obliterate from the law.

I expect that some resistance will be cast up within the states, but I expect that the main weight of the Constitution would be felt on the side of honoring the homosexual marriage accepted in Hawaii. In that event, something truly momentous would have taken place: The judges of one state could accomplish, in effect, the "nationalization" of homosexual marriage. Gay couples would merely need to fly to Hawaii for the ceremony. But that modest requirement would trigger the reflexes of other judges, especially federal judges like Jon Newman in Connecticut, and so we should not be surprised to hear arguments of the following kind: Under the current laws, only gay couples rich enough to afford a trip to Hawaii may have access to the "right" of homosexual marriage. The State of Connecticut preserves that inequality through its refusal to recognize gay marriage. By holding then to its traditional policy, the State of Connecticut denies to poor gay couples the Equal Protection of the Laws. And so, inventive judges, using arguments no more extravagant than arguments they have been shameless enough to use in the past, could strike down the remaining laws, in all of the other states that refuse to recognize gay marriage.

The judges are found in different locales, drawn from different backgrounds, but they are joined by a common outlook, and they seem to be animated toward the same ends. Without the need to pass notes to one another, they are moving in harmony as though they had been arranged, with a deft touch, by the same choreographer. Their immediate object is quite plain, finite, readily within their grasp. They need but one vote to overturn the ruling of the Supreme court in *Bowers v. Hardwick*, and as I say, my surmise has been that the judges see, in the advent of Ruth Ginsburg, the vote that would recast the law. A series of bold, provocative decisions by the judges, on the matter of homosexuality, is likely to propel at least one of those cases to the Supreme Court. Any one of them would make it necessary for the Court to revisit *Bowers v. Hardwick*; and that revisit is likely to result in a decisive turn in the premises and the teaching of the law. And therefore, it is likely to affect also the cast, or form, of our politics, and the direction of public policy.

It is tacitly understood, with knowing glances all around, that this modest step, in overruling *Bowers v. Hardwick*, would have an extended, rippling effect, moving well beyond the rather limited decision that the Court would have to announce in overturning the decision in *Bowers v. Hardwick*. On the surface, of course, the overruling of that case would mean only that the states may not make private, homosexual acts into criminal wrongs, and the objects of prosecution. But that decision would open the spigots of litigation and create vast new possibilities. For that judgment is likely to come along with a new, moral conviction that there is something deeply unreasonable in the state of mind that condemns homosexual acts or regards homosexuality as anything less than a style of life that deserves the respect of the law. The overruling of *Bowers v. Hardwick* would impart a new momentum to the cause of "gay rights," and it would carry well beyond the matter of withdrawing criminal statutes. The decision would provide the premise for a whole new round of litigation to challenge every lingering trace, in which the law withholds its approval or casts an adverse judgment on homosexuality. We can readily expect then a challenge to the laws that refuse to accord rights of adoption to homosexual couples, or of course the laws that refuse to recognize gay marriage.

In this manner do the separate streams of these cases converge—and then they extend again, with currents ever enlarging. Last year, at the beginning of the Clinton Administration, there seemed to be a strong interest in a federal bill on gay rights. That project seemed to recede as the Administration clumsily handled the matter of gays in the military and set off a storm in the country. It became evident to the political weathermen that the climate was no longer exactly congenial to initiatives on gay rights. But this is an Administration that may count now on having, in the courts, a political annex. In fact, the courts may be considered these days the decisive, or even the operational, arm of the party of the Left. As in the case of abortion, the party counts on the courts to enact the parts of the liberal agenda that the party cannot express in public, and which it dare not try to defend openly in the course of a political campaign. The Clinton Administration lost in Congress on the issue of gays in the military, but what it lost in Congress it may recover in the courts, at the hands of judges who are determined to strike down the traditional policy of the military. If the judges succeed in this project, they could conceivably alter the climate of opinion, or they could so alter the cast of the law that it may be more difficult to resist a federal bill on gay rights. For if gays can be described officially as another aggrieved minority; if the rejection of homosexuality can be stamped as a species of discrimination, as illegitimate as the discrimination that is inflicted on the basis of race, religion or gender; then politicians will look quite retrograde if they are not willing to protect yet another group of victims.

But if there is a passage of a gay rights bill, the action would shift to the courts again for the next extension: Groups of gays and lesbians allied with the Administration will move into the courts and invoke the precedent in the case of Bob Jones University in 1983. They will argue that it is now the "public policy" of the United States to recognize the legitimacy of homosexuality and promote gay rights. Therefore, the federal government may not be subsidizing, with tax exemptions, those churches that would deny at the root the premises of our public policy and continue to insist, in fact, on the wrongness of homosexuality.

I would quickly point out that I am offering here a speculation, but it is a conjecture that would move in short, familiar steps, based on arguments and movements we have already seen. Nothing in this chain of conjecture is more extravagant than arguments we have already heard, and if we are guided by experience, we should count ourselves imprudent and naive if we do not work on the assumption that these next moves are just beyond the horizon. But my point here also is that these next phases, in our politics and law, require preparation; and they will arrive more quickly and surely if the judges manage to put into place these simple first steps. All of these possibilities come readily into view as soon as *Bowers v. Hardwick* is set aside, and that setting aside—that dramatic jettisoning of the laws as they used to be—forms the work dear now to the judges, the project that enlists their converted genius. It provides also the only intelligible motive for the decisions they have been delivering in careful, discrete steps.

These judges have apparently determined to give Providence a helping hand, to move history a bit more quickly along the path of what they conceive to be progress. But for the rest of us, the recognition is only now setting in that something is being prepared for our improvement. The experience brings back, quite sharply, Lincoln's words about a similar collusion between the judges and the political class in the middle of the nineteenth century. The object of that collusion was to prepare the public mind for the acceptance of slavery, for its extension into the territories, for its move past the barriers that were cast up in the law to prevent its spread throughout the country. In the aftermath of the Dred Scott decision, the curious, meshing pattern of speeches and decisions became clearer in their design. As Lincoln remarked, "We can not absolutely *know* that all these exact adaptions are the result of a preconcert. But when we see a lot of framed timbers, different portions of which we know have been gotten out at different times and places and by different workmen…and when we see these timbers joined together, and see they exactly make the frame of a house or a mill, all the tenons and mortices exactly fitting, and all…of the different pieces exactly adapted to their respective places, and not a piece too many or too few…—or, if a single piece be lacking, we can see the place in the frame exactly fitted and prepared to yet bring such piece in"—when we see this design worked with such care before us, we are impressed with a vivid sense of the final piece that is about to be put in place. We become aware, in short, of the end that is being so artfully prepared for us.

All of these things, said Lincoln, "look like the cautious patting and petting [of] a spirited horse, preparatory to mounting him."[7] I do not think there can be a reasonable doubt any longer as to the end toward which all of these moves are tending. And I think it is clear that nothing in the courts, no new appointments, or new arguments, are likely to deflect the judges or brake this movement. I have not been exactly shy in expressing, in print, my estimate of the situation. Nor have I held back from recording my judgment that the drift of the courts can be halted only by wresting this issue of homosexuality from the exclusive control of the judges and bringing it back into the political arena, as an object of public discourse and public judgment. To put it another way, referenda can win. And on the matter of homosexuality, a political resistance can draw upon deep reservoirs of sentiment in the public. In framing a political strategy, there would be no need to shape measures to fit the curly reasoning of the courts. The resisters might come forth instead with a simpler, more direct proposal that touches the issue at a strategic place. If the courts in Hawaii follow through, for example, in the decision on gay marriage, there could hardly be a surprise if the decision evokes a reaction in the land. The people who come forward to object would hardly appear to be zealots. But the response may deliver a jolt of sobriety if it suddenly puts forth a clear, comprehensible measure to head the courts off at the pass: The resisters may propose a short, constitutional amendment simply to foreclose the enactment of gay marriage. Charles Rice, at the law school at Notre Dame, struck off the draft of an amendment, which might be confined to one sentence:

> Nothing in this Constitution shall require the United States or any State to treat intimate homosexual activity as a protected right or to accord to homosexual relationships any of the legal attributes of marriage.

Whether that is the final form or not, an amendment of that kind could be initiated within the legislatures of the States. And there is not much doubt that the amendment would quickly gather support, especially in the West and the South. I would point out here that a modest move of this kind could have a substantial yield, even without the need actually to pass the amendment. The fact that the amendment passes in several States, that it seems to be picking up support, that it seems to be a "live" possibility—all of that might be quite enough to concentrate the minds of the judges and induce them to hold back with a certain prudence. Judges like Ruth Bader Ginsburg may prefer then to be cautious, to avoid any provocative new decisions that could irritate the public and stir on the movement for a constitutional amendment. We are likely to discover, too, that the overflow effect works in both directions: The amendment may be confined mainly to gay marriage, but it would reveal a moral resistance, running deep among the public, and the judges are likely to read it in that way. They are likely to recede then, along a broader front, from their willingness to challenge at every point that fixed tendency of the law in favor of the natural family and normal sexuality.

I have suggested in print that there is a connection between this project and the pro-life movement. It should come as no surprise that the judges who have been most aggressive in rooting out from the law any rejection of homosexuality, are the judges who have been most aggressive in promoting the "abortion liberty." Whatever chastens them, whatever checks their confidence, diminishes their authority. And what diminishes their authority, removes the edge of romance from their adventurism, and it dampens their willingness to be brazen.

But at the same time, any political movement that succeeds in chastening the judges, or holding them at bay, will strengthen the political ground for the pro-life cause. A successful campaign, to pass a referendum or an amendment, will bring out people who have not been drawn into politics in the past by other issues. And once engaged, they may be engaged more readily again. New connections are established, new networks spring into existence. Along the way, people may discover the concerns that attach them to other issues, on euthanasia or abortion.

In the late 1970s, a people's movement, stirred on by the redoubtable Phyllis Schlafly, managed to stop the Equal Rights Amendment, when the tide for that amendment seemed inexorable. If it was possible to stop the ERA, how much easier should it be to pass amendments, in several States, simply to insist that the Constitution does not entail gay marriage. But with that small step, a barrier could be cast up against the aggressive promotion of homosexuality on the part of the judges. The concert of the judges could suddenly be disrupted, and the men and women of the bench would find the occasion for some sober second thoughts. They may also turn their minds to better ways of making their living.

As for the rest of us, we may find something quite salutary in bringing this issue of homosexuality out of the courts and into the domain of a public discourse. As Chesterton once suggested, there may be nothing more novel than the rediscovery of orthodoxy. There may be few things more bracing than discovering again the reasons that lie behind the conventions long settled in our lives. And on the matter of sexuality and marriage, even some of the most tutored among us, even our class of writers and jurists, may encounter the pleasures of rediscovering old reasons and learning again things they once knew.

Notes

1. For another statement of this argument, and the analysis of Andrew Sullivan's piece on "the politics of homosexuality," see my own article, "The Closet Straight," *National Review* (July 5, 1993), pp. 43-45.

2. See 92 L Ed 2d 140.

3. This text, and all of the other passages I am citing here, are drawn from the decision of the Supreme Court of Colorado in *Evans et al. v. Romer* (July 19, 1993).

4. Judge Bayless's remarks are drawn from his decision in a District Court in Denver county, as *Evans v. Romer* was remanded to the lower courts. Civil Action No. 92 CV 7223 (December 14, 1993).

5. See *supra*, note 3, decision of the Supreme Court of Colorado, p. 34 of the typescript.

6. See *Baehr v. Lewin*, 852 P. 2d 44 (Hawaii 1993).

7. These passages are drawn from Lincoln's "House Divided Speech," June 16, 1858, in *The Collected Works of Abraham Lincoln*, ed. Roy P. Basler (New Brunswick: Rutgers University Press, 1953), Vol. II, pp. 461-68, at 465.

PART TWO:
THE FAMILY: ITS CORE MEANING
IN A CHANGED WORLD

Chapter 6

"MEDICALIZING"
MORAL DECISIONS
IN REPRODUCTIVE MEDICINE

Thomas Murphy Goodwin, M.D.

Moral decisions related to medical matters require, fundamentally, the unbiased representations of competent medical authority. Information may come from the scientific literature, or from individual physicians who are involved directly in a given case, or are acting as consultants. In each case, suitable moral analysis requires the firm base of unbiased scientific data.

The medical-scientific domain is no less subject to bias than any other. Indeed, much of the emphasis in clinical research in recent years has been directed toward standardizing study design in order to remove bias in clinical investigation. But there are certain sources of systematic bias in the medical community which influence the ability to pose moral questions fairly and have far-reaching consequences for all who come in contact with the medical establishment. I would like to discuss two of these sources of bias in particular. The first is that which arises from the merging of the legal and political dimension of the abortion debate into medical judgment and decision-making.

I would like to develop this idea just as it presented itself in practice, through the case histories of individual patients. I will digress briefly to provide the medical context necessary for some of the cases. My practice and clinical research are in one of the subspecialties of obstetrics and gynecology, maternal-fetal medicine, which is concerned with the whole spectrum of pregnancy complicated by maternal or fetal disease. The cases which I will present provide a vantage point for viewing the landscape surrounding the pregnant woman today.

There are few situations more daunting to those who advocate a consistent ethic of life than the circumstance in which the life of the mother is threatened by the continuation of the pregnancy itself. Although we do not acknowledge this conflict as justifying abortion, even the most dedicated of advocates for the life of the unborn are awed by this dilemma. Indeed, the power of this image has been one of the principle wedges moving forward the advocacy of abortion in general in the United States and elsewhere. What do we know about it objectively?

In Table 1 are listed the conditions which can be diagnosed in advance which are known to be associated with the greatest risk of maternal mortality. Taken altogether, abortions performed for these conditions make up a barely calculable fraction of the total abortions performed in the United States, but they are extremely important to the extent that they have been used to validate the idea of abortion as a whole. They stand as a sign that the idea of abortion is in some sense unavoidable—that it can be the fulfillment of the good and natural desire of the human person (in this case the mother) to live.

The first point I would like to emphasize is how rare these conditions are. Our obstetric service has been the largest in the United States over the past 15 years, averaging 15,000 to 16,000 births per year. Our institution serves a catchment area for all high risk deliveries among 30,000 per year. Excluding cases that have been diagnosed late in pregnancy, we do not see more than 1-2 of these cases per year; these are exceedingly rare conditions; this does not diminish the tragic dimension of these difficult cases but they are seen in perspective when their numbers are compared to the total number of abortions performed.

If we examine other conditions which have been associated with significant, although lesser, risk of maternal mortality for which abortion is often recommended (Table 2), we find that in many cases the prognoses are changing, both because of a better understanding of the natural history of the disease processes and because of advances in therapy. Some examples of this will be seen in the cases which follow.

Here is the paradox: as the actual risks to the mother are diminishing because of medical advances, concern about maternal and fetal risks from complications of pregnancy is still offered as a justification for many abortions. From the case histories which follow, taken from just this last year in our clinic, I will attempt to illustrate the distorted milieu of medical practice into which most pregnant women now enter.

CASE #1

A 21-year-old woman in her 19th week of pregnancy was referred for "immediate abortion." She had complained of shortness of breath and a full evaluation revealed a complex maternal congenital heart lesion, tetrology of Fallot. This is a lesion that is frequently listed as a contraindication to pregnancy because of the increased risk of maternal mortality. The senior house officer who was coordinating the abortion asked for a second opinion from our high risk clinic because the patient was distraught over the recommendation. Despite having been told that she had a significantly increased chance of dying if she remained pregnant, she had not reconciled herself to the abortion.

Repeat evaluation confirmed the diagnosis but showed that the particular manifestations of the condition in this patient were such that she could be expected to tolerate pregnancy without difficulty. She was so-called "pink tet," tetrology of Fallot in which the patient is still receiving adequate oxygen. This could have been determined by the referring physician. As it was, the patient very nearly underwent an abortion for a non-indication. The patient delivered without significant complications following induction of labor in her 38th week of pregnancy.

CASE #2

A 25-year-old woman in the 12th week of her first pregnancy had shortness of breath and was found to have severe narrowing of one of the valves of the heart, mitral stenosis. Her physician recommended abortion and asked our opinion for confirmation. We suggested that the patient be offered the opportunity to discuss balloon valve repair during pregnancy with a cardiologist skilled in that technique. We provided references showing that this could be accomplished safely in pregnancy. Her physician expressed his concern about his liability if there were any abnormality of maternal or fetal outcome. "She's young," he opined. "She can have the valve repaired and try again."

CASE #3

A 38-year-old woman was referred by her pastor. She was 11 weeks pregnant and was found to have breast cancer with spread to the regional lymph nodes. She was told that, for the best chance of long term survival, she should undergo chemotherapy, but that the pregnancy should be terminated first. She was told that her prognosis would be worse if she remained pregnant and that the chemotherapy would definitely harm her baby. Her abortion had been scheduled.

We discussed with her the published experience showing that breast cancer is not affected by pregnancy and that the chemotherapy regimen required for her condition is apparently well-tolerated by the fetus. Of course, the experience with any given chemotherapy regimen is limited, and we were frank with the patient that there were open questions about long term sequelae. When her physician was informed of the patient's desire to undergo chemotherapy and continue the pregnancy, he suggested that we take care of her and accept the liability.

The patient underwent chemotherapy (Adriamycin and Cytoxan) and delivered a baby boy who appeared entirely normal at birth. That many chemotherapy regimens can be continued without apparent ill-effect in pregnancy is information readily available to any interested physician. Why was the patient not informed?

CASE #4

A 20-year-old woman in the 18th week of her first pregnancy presented with severe renal disease which appeared to be due to new onset systemic lupus erythematosus. The first consultant who saw her recommended abortion in anticipation of favorably affecting the course of the disease, and out of concern that the medication required to control her disease might injure her fetus. The patient was anxious not to abort. We were able to tell her that although the chance of successful pregnancy outcome was low, abortion would not predictably affect the course of the disease. We discussed the considerable experience available with the medications that she would require (principally steroids) and the fact that there were no apparent serious fetal affects related to this type of treatment. The patient elected to continue her pregnancy.

Subsequently, a renal consultant recommended kidney biopsy, but not until the patient was aborted. We presented data showing that renal biopsy can be accomplished safely in pregnancy and that the need for this test should not be considered an indication for abortion. Finally, the patient required a lengthy procedure under X-ray fluoroscopy. The radiologist recommended abortion because of significant X-ray exposure. After consultation with the radiation physicist, however, it was clear that the actual X-ray exposure to the fetus in this case posed no significant risk. The patient delivered a grow-delayed baby at 27 weeks pregnancy who did well for one week until dying, suddenly, of an overwhelming infection.

All of the recommendations for abortion in these cases were partly the result of ignorance of the data, but also of something else—a belief that it is better to err on the side of abortion if there are doubts about the effect of the pregnancy on maternal or fetal outcome.

We have discussed cases in which the risk is entirely maternal and some in which both fetal and maternal risks have factored into a recommendation for abortion. In many cases, the risk is entirely fetal.

CASE #5

A 32-year-old nurse had herself tested for cytomegalovirus at 7 weeks gestation. This is a type of virus which is known to be capable of crossing the placenta and infecting the fetus, sometimes resulting in retardation and multi organ system disease, especially if the infection has occurred for the first time in pregnancy. The results of her testing prcfile suggested a recent infection indicating the possibility that her baby could be infected. She was advised to terminate the pregnancy and she had made plans to do so, although with great regret. Her doctor stated that he had confirmed his recommendations with a "high risk pregnancy specialist."

She was referred to us by a physician colleague who was her neighbor. On initial review of the tests, it did appear that there had been an acute infection during the pregnancy. We presented to the patient the data on the likelihood of her child being seriously affected—4/100, one-half of these represented by isolated hearing loss. She was stunned and relieved to learn that the risk was no greater than that. As it turned out, a more specific indicator of infection which we recommended be checked before any decision be made revealed that there had been no infection at all. She delivered a healthy boy at term. She referred frequently to her "miracle baby," a pathetic reflection of the circumstances which nearly took that baby from her.

All this patient received was an accurate assessment of the risk to her child. That was enough for her, even before she learned

84

that there had been no infection. It might not have been for the next woman. In fact, the same woman could have had an abortion for no reason at all the next day. *But it would not have been under the pretense of a medical indication.* The goal is simply to restore a rational medical assessment to these issues. Personally, we may be required to do much more. But in our professional lives, this role of strictly focusing on the issue of medically justified abortion draws attention to the way in which medical judgment has been vitiated in this area.

These cases are just some that we have seen in the last year. They include only women who, usually because of their own convictions, could not easily accept the recommendation for abortion and sought more information. There is no doubt that many others have received such recommendations and proceeded to abort simply on the basis of the doctor's authority.

But the significance of these cases lies not in the individual stories themselves, however disturbing they may be. Such cases are an insignificant number compared to the total number of abortions. In addition, the ethical dilemma in such cases is commonly understood in a context which accepts that abortion would indeed be appropriate if there were a significant risk to the mother or if the fetus were seriously malformed. The real significance of these cases lies in what they reveal about the attitudes of the physicians these women first encountered.

Why are physicians not providing readily available information that could affect their patients' judgment regarding termination of pregnancy? I believe that there are two related reasons for this phenomenon and that they go much deeper than simple ignorance of the facts. One is the transference of the ambivalent attitude toward the developing human, virtually codified in *Roe v. Wade*, into the medical arena. Since the fetus can be aborted for any reason, the physician may see fit to suggest, if not recommend, the alternative of abortion for almost any reason. The basis for such an attitude is closely linked to a second concern: the unbalanced legal burden of informed consent.

When a mother presents with a major medical problem in pregnancy (or indeed any medical problem), the medical record must reflect, in practical terms, the patient's informed consent to continue with the pregnancy despite the risks. By failing to disclose these risks, the doctor is negligent because the patient could have chosen a different course of treatment (abortion). To compound the problem for the physician, there are no clear legal guidelines to determine which risks are so small as to not warrant communication to the patient. A fact is considered to be material if a reasonable prudent person in the position of the patient would attach significance to it in deciding whether or not to submit to the proposed treatment.[1] The accurate assessment of the risks in a given case can be a tedious process. Should any untoward outcome result from the pregnancy (always a possibility), the record may well be scrutinized intensely. No method of documentation is watertight.

The doctor's alternative, to suggest or recommend that abortion is the safest route, carries no such legal liability. There does not appear to be a legal precedent for a physician's liability in a case where abortion was recommended on supposed medical grounds that were subsequently found to be baseless or misrepresented.

With regard to fetal abnormalities, the burden is equally one-sided and even more clearly delineated in law. Physicians have legal and, some would say, ethical duties to inform pregnant women of prenatal tests that would affect their willingness to continue the pregnancy. The concept of "wrongful birth" in law establishes that failure to inform of tests that are widely accepted in the medical community as part of the standard of care could lead to legal liability.[2] The related concept of "wrongful life," although less commonly invoked legally, is instructive for distilling the idea behind the law. In such cases, the child sues, claiming that it would be better not to have been born than to have been born with defects.[3]

The concept of informed consent, simple in theory, is almost impossible in practice. For many physicians it translates into simply recommending every possible test and erring on the side of suggesting abortion whenever there is a question or risk to the mother or fetus. There is a tremendous imbalance between the liability involved in not informing of risks compared to the liability of suggesting the alternative of abortion. All pregnant women, no matter what their personal convictions, are subjected to the effects of this imbalance.

The circumstances where this dilemma arises because of real or even perceived increased risk to the mother or fetus, as I have presented above, are actually relatively infrequent. Much more common in practice is the situation in which a presumably healthy mother (and healthy fetus) are offered screening tests in the hopes of identifying various congenital anomalies of the fetus. Maternal serum alphafetoprotein (MSAFP) screening, capable of identifying fetuses with neural tube defects or Down's syndrome, was introduced into this country in the early 1980s. Its place in practice was virtually mandated by the 1985 liability alert from the American College of Obstetricians and Gynecologists, itself a direct response to the perceived liability under the concept of wrongful birth.[4] Every physician must inform patients about these tests or make himself liable for the results. The patient may refuse the test, but is usually required to make a positive statement refusing the test. The inescapable implication is that the woman who refuses the test is outside of the norm.

More recently, various tests of maternal blood designed to identify fetal Down's syndrome have been introduced into clinical practice. The number of tests on the horizon which will allow identification of other fetal abnormalities appears limitless. The ineluctable logic of these legal precedents affects every pregnant woman and her child. No matter what the personal convictions of the mother, she must receive her care in a system in which every possible problem of maternal or fetal well-being is a test of whether the pregnancy will be allowed to continue. And in that balance, the developing human has little or no value. There is no counterweight to "wrongful birth." There is no "wrongful abortion."

Although few women may actually abort because of this bias, many will learn the lesson: that a new human being is accepted conditionally, one test at a time.

The second source of bias arises, in a sense, from the marginalization of the Catholic view of human sexuality within the medical establishment today. The result of this marginalization is that the scientific discussion of issues that are of particular concern to Catholics is impoverished. Issues such as the proper approach to post-coital contraception in the rape victim, the related subject of the abortifacient vs. contraceptive effects of steroid hormones, Catholic alternatives to the assisted reproductive technologies, the proper approach to the management of ectopic gestation, the systematic study of methods of natural family planning, the scientific basis for "uterine isolation" have rarely been subjected to critical study despite their importance to Catholics. The scientific criteria necessary for adequate moral analysis are often not readily available in standard textbooks and scientific journals. In many such cases, ethicists are left to decide among the varying opinions of self-appointed experts, a process open to tremendous bias and a potential source of scandal because of the wide variation in practices which result. I would like to briefly review the discussion of so-called uterine isolation by way of example.

The debate about surgical sterilization in Catholic health care institutions has been carried on for more than 50 years. The basis for defining an acceptable rationale rests, medically speaking, on the concept of the "weak uterus." Gerald Kelly, S.J., summarized the position in his 1958 text *Medical Moral Problems*: "...when competent physicians judge that, by reason of repeated cesareans (or some similar cause) a uterus is so badly damaged that it will very likely not function safely in another pregnancy, they may, with the consent of the patient, remove the uterus as a seriously pathological organ."[5] The specific example which Kelly used, the "paper thin" uterine wall, will be of interest to us later.

The scientific premise is that there are conditions of the uterus which render it so damaged that it cannot be expected to carry a subsequent pregnancy (i.e., it is likely to rupture). Further, it is assumed that such conditions can be identified at the time of cesarean delivery. Unfortunately, there is no development of medical-scientific support for this premise in Father Kelly's treatise. It appears to have been accepted *a priori*, perhaps reflecting the general opinion among obstetricians at the time.

Having conceded that removal of the weak uterus (hysterectomy) was acceptable, Thomas J. O'Donnell, S.J., developed the idea further, introducing the concept of "uterine isolation." Instead of removing the damaged uterus, why not *isolate* it by cutting the fallopian tubes? This procedure, it was argued, would fulfill the criteria of the double effect while minimizing the medical risks to the patient in that a much less extensive surgical procedure could be employed.[6] The fundamental medical-scientific premise is the same—that the doctor can judge that he will be unable to repair the uterus in such a way that it will safely support another pregnancy. Although O'Donnell himself came to question the application of the concept, he and others have continued to defend it conceptually.

For a subject of considerable practical importance, there has been remarkably little formal discussion of uterine isolation. What discussion has taken place has focused on the moral aspects of the question. Virtually no attention has been directed to the scientific premise that underlies the argument. The entire concept of the "weak uterus" has remained in the realm of plausible conjecture. Yet, it reportedly forms the basis for virtually all policies allowing tubal ligation in Catholic institutions in the United States.[7]

Part of the reason for lack of formal discussion is that the subject is not of interest to the medical community in general. The issue is seen as a Catholic one. Thus, there has not been, nor is there likely to be, any systematic research directed toward describing the "weak uterus." Even more significant, perhaps, is that contemporary obstetricians in Catholic institutions have little desire to participate in a critical analysis of the argument which underlies the only avenue to providing sterilization in the Catholic hospital.

The discussion of the weak uterus began in a time in which sterilization was an uncommon surgery, not widely accepted even in the general community. Physicians on staff at Catholic hospitals and Catholic physicians in particular, were likely to have accepted the Church's position on sterilization. This is no longer the case. Few obstetricians, even at Catholic hospitals, object to sterilization per se.

Other factors have tended to color the medical debate as well. The popularity of sterilization as a method of contraception has grown tremendously. It is now the most commonly used method of contraception. In many communities, the Catholic hospital may be the only health care institution. Even in larger communities, the need for institutions to provide comprehensive services in managed care also provides impetus for health care providers in

Catholic institutions to find some way around difficult moral prohibitions. Catholic health care providers and institutions will continue to feel considerable pressure to provide this service, especially at the time of repeat cesarean delivery where it adds little expense and morbidity.

These impediments to customary medical-scientific discourse have resulted in a situation in which the experience of individual practitioners is the only source of medical information on which to base these moral judgments. Left to decide between opinionated doctors of differing opinion, the moral theologians have tended to cite the schoolmen to the effect that *doctores scinduntur* (the experts are divided). Policies allowing uterine isolation have thus been granted on the basis that the scientific evidence is at least probable.

What do we know objectively about the "weak uterus?" (In addressing this question, I am presuming medical conditions that prevail in the United States at the present time.) There is no doubt that conscientious physicians have accepted that such an entity exists. Nevertheless, the first thing that strikes one who seeks information about it is that the general concept is not well-attested. There is not a single reference to the concept or any related idea in the English language medical literature in the last 30 years. This lack of mention does not prove that the entity does not exist, but the fact that the weak uterus has never been formally characterized should cause us to proceed cautiously in accepting it as the basis for a critical ethical decision-making process. Beyond this lack of definition, there is recent evidence, albeit indirect, which casts doubt on the weak uterus as an entity.

A natural opportunity for considering the criteria for the weak uterus is afforded by examining a policy on uterine isolation which was recently proposed at a Catholic institution in this country. This policy is representative of several that I have had occasion to review. It is instructive because it provides a broad definition of the weak uterus, allowing us to consider each of the proposed criteria for this condition.

Uterine isolation may be performed in conjunction with a cesarean delivery when a subsequent pregnancy cannot be considered due to possible rupture of the uterus. The conditions which may lead to this include the following:

90

Thin lower uterine segment
Classical cesarean delivery
Transverse incision with extension into:
 the upper uterine segment
 the cervix
 the broad ligament
Spontaneous rupture of the uterus

Let us consider these conditions individually with particular emphasis on spontaneous rupture of the uterus, which is the most extreme example of the weak or damaged uterus.

THIN LOWER UTERINE SEGMENT

The thin lower uterine segment is not a recognized condition of the uterus as such. It is not described in textbooks of obstetrics nor referenced in the English language medical literature of the last 20 years. There are no objective criteria defining this condition. (It could be argued that a thin lower uterine segment is objectively identified when the lower segment scar is so "thin" as to have separated, but this condition is more properly classified as a dehiscence of the uterine scar and will be treated below in the discussion of that entity.) It is present if the attending physician says it is present. Although it is common to note that the lower segment is thin or "thinned out," no pathologic correlates of this condition have ever been described. Specifically, there is no published account of its association with a risk of uterine rupture in a subsequent pregnancy.

It is my experience that the thin lower uterine segment is the most common indication for uterine isolation. It constituted over 90% of the indications for uterine isolation in one institution where I reviewed the uterine isolations.

CLASSICAL CESAREAN

This is defined as a vertical incision of the uterus which extends into the muscular portion of the uterus (Figure 1). It is used in less than 2% of cesarean deliveries, generally in cases of extreme prematurity or certain abnormalities of fetal life. It is well established that women in whom the uterus is incised in this fashion are at increased risk for uterine rupture in a subsequent pregnancy. The chance of rupture with this condition is thought to be as high as 5% if labor is allowed to take place in a subsequent pregnancy. If elective cesarean is performed before labor, however, the risk is substantially reduced. For this reason, trial of labor is contraindicated in women with a prior classical cesarean delivery. On the other hand, there is no suggestion that subsequent pregnancy itself is contraindicated or even inadvisable. There are no recommendations for sterilization after classical cesarean delivery.[8]

TRANSVERSE INCISION WITH EXTENSION INTO THE UPPER UTERUS, BROAD LIGAMENT OR CERVIX.

The lower segment transverse cesarean delivery incision is shown in Figure 2. This is the standard incision employed in the United States today. Extension of the low segment transverse incision into the upper portion of the uterus, the broad ligament, and toward the cervix are shown in Figure 3.

Extension into the upper segment is thought to pose a risk for rupture in subsequent pregnancy which is equivalent to that seen with a classical cesarean. The discussion above applies to this entity. There is no data in the literature to support an association between extension of the transverse incision into the broad ligament or lower segment and the risk of rupture in a subsequent pregnancy.

SPONTANEOUS RUPTURE OF THE UTERUS.

The most dramatic and severe form of the weak uterus occurs with catastrophic rupture. Because of the severity of this condition, a considerable body of experience has accumulated with regard to its evaluation and treatment. The largest reported experience is contained in a series of publications from the University of Southern California in Los Angeles. The data which follows is summarized from that experience.

From 1983 through 1992, there were 166,851 births at LAC-USC Women's Hospital. 17,521 (10.6%) of these were to women with a prior cesarean delivery. 12,796 of these women attempted a trial of labor after cesarean, and 10,478 were successful in delivering vaginally. Uterine scar separation was noted in 310 (1.7%) cases, the majority (1.1%) of which were asymptomatic uterine dehiscences. Catastrophic rupture requiring emergency surgery occurred in 0.7% (117 cases). The analysis of these cases of catastrophic rupture allows the most direct insight into modern obstetric practices related to injured or weakened uterus.

It is interesting to note that hysterectomy was required in only 30 of 310 uterine scar separations (9.7%). In each case, hysterectomy was performed because of massive, uncontrollable hemorrhage from the ruptured uterus, or because the patient had previously indicated in writing a desire for permanent sterilization. No patient with asymptomatic separation of the uterine scar underwent hysterectomy. Patients who had the ruptured uterus repaired and who still desired to conceive again were advised to undergo elective cesarean delivery before labor in the next pregnancy. In no case was sterilization or hysterectomy performed except to save the life of the mother unless there was documented desire for permanent sterilization.

The argument can be simply put. If the ruptured uterus, clearly the most significant type of traumatic uterine injury, can be repaired and the patient allowed to conceive again, how can this or lesser degrees of uterine injury be indications for hysterectomy or "uterine isolation" in and of themselves? I believe that such data should lead us to revisit the medical-scientific basis for the uterine isolation argument.

I do not propose this brief discussion as the "last word" on uterine isolation. It is difficult, after all, to prove that something (the weak uterus) does not exist. But I do intend this to serve as a call to debate the scientific premise of uterine isolation on its own merits. The failure to appeal to a common body of objective medical-scientific data is one of the reasons for the confusing variation in Catholic medical practice from region to region. The same may be said of protocols for management of rape victims in Catholic institutions and the other questions which I outlined at the beginning of this talk. Is it really necessary for each hospital or diocese to explore these complicated subjects individually? If I may be permitted a few concrete suggestions:

1. The time is right for the responsible authorities to support efforts to achieve a scientific consensus on these issues to the extent that that is possible. Where further study is needed, this should be supported as well. Such support will signal the medical-scientific community that Catholics are serious about these questions.

2. Encourage the Catholic medical schools or support independent institutions dedicated, at least in part, to the study of these issues of concern to Catholics that do not receive attention from the medical community in general.

3. Encourage young Catholic men and women to seek careers in obstetrics and gynecology. The Catholic understanding of human sexuality is poorly represented within the profession, often leading to confusion and misunderstanding for Catholic women seeking care within the system.

Notes

1. Lenke, R. R., Nemes, J. M., "Wrongful Birth, Wrongful Life: The Doctor Between a Rock and a Hard Place," *Obstet. Gynecol.* 66 (1985):719-22.

2. Robertson, J. A., "Legal and Ethical Issues Arising from the New Genetics," *J Reprod. Med* 37 (1986): 521-4.

3. Pelias, M. Z., "Torts of Wrongful Birth and Wrongful Life: A Review," *Am J Med Genet* 25 (1986):71-80.

4. American College of Obstetricians and Gynecologists professional liability alert, 1985.

5. Kelly, Gerald, S.J., *Medico-Moral Problems*, (The Catholic Hospital Association, 1957).

6. O'Donnell, Thomas J., S.J., *Medicine and Christian Morality*. Second revised and updated edition, (New York: Alba House, 1991), pp. 138-144.

7. Peter Cataldo, Ph.D., Pope John XXIII Center. Personal communication.

8. Committee on Obstetrics: Maternal and Fetal Medicine, "Guidelines for Vaginal Delivery After a Previous Cesarean Birth," ACOG Committee Opinion No. 64, (Washington, DC: American College of Obstetricians and Gynecologists, 1988).

9. Farmer, R. M., Kirschbaum, T., Potter, D., Strong, T. H., Medearis, A. L., "Uterine Rupture During Trial of Labor after Previous Cesarian Section," *Am J Obstet Gynecol* 165 (1991): 996-1001.

10. Leung, A. S., Leung, E. K., Paul, R. H., "Uterine Rupture After Previous Cesarian Delivery: Maternal and Fetal Consequences," *Am J Obstet Gynecol* 169 (1993): 945-50.

11. Miller, D. A., Paul, R. H., "Vaginal Birth After Cesarean Section: A Ten Year Experience," *Am J Obstet Gynecol* (in press).

TABLE 1.
CONDITIONS ASSOCIATED WITH A GREATER THAN 20% RISK OF MATERNAL MORTALITY.

Pulmonary hypertension

  Primary

  Eisenmenger's syndrome

Marfan's syndrome with aortic root involvement

Complicated coarctation of the aorta

Peripartum cardiomyopathy with residual dysfunction

TABLE 2.
OTHER CONDITIONS ASSOCIATED WITH SIGNIFICANT RISK OF MATERNAL MORTALITY.

Severe aortic or mitral stenosis

Prior myocardial infarction (especially in diabetic)

Marfan's syndrome

Uncorrected tetrology of Fallot

Coarctation of the aorta

Classical cesarean

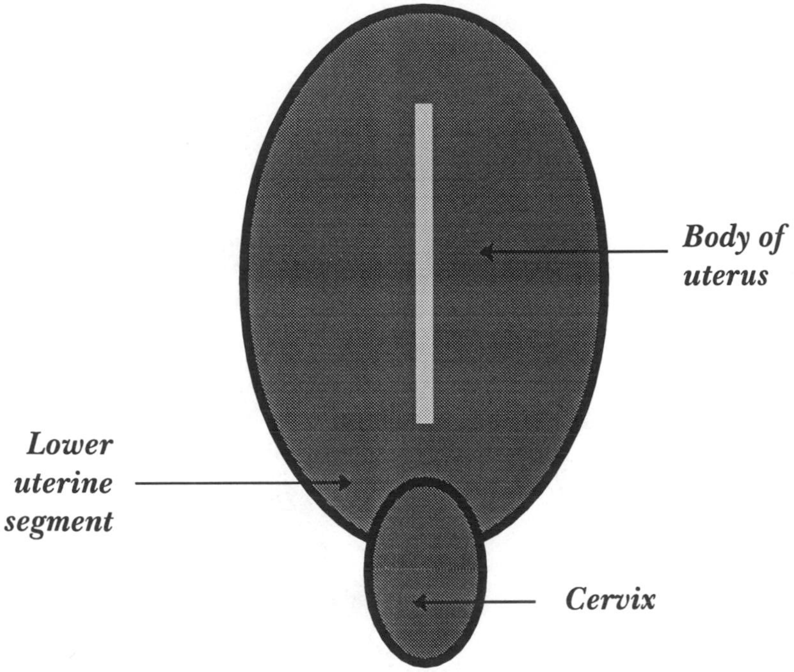

figure 1

Cesarean with transverse incision

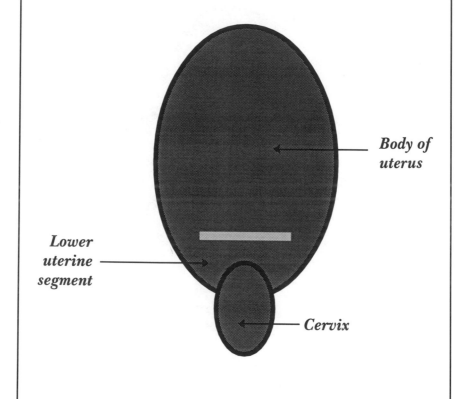

figure 2

Transverse incision with extension

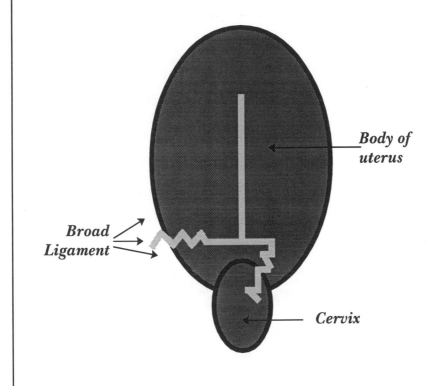

figure 3

Chapter 7

MARITAL LOVE AND THE FLAWED LOVE OF QUASI-MARITAL TIES

The Reverend Monsignor Cormac Burke, J.C.D.

Skepticism about binding commitments?

There has been no period in history without its own particular crises. One of the greatest of the present day, it seems to me, as well as one of the most peculiar, is the growing rift between men and women. The relationship between the sexes is marked more and more by suspicion and tension, division, and even antagonism.

The idea that man and woman are somehow made for each other, and made for union of a particular type called marriage—an idea that has come down the centuries—is under threat. Unions still occur or are attempted—in some marital or quasi-marital form—but they tend not to last.

People, at least in Western countries, have become deeply skeptical about a permanent husband-wife relationship. They are no longer convinced that it is worth making and can be stuck to. This loss of faith in marriage, with the fundamental pessimism it denotes about the possibilities of finding a happy and lasting love in life, implies a major crisis for humanity.

Catholics too, in ever larger numbers, are coming to think that marriage-open-to-divorce is better than marriage-bound-to-indissolubility: a situation that must give us pause. In theological terms, this could be seen as a temptation against faith, since indissolubility is a defined dogma (Denz., 1807). As such, it is no small temptation. Yet its possible occurrence should come as less of a surprise when we recall the reaction provoked by Jesus when he insisted that according to the original divine plan, the marriage bond is unbreakable: if things are so, his very Apostles felt, then it is better not to marry (Mt 19, 10). But of course they were wrong. Things are so; and it is still good—a great good—to marry.

Current misgivings about the value of indissolubility have no less serious anthropological implications, reflected in the idea that faithfulness to a lasting commitment, however freely undertaken, is not reasonably to be expected; it is something beyond human nature and people are not capable of it. As this idea spreads, it creates a mindset hostile to any type of permanent commitment: the priesthood and religious life included, as well as marriage.

The idea that "indissolubility is a bad thing"—for which there must be a way out—has effects on both people and pastors. Those contemplating marriage approach it less seriously; and when they do marry, strive less to keep their marriage going later on as it becomes subject to stress. For their part, pastors and counselors may tend to prepare couples less in pre-marriage instruction for the difficulties they are going to meet, and may not be sufficiently positive and supportive with couples who are going through the actual experience of difficulty. We have a real problem on our hands when the "solution" being offered for difficult marital situations is not "try to make a go of it, pray, rely on grace," but more and more: "seek a way out, a 'good faith' solution, an annulment..." Things will continue to deteriorate unless we can achieve a re-evaluation of married indissolubility. This has to be a central point of pastoral reflection and responsibility, especially in the formation of priests and counselors.

Christian and secular anthropology

Vatican II sought to offer a renewed vision of marriage, of marital love and commitment. How is it that this renewed vision seems so infrequently to have been translated into practice? One reason, I feel, is that much post-conciliar reflection on marriage has not always grasped the Christian anthropology which is a key to conciliar thinking about human realities, especially as applied to the marital covenant. The result is that much recent understanding and presentation of marriage has been largely, though no doubt unconsciously, colored by the anthropology dominant in our secular world.

The "secular anthropology" I refer to is an individualistic view of man, which sees the key to human fulfillment in self: self-identification, self-assertion, self-concern.... The current crisis about indissolubility—the tendency to look on it as an "anti-value"—finds much of its explanation in this individualism, present outside and inside the Church. Individualism fosters a fundamentally self-centered approach to marriage, seeking to get from it rather than being prepared to give in it: will this—this union, this liaison, this arrangement—make *me* happy?

Then marriage becomes at best a tentative agreement between two individuals, each inspired by self-interest, rather than a shared endeavor where a couple want to build together a home for each other and for their children.

Married personalism

By the distinctive anthropology of Vatican II, I mean that Christian personalism which is so present in conciliar thinking, especially in *Gaudium et spes*. Developed in great power by Pope John Paul II, it is fundamental to a deeper human understanding of Christian life and of marriage in particular.

The essence of true personalism is expressed in *Gaudium et spes*, no. 24: "man can fully discover his true self only in a sincere giving of himself." We can only "realize" or fulfill our self, by giving our self. Here is a gospel program of life in direct contrast with the prescription for living so commonly offered by contemporary psychology: seek self, find self, identify self, care for self, hold on to self, don't let go of yourself.

Marriage represents the most concrete natural type of self-giving for which man and woman are made. As *Gaudium et spes* also says: the "partnership of man and woman constitutes the first form of communion between persons" (no. 12). Major texts of the magisterium have continued to expound marriage in a personalist light.[1] Strikingly enough, the revision of the Church's law has contributed notably to the personalist analysis of marriage. Two canons in the 1983 Code of Canon Law merit special attention.

Canon 1057 says, "Matrimonial consent is an act of the will by which a man and a woman, through an irrevocable covenant, mutually give and accept each other in order to establish a marriage." The very object of conjugal consent is thus presented in terms of mutual self-donation—in most striking contrast with the "ius in corpus" phrase with which the 1917 Code expressed the same object.[2] The man gives self as man and husband, the woman as woman and wife; and each receives the other as spouse. One wonders if the scope and power—the beauty and the demands—of this new formula have been fully appreciated, especially in the fields of seminary training, marriage counseling, and tribunal work on marriage cases.

Married personalism particularly characterizes another remarkable canon, c. 1055, above all when it speaks of the *ends* of marriage. "The matrimonial covenant...is by its nature ordered to the good of the spouses and to the procreation and education of offspring."[3] To my mind there is something extraordinarily significant in this modern magisterial choice of the term "good of the spouses" to express one of the ends of marriage. It should be stressed that it is not presented as a personalist end, in *contrast with* the institutional end—which would be procreation. The good of the spouses is equally an institutional end, just as much as procreation. This is evident from the dual account given by Genesis of the creation of man and woman. The first account—"God created man in his own image, in the image of God he created him; male and female he created them...and said to them, 'Be fruitful and multiply'" (Gen 1, 27-28)—is clearly procreational. While the second—"Then the Lord God said, 'It is not good that the man should be alone: I will make him a helper fit for him'" (Gen 2,18)—is clearly personalist. Therefore, while the two ends can be distinguished, they should not be over-contrasted, for *both* are institutional ends.[4] More than any possible hierarchy between them, it is their inseparability which needs to be understood and stressed. Since time does not permit going into the personalist value of procreation,[5] let us briefly examine the idea of the "good of the spouses," concretely too in the light of indissolubility.

Indissolubility and the "good of the spouses"

God could have created the human race in a unisex—sexless—pattern, and provided for its continuation otherwise than by sex. Genesis seems to make it clear that creation would have been less good if he had done so; "it is not good for man—or woman—to be alone." So sexuality appears in the Bible as part of a plan for personal fulfillment, a factor meant to contribute to the perfecting of the human being. The basic anthropological point is that the human person is not self-sufficient, but needs others, with a special need for an "other," a partner, a spouse.

Each human person, in the awareness of his or her contingency, wishes to be loved: to be in some way unique for someone. Each one, if he or she does not find anyone to love him or her, is haunted by the temptation to feel worthless. Further, it is not enough to *be* loved; it is necessary to *love*. A person who is loved can be unhappy, if he or she is unable to love. Everyone is loved (at least by God); not everyone learns to love. To learn to love is as great a human need as to know oneself loved; only so can a person be saved from self-pity or self-isolation, or from both.

To learn to love demands coming out of self: through firm dedication—in good times and bad—to another, to others. What a person has to learn is not passing love, but *committed* love. We all stand in need of a commitment to love. Such is the priesthood, or a life dedicated directly to God. And such is marriage, the dedication to which God calls the majority. To bind people to the process of learning to love was God's original design for marriage, confirmed by Our Lord (Mt. 19, 8ff.). The married commitment is by nature something demanding. This is brought out by the words with which the spouses express their mutual acceptance of one another, through "irrevocable personal consent,"[6] "for better or for worse, for richer or for poorer, in sickness and in health...all the days of my life."[7]

While this commitment is indeed demanding, it is also deeply natural and attractive. Real love means it, when it says, "I'll love you for always." Among other things, this could suggest that in the education given to our young people, clearer stress should be placed on the fact that human beings, in distinction to animals, are created not just with a sexual instinct, but with a *conjugal* instinct.[8]

Sexual instinct: conjugal instinct

The sexual instinct is natural, developing by itself and quick to make itself present. More than development, it needs control; it is often more intense toward one person, but not normally limited to one. The conjugal instinct is also natural, though slower to make itself present; it needs to be developed; it scarcely needs to be controlled; it is generally limited to one person.

The conjugal instinct draws man and woman to total commitment to one person, to a permanent association or covenant of love, and to be faithful to that freely assumed commitment. The widespread frustration in the area of sex which people sense today is a frustration of conjugality rather than of mere sexuality. As the conjugal instinct is understood, developed and matured, it tends strongly to facilitate sexual control by inducing sexual respect. It is normal for a young couple in love to have an *ideal* of marriage before them: each sees the other as possible life-companion, and mother or father of one's future children; someone therefore who can be absolutely unique in one's life. These are primary truths of conjugal sexuality which our modern world seems to be losing sight of; hence the gradual loss of mutual esteem between the sexes. While this applies reciprocally in the sexual relationship, it has a particular application in how a man relates to a woman. If nothing so much as motherhood or potential motherhood makes a man respect a woman, this is because it raises her above the category of an object to be possessed and establishes her in that of a subject to be revered.

Marital love and marital defects

It is easy to love good people. The program of Christianity is that we also learn to love "bad" people, i.e., people with defects. Within our present context, its particular program is that whoever freely enters the marital covenant of love and life with another —no doubt because he or she sees unique goodness in that person—should be prepared to remain faithful to the covenant, even if later on objective or subjective considerations make the other seem to have lost any exceptional goodness and to be characterized rather by a series of maddening defects.

The discovery of mutual defects in marriage is inevitable, but not incompatible with the fulfillment of the good of the spouses. On the contrary, one can say that the experience of mutual defects is essential if married life itself is to achieve the true divine idea of the "bonum coniugum." As effortless romance fades, the stage is set for each of the spouses to get down to the business of *learning to love* the other *as he or she really is*. It is then that they grow as persons. Here lies the seriousness and beauty of the challenge contained in marriage: it remains a critical point to be stressed in education and counseling.

Romance is almost sure to die; love however does not have to die with it. Love is meant to mature, and can do so if that readiness for sacrifice implied in the original self-giving of marital consent is alive or can be activated. The idea that true love is prepared for sacrifice strikes a chord which perhaps our preaching needs to touch on more. As Pope John Paul II says: "It is natural for the human heart to accept demands, even difficult ones, in the name of love for an ideal, and above all in the name of love for a person."[9]

Human nature is a mixture and conflict of good and bad tendencies. Are we appealing sufficiently to the good tendencies? Or do we yield at times to the temptation to think that the bad are more powerful? We need to strengthen our faith not only in God, but also in the goodness of his creation, recalling what St. Thomas Aquinas teaches, "bonum est potentius quam malum":[10] good is more powerful than evil, and its appeal strikes deeper into our nature, for goodness rooted in truth remains the most fundamental need of the human person. We have lately been once more reminded of this in *Veritatis splendor*. It is from our natural quest or thirst for the good that Pope John Paul II there builds up his presentation of the splendor and attraction of the truth.[11]

Contrary tendencies can be natural. In the face of danger it is natural to feel tempted to be a coward and run away. But it is also natural to want to be brave and face the danger. A mother or father may have a natural tendency toward selfishness; yet they have a no less natural tendency to care for their children: a maternal or paternal instinct. Similarly, while it is natural for strains to develop between husband and wife, it is also natural for them to want to preserve their love from the threat of these strains. What we have called the conjugal instinct calls them to be faithful, whereas a person senses something soft, mean and selfish, in a refusal to face up to the challenge of fidelity.

As against this, there would seem to be little that is natural, and nothing that is inevitable, in the phenomenon that two people who at one moment thought each other absolutely unique, should end up five or ten years later unable to stand one another. "My love for him or her has died...." If such were to happen, it would have been a gradual death, and one that could often have been prevented by good counsel from relatives, friends, pastors.

"Trial" commitments

It is not good for man to be alone; or to "half" give himself. Hence derives the radically unsatisfying and frustrating nature of "quasi-marital" ties: i.e., where there is no binding commitment. I refer here not to simple promiscuity, but to couples who want some sort of semi-conjugal relationship, where there will be a certain sense of belonging to each other; but not definitively, always with a way out.

Such a relationship is something so much less than marriage, that a couple experimenting with it are not likely ever to marry; or if they do, it is not likely to last. Their approach is too flawed. Each one remains fundamentally his or her own project; there is no *shared* enterprise. "I" rather than "we" remains the reference point and center for each. The other is never regarded as more than a "trial" partner.

They don't *give* of selves; each one only lends to the other, only gives in part. Their subsequent lives can seldom shake off the feeling: "I have never found anyone worth giving myself to," or "I have never been capable of giving myself"; or perhaps simply: "I have never been accepted; nobody ever thought me worth accepting unconditionally."[12]

People who do not love cannot find love; people who do not give themselves cannot find themselves. The way of quasi-commitment is a way of self-frustration.

Now let us try to draw practical conclusions from these points. We could first consider preparation for marriage; and then, care during marriage.

Pastoral preparation for marriage

We have to try to ensure that education given to young people, at least in Catholic institutions, is inspired by a truly Christian anthropology, which restores the sense of the naturalness and attractiveness of the call to marriage, with special insistence on the goodness of the commitment to an unbreakable bond of love. Two aspects of this education could be distinguished.

a) *Love-education*, which really means education in giving. If frustration is inevitable and fulfillment not possible without giving self, then three main problems face the life of each one: (i) to find something—some ideal, some person—worth giving self to; (ii) to be able to give self (for this, one must first possess self); (iii) to be able to stick to the gift (because fulfillment is not a momentary but a life-long process).

Corresponding to these problems, perhaps three rules could be put to our young people. First, don't be afraid to give *of* yourself, now. Practice self-giving *now*, in your teens, at home, in service activities. Second, don't give yourself sexually until the moment comes; and that moment is marriage. Giving yourself before, you give in parts and too easily, and have little or nothing left to give when the moment comes (a powerful argument in favor of pre-marriage chastity). Third, when the moment does come for marriage (if that is your vocation), give yourself really, in the full gift of your conjugal self.

b) *Sex-education*. Though some would deny it, the contemporary attitude not just toward marriage but toward sexuality is tinged with profound pessimism. When sex is presented as easily-accessible pleasure, it becomes almost impossible for people to understand its importance and its fragility in so many aspects of human development. Proper sex-education must help young people:

- understand the truly human side of sexuality: not only the equal dignity of the sexes, but especially the value of sexual complementarity. Here we are up against a pervasive unisex culture and philosophy.

- achieve proper sexual identification, seeing the development of masculinity and femininity as goals to be pursued. Many girls (just to take one example) seem today to have little idea of those traits of feminine nature which can captivate a man, and hold him captive, even as physical charms may wane.

- understand the delicacy of the sexual relationship.[13] Sex used to be an area of happiness—a promise or a hope of happiness—surrounded with danger. The danger has been taken away, but with it the hope of happiness seems to be going too.

In this work, our educators ought to be the first to realize that when sexuality is reduced to the level of physical differences, women are the losers; for on the merely physical level, man is the stronger and can easily dominate. Whereas, when the more truly human and spiritual aspects of sexuality are operative, women tend to acquire a special ascendancy and superiority.

Educators need equally to realize that an over-emphasis on independence with an under-emphasis on complementarity, can make the achievement of true sexual identity almost impossible. Many marriages fail today because there is not enough masculinity or femininity to keep them together. No preparation for marriage is adequate if it does not help toward spousal role identification.

Pastoral care during marriage

a) *toward a couple as spouses*. It is easy to make the marital commitment. It is not easy to maintain it, to perfect it, so reaching, as *Veritatis splendor* says, "that maturity in self-giving to which human freedom is called."[14] Along with prayer and the sacraments, people need to be reminded of a main key to success in conjugal love (i.e., the love that binds together two persons with defects): learning to forgive and asking for forgiveness. Each time husband and wife acknowledge his or her defects to the other, he or she becomes more human, and therefore more lovable. The husband or wife who denies their defects or seeks to justify them, becomes more proud, more isolated; less loving and less lovable.

110

Not only the spouses themselves, but their relatives and friends need to be taught to understand and respect the demanding beauty of the conjugal relationship, in the life-long task of learning to love. People need support: from relations and friends first; and then from pastors and counselors. There is need for a constant catechesis which shows a new appreciation of the commitment involved in marriage, especially of the goodness of the bond; so that the very *beginnings* of trouble are met with positive help and advice, not with encouragement to seek an annulment (which may not be granted in the end). Friends and neighbors need all to be reminded of their grave responsibility to be a help and not a hindrance to the perseverance of married persons.

b) *toward a couple as parents*. Wise spouses learn how to distribute parental roles. As in any team, this approach of complementing one another obviates difficulties in getting along. But if the team approach is lost, if they let themselves be pushed into a power struggle, the family enterprise is almost bound to end in failure.

The help that families need cannot come mainly from outside, nor will it suffice if provided on a merely collective or social level: e.g., family days or activities organized by the parish. It is in the home itself that families need to develop their personality and strength. The family life of each Christian home needs to take on a forceful quality, expressed in family conversations, plans, projects, which are humanly attractive. No easy task, given the attraction of other forces? Agreed; but there is the challenge to parents to be the creators of something unique. They need to find encouragement from their pastors in this, just as they certainly will find the grace of God.

In Summary:

a) The true commitment and binding relationship of marriage attracts powerfully, for there is something deeply natural to it. However, for our nature in its present state, there is also something deeply difficult to it. To achieve the fulfillment promised by marriage is not possible without grace; it is possible with grace.

b) Our pastoral presentation of marriage must be optimistic: showing the natural attraction, without underplaying the natural difficulties; and emphasizing the supernatural help;

True pastoral care for marriage must therefore be based on:

—sound anthropology, which on the one hand stresses the complementarity of the sexes and of sexual roles no less than the equal dignity between man and woman; and which then particularly underlines the main aspects that make marriage attractive and worthwhile, especially offspring and indissolubility;

—sound psychology, which helps people realize that difficulties, even severe ones, must arise in marriage; and that it is there that love, which means giving, is tested and grows or fails;

—sound pastoral and sacramental theology, which equips married people to face difficulties with full reliance on sacramental grace, and on prayer and guidance;[16]

—sound ascetical theology, which reminds those preparing for marriage, and in marriage, of what Vatican II so stressed: that marriage is fundamentally and ultimately a vocation to holiness;[17] it means constant exercise in true love, which consists in self-giving, self-sacrifice, losing self for others and so finding oneself.

In the end we cannot and should not want to get away from the fact that happiness—also that which marriage promises—is not possible without generosity and sacrifice. I often heard Blessed Josemaria Escriva, the Founder of Opus Dei, say that happiness has its roots in the shape of the Cross.[18] It is the rule and apparent paradox of the Gospel: Only by "losing" and giving ourselves—the essence of love—can we begin to find ourselves and, even more than ourselves, the happiness we are made for.

Our preaching on marriage will produce no renewal if it does not reflect this basic truth. As the Cathechism of the Catholic Church says: "Following Christ, denying themselves, taking on themselves their own cross, the spouses can "understand" the original sense of matrimony and live it with the help of Christ. This grace of Christian matrimony is a fruit of the Cross of Christ, the source of all Christian life."[19]

Notes

1. Cf. *Humanae vitæ*, no. 9; *Familiaris consortio*, no. 13; *Mulieris dignitatem*, no. 7, etc.

2. Bearing in mind that the idea of "giving oneself"—*se tradere*—can only figuratively imply a gift of one's actual person, the gift involved is rather the fullness of complementary conjugal sexuality.

3. The *Catechism of the Catholic Church* (no. 2363) insists on the "double end of marriage: the good of the spouses themselves and the handing on of life."

4. Cf. C. Burke: "Marriage: a personalist or an institutional understanding?": *Communio* 1992-III, 287ff.

5. *Nevertheless*, since the contraceptive mentality certainly provides part of the explanation why spouses stick together less, *this point—the personalist value of procreation*—is a theme that urgently needs to be developed: cf. C. Burke: "Matrimonial Consent and the *Bonum Prolis*" *Monitor Ecclesiasticus* 114 (1989-III), 397-404.

6. *Gaudium et spes*, no. 48.

7. *Ordo Celebrandi Matrimonium*, no. 25.

8. Cf. C. Burke: "Personalism and the *bona* of Marriage" *Studia Canonica* 27 (1993), 411-412.

9. General Audience, April. 21, 1982 (cf. *Insegnamenti di Giovanni Paolo II*, V, 1 (1982), p. 1274; cf. *Familiaris Consortio*, no. 34: "sacrifice cannot be removed from family life, but must in fact be wholeheartedly accepted if the love between husband and wife is to be deepened and become a source of intimate joy."

10. *Summa Theol.* I, q. 100, art. 2.

11. Cf. VS, Chap. I: "What good must I do?"

12. Psychiatric studies show that the choice to live together instead of marrying, easily induces deep-rooted anxiety and insecurity: cf. *Nadelson-Notman*: "To Marry or Not to Marry: a Choice" *American Journal of Psychiatry*, 138 (1982), p. 1354.

13. Cf. *Catechism of the Catholic Church*, 1607.

14. VS, no. 17

15. Cf. VS, no. 102f.

16. Married couples "have need of the grace of God.... Without this help, man and woman cannot achieve that union of their lives for which God created them at the beginning:" *Catechism of the Catholic Church*, 1608.

17. Cf. *Lumen Gentium*, 39-41; *Gaudium es spes*, 48-49.

18. Cf. *The Forge*, Scepter Press, New York, 1990, no. 28.

19. No. 1615.

Chapter 8

CHILDREN: THE SUPREME GIFT OF MARRIAGE

Janet Smith, Ph.D.

To Children

The sociologists and psychologists who are addressing this distinguished assembly will have laid out the dimensions of the sociological and psychological dysfuntionality of the family; which includes, for example, the incidence of divorce, the amount of sexual and psychological abuse, the alienation and isolation of children, the easy slide that such alienation and isolation facilitates into drug abuse, sexual license and other modern forms of escapism.

What I wish to explore here is how the modern age has a philosophical and theological dysfunctionality in respect to its understanding of children and their intrinsic importance, and of the importance of children to their parents and society. At the risk of sounding unduly alarmist, I must observe that our society has nearly reached a state of philosophical insanity in respect to the value of human life, the value of babies and the meaning of sexuality. A state of philosophical insanity means that we are fundamentally and basically denying the reality of fundamental and basic truths to the point that our behavior is dangerously self-destructive.

Babies are gifts, wonderful gifts from God that should rightly be the focal point of any marriage. But in our society babies are rarely considered as gifts from God. Certainly parents still naturally want to have children (if only a few well-planned and genetically well-designed ones) and they still delight in their children but even so children are more often considered a possession that couples—or single individuals, homosexual or heterosexual—may opt to have or even opt to have made for them; they are an option, not the reason for marriage.

It is even considered a luxury and often an irresponsible luxury for couples to have more than two children; those who have many are considered ignorant or self-indulgent. They are not understood to be doing a generous service for God and man; they are adding to the problem of overpopulation; they are producing enemies of the environment who will consume too many of the world's resources. Any mother of three or more children has horror stories to tell of the rude comments about her childbearing practices, made by perfect strangers. Many of those who are infertile, on the other hand, think they have a right to a baby and think that there are no ethical limits to the reproductive technologies.

A further irony is that the epidemic in infertility that we seem to be facing has its cause in great part in scarring created by pelvic inflammatory diseases, largely contracted through sex outside of marriage and in reduced fertility attributable to prolonged use of contraceptives. So we have women who for years suppress their fertility so they can have sexual intercourse without babies and who then spend considerable private and public fortunes so they can have babies without sexual intercourse.

The ready availability of abortion speaks volumes of our devaluing of human life and children as do the new industries we have that specialize in baby making, that allow any woman who has money to pay for it to be artificially inseminated and that allow parents literally to design what kind of children they are going to have. As I wrote this talk, there was the flare up of the ethical issue of taking eggs from aborted fetuses to use for *in vitro* fertilization. I watched a brief discussion between a doctor and a woman representing a pro-life organization. He was arguing that since the procedure was scientifically possible and since it would help infertile women conceive, it was a good and ethical procedure. He simply could not see the absurdity of the procedure so well pointed out by the pro-life woman; it is absurd to take eggs from a baby being aborted, to help another woman have a baby; why doesn't she simply adopt the baby being aborted?! If we valued life at all, this absurdity would be blatantly obvious to all; that it is not indicates how lost we are.

A few weeks earlier we had all pondered the meaning of "cloning" or twinning embryos. A friend was quick to point out the near-certain implications of this procedure. One could gestate one twin and freeze the other; the frozen one could be activated if the gestated twin needed spare parts or could be sold if some couple especially liked the gestated twin and wanted a child just like him or her. We long ago passed through the door of absurdity in these matters and now are just multiplying absurdities.

I apologize if I use the word "absurdity" too liberally, but we are living in a time when the shocking and unthinkable has become ordinary; our instincts that should by virtue of a gut reaction, so to speak, cry out that "such things" ought not be done have been dulled by the proliferation of abuses to human life in this century. At least in the early and middle decades of this century, such absurdity was inflicted on the born; the perpetrators of great crimes against humanity tried to hide these crimes, but at least victims and potential victims could to some extent fight for themselves and their neighbors could be moved to fight for them. The

116

invisibility of the unborn, the seeming insignificance of the fertilized egg, makes it much harder to protect the unborn from the great indignities and vile crimes we wreck upon them.

To Parents

Another great harm done to children is intimately related to the harm done to parents—babies are generally received into the world by parents who are not mature themselves and who, sadly, have been formed by the values of their dysfunctional society. They have too little sense of the value of life and a great deal of this lack of value comes from the severe misunderstanding of the meaning of sexuality in our culture. Whereas in other decades of this century, it was political utopianism that led to the hostility to life which resulted in massive killings of the innocent, in our age, it has been an attempt to establish a sexual utopia that has led to the massive killings of the unborn and the great devaluing of the lives of their living brothers and sisters.

In the final decades of this blood-soaked twentieth century, it has not been the teachings of a man such as Marx or the political machinations of a Hitler that has led us to wage what at times seems to be a systematic pogrom on the unborn. Rather, it has been the proliferation of sexual activity that has no ordination to the care of the babies that may issue from that sexual activity.

This devaluing of the meaning of human sexuality is a primary cause of the devaluing of human life and the devaluing of children we have seen in these last several decades. When contraceptives became widely available we had the igniting of the sexual revolution which separated having babies from having sex. When that separation happened, babies were no longer welcomed as the natural and right outcome of sexual intercourse, but were considered an accident of sexual intercourse, an inconvenient burden, so inconvenient that we argue that we need abortion to keep our life-styles going. The easy availability of contraception has led millions to take up life-styles they simply were not able to pursue before the availability of contraception—life-styles that include sexual relations with several partners before marriage, relations that often lead to abortions. Indeed, one of the most telling items of evidence that our society has gone haywire in its understanding of sexuality and the value of life is a statement from the Supreme Court decision about the *Casey vs. Planned Parenthood* case. There it made the connection between contraception and abortion in a blatant fashion. It stated "in some critical respects abortion is of the same character as the decision to use contraception...for two decades of economic and social developments, people have organized intimate relationships and made choices that define their views of themselves and their places in society, in reliance on the availability of abortion in the event that contraception should fail." What this passage is saying is that because of the life-styles that contraception has made possible, abortion is a necessity in our society. In even more blunt speech, what this passage is saying is abortion is necessary because contraception has enabled individuals to engage in sexual relationships that are not in the least receptive to children.

Moreover, the notion that children are an optional offshoot of sex and not the reason for sex or marriage leads individuals to make bad choices for n.arriage partners. Those who marry, are often simply marrying a sexual partner that they have become used to. Sexual attraction and sexual compatibility become the chief foundation for relationships. Often when I suggest to young people that the primary question they should ask themselves when they are looking for a spouse is "Would this individual be a good parent to our children?" they are astonished by the question and realize that it would radically influence their choice of a spouse—and they admit that such a consideration has been far from their minds!

Most couples who get married have lived together before marriage (and most have had other sexual partners as well) and have contracepted. Their contraceptive practices have shaped their view of the purpose of sexuality and this carries over into marriage. The contraceptive view of sexual intercourse conveys that sex is for pleasure and that children are an option and largely an unwelcome option. This view of sex is, of course, completely contrary to the Catholic understanding of sex. In the Catholic understanding, sexual intercourse is a great gift of God to spouses wherein he enables them to share in his great mission of bringing new souls into existence to share eternal bliss with him (I shall say more about this in a moment). It is meant to be engaged in only by those who are prepared to be parents. Not only is this view of sex completely foreign to our culture, but it is also foreign to most Catholic couples who have also jumped on the contraceptive bandwagon.

The erroneous view of the purpose of sexuality flows over into an erroneous view of the purpose of life. If sex can be used strictly for the satisfaction of our own pleasures, then it seems like life itself is meant to be lived in the pursuit of satisfying our desires—not in the pursuit of serving God. Those who have been sexually active since their teen years enter marriage as quite selfish individuals in regard to sexual intercourse. They have not learned self-restraint in respect to their sexuality nor likely in respect to the indulgence of other desires as well.

Most of these young people who have lived a life of indulgence before they got married have also been parented by parents who lived a contraceptive life-style. My generation has been dreadfully self-indulgent in sexual matters—and otherwise—but many of us at least had the example of generous and selfless parents that lurked in our memories. The present generation has been parented for the most part by my selfish and self-indulgent generation and have few examples of lives lived in the service of raising good children. Their parents, my generation, have largely put careers, the acquisition of material goods and self-fulfillment at the center of their lives—children fit in as one more life-enriching experience but not as the very reason for the vocation to marriage. When I suggest to young women that instead of pursuing careers they should consider devoting themselves to being a wife and mother full time, they don't much know what I am talking about since many have known no women who have done such!

Young adults of today purchase at great volume books on parenting; that they need books suggests that few of them enter marriage with much of a notion of how to be a parent. Many of my friends are astonished at how well I do with children and how much I know about children since I am a single woman without children. But my mother had two babies when I was a young teenager and I started parenting from that day forth. Few people these days have the wonderful advantages of growing up in a big family, one of them being the advantage of practicing parenting from quite an early age. Now I have taken to recommending to my friends that when their first child reaches the age of about twelve or thirteen that they have at least one more baby so that their children may enjoy the experience of parenting at that age. I think teenagers who are raised in a house with small children are much more likely to have a responsible view of sexuality since they have a sense of what it means to take care of babies, the consequences of sexuality. Once their youngest sibling reaches puberty, they themselves may well be married and having children, so now the cycle can continue as these youngsters can practice parenting on their nieces and nephews!

Children as a Gift to Spouses from God

The title of this paper "Children as the Supreme Gift of Marriage" is from *Gaudium et Spes*; this phrase is part of a sentence that reads: "Children are the supreme gift of marriage and contribute to the greatest extent to the good of the parents themselves." We often think—and rightly—that parents give the gift of life to their children and that they are the great benefactors of their children. But it is equally true that children are a gift from God to the parents, a gift that helps them become adults and gives great meaning to their lives.

Babies do tend to make those who care for them more mature. One of my favorite encounters on the face of the earth is meeting a new father. I have had the good fortune of speaking to several of my male friends shortly after they witnessed the birth of their first child. They float about six feet off the ground and make remarks like "Everything is different now." And it is; they will begin to be more responsible in how they spend their money and time; they will begin to care more about the kind of community in which they live, the quality of the school system and government and what is shown in the media. Those who have responsibilities for the next generation are the ones primarily interested in the kind of world in which we live. They also tend to be concerned about their own virtue or lack thereof since they know they will be models for their own children. Parents will tell you how much they need patience and kindness, courage and hope, for instance, in order to be good parents. If they don't have these naturally, they tend to acquire them through the very process of parenting. Many start going back to church and start to learn something about their faith (many for the first time) since they wish to pass on good values to their children.

Adults without children need to make a much more conscious effort to be generous and other-directed than do those who have children. Having children in a sense forces selflessness upon one. One has to learn to live for another. Some, of course, successfully resist the formation in virtue that having children can bring, but most people find that they are much better people precisely for having children. They find it quite natural and easy to love someone else more than themselves and to work energetically for someone else who can only give them love in return. God wants us all to be loving, self-sacrificing, and generous. The most natural means he uses for inculcating these virtues in us, is to make us parents. Children also help us acquire supernatural virtues; as I mentioned, many upon becoming parents return to church; they begin to worship and pray in ways that they may have abandoned since their own childhoods. The natural piety and responsiveness of children to the claims of religion can help enforce a wobbly faith in parents. I think parishes could achieve many evangelical goals by having seminars on parenting and teaching the Faith to one's children, for as the children as taught, so too are the parents.

Children as Gift to God from Spouses

What parents need to learn as they learn their faith is what the vocation to marriage entails. Very few of them understand that marriage is a Christian vocation and is a means of serving God— marriage in our society seems an altogether selfish institution —even if a *mutually* selfish institution. In the modern view, marriage simply ensures one a companion—for however long one remains married. Few who get married have a sense that what they are doing is embarking upon the adventure of building a family together. In our time, home is not the focus of one's life from which one's energies radiate out to the rest of the world, as it is in the Christian vision; rather home is where one relaxes and unwinds after a hard day at work—work, not family, being the center of one's life. One may raise a few children as a kind of hobby, but few think that all one's decisions should revolve around fulfilling one's Christian commitments, which, for a married individual, mean first and foremost being a good spouse and parent.

The first paragraph of *Humanæ vitæ* is in itself a brief catechesis on marriage; it states:

> God has entrusted spouses with the extremely important mission of transmitting human life. In fulfilling this mission spouses freely and deliberately render service to God, the Creator. This service has always been a source of great joy, although the joys are, at times, accompanied by not a few difficulties and sufferings.

Spouses should reflect deeply on this notion that God *entrusts* new life to them and that they are *transmitting life* that comes from God.

One reason that we so little understand the value of life and of children is that we don't really grasp the Christian message. Again, the current generation by all reports is abysmally religiously illiterate, not often through its own fault. The religious education programs that today's young people endured largely focused on Christianity as a form of social service; few young people have been educated in the meaning of salvation history, in the meaning of the Church and the sacraments, for instance. In my public speaking, when I speak of God the creator who has made the whole universe so that human souls may enjoy eternal bliss with him and that the chief goal of all of us is to bring ourselves and others to salvation, this is often greeted as a message never or rarely heard.

In our day when some animals have more rights than some humans, people are hard pressed to understand what it means to have an immortal soul and what a grand privilege it is to be able to participate in the bringing forth of new human souls. Contraception is so thinkable and doable because couples do not realize what a great affront it is against children as a gift from God. Those who engage in contracepted sexual intercourse are engaging in an act

122

that God designed as a means of conferring a great gift on them; indeed, one thinks he made it so pleasurable so that they would engage in it often, thereby increasing the number of gifts they are likely to receive. Contraception is an emphatic embrace of the pleasure that comes with the act.

Many have trouble distinguishing natural family planning from contraception; I haven't the time to go into the differences here, but let me note that those who use NFP do not reject and attempt to negate the baby-making power of sexual intercourse; rather they exhibit great reverence for it. They refrain from engaging in sexual intercourse when a baby is a likelihood; this refraining is not a slap in the face to God, where contraception is. It is rude to reject gifts when one arrives at the party where they are being distributed, but it is not rude to say that it would be inconvenient to have a party at certain times when one cannot accept the responsibilities that may come with it! Those using NFP do not reject the gift of children; they simply postpone the reception of the gift. Contraceptors, however, treat the baby-making power of sexual intercourse with contempt by insisting upon engaging in a potentially fertile act while at the same time attempting to make it an infertile act.

Contraceptors, through their contracepted acts of sexual intercourse, are saying to their spouses: "I want to have sex with you, but I do not want to have babies with you"—which is a statement one makes to one's mistress or paramour but not to one's beloved spouse. Those who do not contracept are preserving the baby-making meaning of the act, and their acts are always saying "I reverence the baby-making power of sexual intercourse, and am open to being a parent with you." To be willing to be a parent with another is to confer a very great honor on that other; one is willing to make another like one's beloved and to join in the absorbing process of raising that child with another. Lovers who become spouses pledge and want a lifetime bond with one another; they achieve this through children. Sexual acts that say something less than "I want a lifetime union with you"—and contracepted acts emphatically do not say this—are acts that enter an alienating note into an act that should be profoundly unitive. Now, I am not saying that most contraceptors are consciously contemptuous of God; I suspect most are good-willed and subjectively innocent; nonetheless, their act has a certain meaning that they cannot help absorb as they perform the act. They are acquiring attitudes and values that they may well reject if they were conscious of them.

Few, indeed, have any clear sense of what the Catholic Church teaching about sexuality and the value of human life is. Simply stated, the Catholic Church teaches that those who are not prepared to be parents should not be having sexual intercourse. Think of what radical changes would come about in our society if more were living by the Church's teaching. The Catholic ethic of sexual responsibility would abrogate many of the most bizarre problems we have in our society. People would be waiting to have sex and children until they married; think of the troubles we would avoid if this came to pass! Think of the reduction in abortions; think of the reduction in the number of babies born out of wedlock; think of the young women free to finish their schooling and free to enter wholesome marriages. Those who wait to have sexual intercourse and babies within their marriages have a phenomenally low divorce rate compared to the rest of the population; those who do not contracept have a virtually nonexistent divorce rate. Think of how many evils we would avoid if we had stable families. It is living by the Catholic sexual ethic that would ensure such a happy situation.

But don't think we will be hailed as prophets and heroes if we preach such an ethic in season and out from the rooftops as we ought. Those many who speak out against abortion and those few who speak out against premarital sex and contraception are perceived by the media and much of our society as being similar to members of the Ku Klux Klan; they are perceived as narrow and repressed people who wish to impose their restrictive values on others. Last year, in an episode of the sitcom "Picket Fences," a Catholic priest, who had weakly articulated the Church's opposition to contraception, was warned that because of the world's population problem and the problem with unwanted pregnancies, soon Catholics would no longer be permitted to speak out against abortion and contraception. Pro-lifers are now under threat of great persecution for peaceful protest outside of abortion clinics, for activity that is constitutionally protected for any other protest group. Objection to abortion and its natural counterpart, contraception, is an incredible threat to the life-styles of so many in our society. In spite of the fact that President Clinton is now touting the values that Dan Quayle was mocked for promoting, the policies of the current administration and the whole Zeitgeist is against Catholic morality. I suspect the Church is in for some severe persecution and suppression in not too many years time.

Yet in certain ways, it is easy to proclaim Christian truth in our times. We can see clearly what a world from which Christian values are absent, looks like. At home, we find drugs, pornography, divorce, adultery, abortion, child abuse, violence in our schools and streets, to name some of the more manifest evils. Abroad, what is going on in Bosnia alone is enough to make us see what the darkness looks like. We need the light of Christ or we will continue to sink into a deeper darkness which houses more monsters for children than for any one else. It is only the incessant proclamation of the Christian message, and in this matter, the incessant proclamation of the Christian understanding of sexuality and marriage that will save us and our children from the darkness. We must proclaim it while we can.

Chapter 9

THE FAMILY AS THE FIRST SCHOOL OF LIFE AND LOVE: ITS COMPETITORS

Joyce Little, Ph.D.

In 1983, Walker Percy, doctor-turned-novelist and convert to the Catholic Church, wrote *Lost in the Cosmos: The Last Self-Help Book*, a satire on contemporary American life. Percy believed that most Americans today are lost, which is bad enough in itself, but even worse, that most Americans don't have any idea they are lost. The root cause of this lostness, as Percy diagnosed it, is the absence today of any coherent view of what it means to be human.

> Despite the catastrophes of this century and man's total failure to understand himself and deal with himself, people still labor under

the illusion that a theory of man exists. It doesn't. As bad and confused as things are, they have to get even worse before people realize they don't have the faintest idea what sort of creature man is.[1]

Until fairly recently, the Judaeo-Christian view of man as created in the image of God, called to live his life out in accord with God's will and destined to share in God's life and love, could have been said to inform Western institutions, especially that of the family, but this is no longer the case. James Madison, one of the framers of the Constitution, said, for example, that "We have staked the whole future of the American civilization, not upon the power of government, far from it. We have staked the future...upon the capacity of each and all of us to govern ourselves, to control ourselves, to sustain ourselves, according to the Ten Commandments of God." So far removed are we from his view of things that it is today regarded as unconstitutional to hang the Ten Commandments on the wall in a public school classroom. As for the family, as Robert Nisbet, social historian, has pointed out, "On no single institution has the modern political state rested with more destructive weight than on the family. From Plato's obliteration of the family in his *Republic*, through Hobbes, Rousseau, Bentham, and Marx, hostility to the family has been an abiding element in the West's political clerisy."[2]

The Family: Its Competitors

"Crisis" is an overworked word today, but it is also too mild a word to characterize the situation we face, for our situation is more desperate than that. We are on the brink of catastrophe in this country. Nowhere is this more apparent than in the current state of American family life, or rather the lack thereof.[3] The supreme irony today, in fact, is that while the devastation wrought on American families has finally become so obvious that no talk show, newscast, newspaper, magazine, or politician can any longer avoid deploring it, the society itself if clearly committed to the very things guaranteed to present any real reversal of this devastation. The most obvious competitors to, and the most destructive elements of,

127

family life today clearly include our educational system, psychology and the government itself.

Education. Public education, whether grades K-12 or university-level, has become one of the biggest competitors to the American family—for several reasons. First, compulsory public school education has had the effect, more often than not, of misleading parents into thinking their children's education is primarily the state's responsibility, not theirs.[4]

Second, our schools are failing woefully to educate our children. We are all now accustomed to those grim annual international test results, in which our students, in science and math, routinely come in last or next to last among the industrial nations. In another sense, however, our schools aren't failing at all. They have simply shifted their focus from such things as science and math to the emotional and psychological well-being of the students. Concerned these days primarily with students' self-esteem, our teachers employ holistic grading and outcome-based methods which guarantee that no one shall fail and everyone shall feel good about himself.[5] So successful are our schools at engendering a sense of self-esteem that our students last year not only came in last on those international tests, but, when asked how well they thought they knew the material, turned out to think they knew it better than did the students from any other country. This self-indulgence engendered by our schools makes it difficult for parents to instill within their children any sense of self-discipline.

It furthermore makes the teaching of the Catholic faith to anyone a very difficult, if not impossible, task. For the Catholic faith is a complex, highly nuanced business which cannot be contained in a sound bite or on a bumper sticker. But we are living in a society where half of the adults are functionally illiterate and most of them are culturally illiterate. As one social critic has observed,

> ...we have arrived at a point where any hope of conveying the subtle realities of existence, private or social, to a large number of people must be abandoned as feckless, an example of the innocent and very old-fashioned idealism spinning its wheels. The reason is simple: there is no substantial number of people in the society capable of comprehending, much less writing, the language required for such an understanding.[6]

Third, the ideologizing of American education, especially as reflected in the "politically correct" movement, more often than not runs counter to the teachings of the Catholic Church, putting parents and/or students in the position of having to make a choice between being politically correct or being Catholic. And, to make the situation worse, so many of the issues bound up with political correctness have a direct and destructive bearing on family life. Political correctness, for example, dictates that no significant differentiation be recognized between men and women or between heterosexuality and homosexuality. Sex education must be taught in a value-neutral fashion. Indeed, everything must be taught in a value-neutral fashion, including values themselves. Thus, we have courses not in morality per se, but in values clarification, courses specifically designed to leave students with the impression that all values are equal, that no moral stance is superior to any other. Safe, not moral, behavior is the goal sought, and if this requires the distribution of condoms or contraceptives, so be it.

Psychology. Perhaps the chief competitor to the family today is psychology. As Christopher Lasch has observed, "It is a commonplace that twentieth-century psychiatry serves as a substitute for religion, promising the traditional consolations of personal mastery, spiritual peace, and emotional security."[7] So much has psychology taken the place of religion that Philip Rieff, the sociologist, in his classic work *The Triumph of the Therapeutic*, rightly notes that "For more than a century now, theologians have been screening psychologists in the hope of finding one who could rescue theology for them."[8]

The most damaging effect of psychology today is its assumption that the individual is the primary center around which all things revolve. This has produced what has been called the imperial or autonomous self, intent on its own well-being at virtually any cost.[9] This new self is encouraged to see the community, any community, as the source of its difficulties. Hence today the emphasis on dysfunctional families and culturally-conditioned biases as the cause of so many people's problems.[10]

If psychology has replaced religion, so also has the search for the right therapy replaced the search for salvation. To cite Rieff again, "Religious man was born to be saved; psychological man is born to be pleased. The difference was established long ago, when 'I believe,' the cry of the ascetic, lost precedence to 'one feels,' the caveat of the therapeutic."[11] If people are no longer lined up at the confessional, it is largely because they are reading self-help books, consulting therapists and participating in support groups which promise self-esteem, not forgiveness, and self-fulfillment, not salvation.

Nowhere is the family more at risk from psychology than in its rejection of sexual self-restraint. As Rieff rightly observes, "Historically, the rejection of sexual individualism (which divorces pleasure and procreation) was the consensual matrix of Christian culture."[12] Sexual individualism today, however, is at the center of most therapies.[13] Rieff maintains that "The systematic hunting down of all settled convictions represents the anti-cultural predicate upon which modern personality is being reorganized, now not only in the West, but, more slowly, in the non-West."[14] The one conviction above all others which is systematically hunted down today is sexual self-discipline.

The family as we have known it is the primary victim of this new sexual freedom. Divorce and remarriage are commonplace, despite growing evidence that children are almost always seriously harmed by this. Out-of-wedlock pregnancies are now a national epidemic, creating, as Charles Murray pointed out in his recent article in *The Wall Street Journal,* a new underclass not only in the black but now also in the white community.[15] And, despite sex education and the growing practice of distributing condoms to high school students, the number of unwanted pregnancies and abortions among teenagers is simply endemic. AIDS and other so-called social diseases are at all-time highs.

Apart from families themselves, children are the greatest victims of today's sexually-autonomous adults. They are of course victims of abortion, in a society which has few moral qualms in proclaiming that it does not want at least 1,600,000 of its own children every year. They are victims of so-called single-parent families, in most of which no responsible adult male can be found. And they are also victims in today's climate of easy divorce and remarriage. As a recent cover article in *The Atlantic Monthly* on the current state of family life details, divorce is encouraged by our society,

130

with unhappy spouses offered the enticement of new growth and maturity, new freedom, new opportunities for personal happiness once the old marriage has been shed. Children, on the other hand, are counseled, in the new books for them on divorce, to recognize and sympathize with the difficulties of their parents, to accept the fact that there will be less money and more need for self-restraint. To cite the article,

> Children are called upon to invest in the emotional well-being of their parents. Indeed, this seems to be the larger message of many of the children's books on divorce and remarriage. *Dinosaurs Divorce* asks children to be sympathetic, understanding, respectful, and polite to confused, unhappy parents. The sacrifice comes from the children: "Be prepared to give up some things." In the world of divorcing dinosaurs, the children rather than the grown-ups are the exemplars of patience, restraint and good sense.[16]

Even when marriages don't end in divorce, children are frequently victimized by the shoddy upbringing to which they are subject.[17]

Finally, to make things worse, there has been little attempt by Christian theologians to counter the new psychological claims to sexual freedom. The imperial self has all too often been embraced rather than rejected by those who ought to know better. Rieff comments upon this strange situation in which those entrusted by the Christian community with the cultural function of defending traditional sexual constraints actively participate in the destruction of those constraints.

> Contemporary churchmen may twist and turn while they try to make themselves heard in a culture that renders preaching superfluous: the fact remains that renunciatory controls of sexual opportunity were placed in the Christian culture very near the center of the symbolic that has not held. Current apologetic efforts by religious professionals, in pretending that renunciation as the general mode of control was never dominant in the system, reflect the strange mixture of cowardice and courage with which they are participating in the dissolution of their cultural functions.[18]

The desperation of our situation is perhaps nowhere made more apparent than in President Clinton's appeal to Americans to fight violence with values. How can this be done, in a society which cannot display the Ten Commandments in public places, whose schools cannot teach values but only values clarification, whose families are daily subject to the assault of the imperial self intolerant of the imposition of any values, and whose professional, academic and religious elites, aided by mass media, connive at the destruction of all of this culture's settled convictions?

Government. A third major competitor to and destroyer of the family is the American government itself, for several reasons. First, of course, is the welfare system which subsidizes both fatherless homes and illegitimate children. As Charles Murray pointed out in 1984, in his seminal work *Losing Ground*, what we subsidize we get more of, and we now have overwhelming numbers of fatherless children and unwed mothers. Thirty years ago, when Daniel Patrick Moynihan first warned us of the underclass being created in the black community because of out-of-wedlock pregnancies, the illegitimacy rate among blacks was 26%, while among whites it was virtually nil. Today the illegitimacy rate among whites is 22%, almost as high as the black rate was then, while the illegitimacy rate among blacks has soared to 68%. This means that about 30% of all births in this country today are illegitimate. As Archbishop J. Francis Stafford recently and very pointedly remarked, "It is the unwillingness of man to face responsibility for his sexuality that is the basis of evil in our society. The big problem is our increasing incapacity to socialize the American male as father and husband. His infidelity to his children and to the women who bear those children is evil."[19]

According to Murray, "the brutal truth is that American society as a whole could survive when illegitimacy became epidemic within a comparatively small ethnic minority. It cannot survive the same epidemic among whites."[20] He thinks we ought to abolish the welfare system altogether. Lasch, noting that "capitalism has evolved a new political ideology, welfare liberalism, which absolves individuals of moral responsibility and treats them as victims of social circumstance," concludes that "The rehabilitation of parenthood, it appears, implies an attack on professionalism and the welfare state."[21]

A second and much worse problem has been the decided turning interpretations of law and the Constitution toward protecting the rights of the individual at the expense of the family and the larger community itself. The Supreme Court today clearly understands the individual, not the family, to be the basic cell of society. Hence, interpretations of the First Amendment guaranteeing free speech have favored the rights of individuals at the expense of the community regarding, for example, pornography, against which the Church teaches that families have the right to protect their children. Consistent with this are laws allowing women to get abortions without the consent of their husbands or of the fathers of their children and minor girls to get abortions without parental consent. Condom and contraceptive distribution in the schools, without parental knowledge or consent, is another example of the triumph of the imperial self at the expense of the family.

Most alarming of all is the fact that the Supreme Court has recently thrown the full weight of its authority behind this notion of the imperial self, telling us, in *Planned Parenthood v. Casey*, that abortion is a right because personal autonomy is central to that liberty protected by the Fourteenth Amendment, since "At the heart of liberty is the right to define one's own concept of existence, of meaning, of the universe and of the mystery of human life."[22] The autonomous self could not ask for more than this.

Third, we face the inroads made by feminists, gay rights activists and other proponents of political correctness in the corridors of governmental power, resulting in political support for such things as family diversity by which almost any collection of individuals or even one individual all by himself is regarded as a family, of homosexual rights equivalent to spousal rights, of equal pay for equal work, of publicly-subsidized abortion, every one of which undermines the family.[23]

Finally, and most ominously, we are confronted, under the rubric of separation of Church and State, with the deliberate expulsion of religion from government, from the public square. As Stephen Carter, a liberal African American law professor at Yale, observes in his recent work, *The Culture of Disbelief*, "the metaphorical separation of church and state originated in an effort to protect religion from the state, not the state from religion."[24] Today the separation of Church and State has come to mean that religion has no place in the life of the State. The refusal to display, much less teach, the Ten Commandments is but one deadly result of this novel interpretation of the Constitution.[25]

The Family: In-House Problems

In order for the family to be the first school of life and love, two things are necessary: first, intact, sacramentally-imbued families, and second, parents informed of the nature of the family and of the nature of life and love. Unfortunately, when we turn specifically to the subject of Catholic families in America, we discover two tragic facts: a dearth of intact, sacramentally-imbued Catholic families and an unprecedented degree of ignorance among Catholics about the nature of family, life and love. Catholics are divorcing at about the same rate as non-Catholics, Catholics are dissenting from Church teachings on sexual matters and even on abortion at about the same rate as non-Catholics, and Catholic parents today are far less informed about their faith, generally speaking, than were previous generations of Catholics in this country. The reasons for this are not difficult to discover.

First, Catholics hear almost nothing in church these days which has any bearing on the family. I recently asked some of my older, nontraditional students, married women with children, when last they heard a sermon on the family at Mass. Each one of them thought about this for a moment and then replied that she could not remember having heard any sermons at all on the family. This did not surprise me. I can't remember having heard any sermons about the family in at least the last ten years.

The Catholic students I have every semester are as surprised as their non-Catholic counterparts to learn the Church teaches that the family, not the individual, is the basic cell of society. It also comes as a surprise to them that human beings are communal by nature, not individualistic, and that love is not a feeling, but an act of the will, requiring self-sacrifice for the sake of the one loved. Might this dearth of sermons on the nature of love help explain why, as the *Atlantic Monthly* article points out, more than half of the adult population in this country no longer regards self-sacrifice as a virtue.[26]

Not that we have any lack of sermons on love, at least on God's love for us. One of the most common complaints I hear from Catholics today is that their priests seem to have nothing to say except that God loves us. I actually had a student last year who had completed a B.A. at a state university, but who enrolled in and paid the tuition for my undergraduate course, "Teachings of the Catholic Church," even though she could not apply the hours to any degree program. Her reason for doing so was simple and speaks volumes for the situation so many Catholics find themselves in today. As she put it, she as a child had been given almost no education in the faith and all she heard at Mass on Sundays was that God loves us, but she was pretty sure the Church teaches more than that. Most Catholics have neither the time nor the money to do what she did, and so they drift through life with little more than weekly assurances of God's love.

After reading *Veritatis splendor*, I told my mother about it, as I have told her of other writings by the Pope. Her response also speaks volumes for the situation the laity find themselves in. "I've heard about this encyclical on television," she said, "but am I ever going to hear about it in church? What good" she asked, "does it do for the Pope to write all these things when we never hear about them in church?" There was little I could say, especially given the fact that I've not heard a word spoken from the pulpit about anything this Pope has written, not one single word in the fifteen years of his papacy. No pope in the history of the Church has addressed with such frequency and cogency these issues of marriage, family, human sexuality and morality as has he, and no pope has ever done so with the freshness and originality of thought he brings to them, and yet no Catholic in this country could speak intelligibly for two minutes on anything he has written.

Every day I turn on the television and am confronted by the enormous problems this country faces with drugs, violence, broken families, sexual promiscuity. Every week I read magazines detailing our various crises regarding education, AIDS, unwanted pregnancies, sexually abused wives and children. Every Sunday I go to Mass, and there I find my one weekly respite from all these problems. Nothing is said about any of them. Generally speaking, nothing substantive is said about anything. We've heard so much in the post-Vatican II Church about the need to be relevant. We have the very teachings this society needs above all else to confront those problems associated with the disintegration of family life, and yet in so many parishes not one relevant word is uttered which would have any bearing on the anarchy into which we are moving.

A second failure within the Church in this country has been our Catholic school system. My experience, and that of my colleagues in other parts of the country, teaching in small Catholic colleges and universities, is that the great majority of students who come to us straight from the parochial school system know little more about their faith than do Catholics coming from the public school system, and in fact very little more about the Catholic faith than do Protestants and even non-Christians.

The situation within our Catholic colleges and universities is no better. Although I work at a university which requires of its theologians loyalty to the Magisterium, the same cannot be said for most of our institutions of higher learning. Nowhere has my own work in theology met with more antagonism than from Catholic theologians. My first theological talk at a national convention, given to an audience made up primarily of self-proclaimed Catholic theologians and based mostly on theological sources such as Scripture, tradition and the Magisterium, generated hostility such as I had never before in my life encountered. Most of my theology professors in graduate school hung very loose to the Catholic faith. One of them, angry that loyalty to the Magisterium might be required of Catholic theologians, told me that were such a thing to happen he would leave theology, because, as he put it, "I am first and foremost a theologian who just happens to be a Catholic." It is, as Rieff says, the cultural elites within our religious institutions who, more than anyone else, conspire in the downfall of those things for which their religions stand.[27]

A third failure has been a lack of episcopal leadership in this country. The failure has been two-fold. The first failure has been at the level of the National Conference of Bishops. While Catholic marriages and family life have been under attack from various competitors in the society as a whole, the NCCB has been issuing pastorals on such things as the economy, capital punishment and nuclear weapons. Beyond that, enormous time, effort and money have gone into the now-defunct pastoral on women in the church and into creating inclusive language translations of liturgical documents, none of which reflects any of the most pressing needs of ordinary Catholics in ordinary parishes out there today. It is encouraging that the NCCB has recently addressed itself specifically to the family, but this will have little impact unless local churches follow it through with serious teaching on the family and the NCCB follows it up with teachings on related issues such as marriage and sexual morality.

Second, there has been a near dearth of teaching by individual bishops in their own dioceses. Is this because the NCCB is now thought by most bishops to have assumed that responsibility? Whatever the reason, most Catholics get little or no instruction from their own particular bishops. I have spoken here about societal competitors to the family, and undoubtedly there are an enormous number of such competitors today. But one cannot really speak of competitors to the Catholic faith, because a competitor requires something to compete against, and right now there is to a very large extent no Catholic faith against which anyone has to compete. A bumper sticker from the Vietnam War era read, "What if somebody declared a war and nobody came?" In effect, competitors against the family have declared a war, and to date the Catholic side has yet to show up. Daily Catholics are bombarded by the media, seduced by psychology, their children virtually held hostage against what the Church teaches in a public school system purged of all religion and morality, their responsibilities as parents increasingly undermined or co-opted by the government, and hardly a word is heard from anyone in the Church condemning, criticizing or even challenging what is happening to them.[28]

Conclusion

American democracy was fashioned within the context of the Judaeo-Christian culture of the West. The Constitution is perhaps

137

the last great document of the West to have been formulated within that tradition. The Constitution presupposes that culture has its own context and cannot be made to work in the absence of that context. As Madison put it, the American civilization is staked not on the government, but on the willingness of the American people to abide by the Ten Commandments. Or, as Paul Johnson, former editor of the *New Statesman*, puts it, "the eclipse of Christian theodicy is certain to lead to more revolution and violence. For if the Christian theory of the world, and its explanation of the miseries all of us undergo, no longer holds, then the Christian legitimation of social order, law and communal self-restraint cannot be maintained very long either, and the violent revolution, from being an aberrant interruption of customary stability, becomes the normal feature of life."[29]

Unfortunately, we are all witnesses to the kind of violence which ensues from the moral breakdown of a community. As one columnist recently described our situation, "Without a moral anchor, we're adrift in a sea of immorality, headed toward economic and social chaos."[30] In point of fact, however, the ultimate result of this breakdown is more likely to be tyranny than revolution. People will not long suffer anarchy in their streets, and will gladly exchange their freedom for safety and security. Charles Murray points out that, as recently as the administration of John F. Kennedy, "America's elites accepted as a matter of course that a free society such as America's can sustain itself only through virtue and temperance in the people, that virtue and temperance depend centrally on the socialization of each new generation, and that the socialization of each generation depends on the matrix of care and resources fostered by marriage." He himself concludes that "A society with broad legal freedoms depends critically on strong nongovernmental institutions to temper and restrain behavior. Of these, marriage is paramount. Either we reverse the current trends in illegitimacy—especially white illegitimacy—or America must, willy-nilly, become an unrecognizably authoritarian, socially segregated, centralized state."[31]

Already we see signs of this kind of tyranny in America. People today murmur no protest at all when police set up roadblocks and check every third driver and car for alcohol and drugs, even though the Constitution guarantees us protection from arbitrary search and seizure. Every day in the newspapers, magazines and on television, we hear proposals for more police, more prisons, tougher laws, stiffer penalties, and more gun control, as the way to deal with the growing anarchy. All of this is nothing more than a recipe for a police state.

The Catholic Church is the only institution within this society with both the message Americans most need to hear and an intact authority with which to deliver that message. In this sense, Richard John Neuhaus is right in proclaiming this to be "The Catholic Moment" in American history.

First, we know that the family is the basic cell of society, and that, as Pope John Paul II puts it, "The future of humanity passes by way of the family" (FC 86). We also know, as he says, that

> Everything depends in principle on the way parents and family have fulfilled their first and fundamental duties, on the way and in the measure that they have taught "to be human" that creature who thanks to them has become a human being, has obtained "humanity."
>
> In this the family is irreplaceable. Everything must be done to ensure that the family will not be replaced.[32]

Second, we know that freedom, especially in a democracy, cannot long be maintained if the sort of freedom people have in mind is that of the imperial self doing whatever it pleases, a freedom either divorced from truth or creator of its own truth. In *Veritatis splendor,* the Pope speaks of the enormous destruction wrought by modern efforts to divorce freedom from truth. We as Christians know that truth is the only path to true freedom, because true freedom is the freedom to do good, not the freedom to do as we please.

Third, we know, as the Pope puts it, that "the most dangerous crisis which can afflict man [is] the *confusion between good and evil,* which makes it impossible to build up and to preserve the moral order of individuals and communities" (VS 93). When our own Supreme Court insists that "freedom" means the right of each person to define for him- or herself the meaning of existence and the value of human life, all one can say is that confusion about good and evil just can't get any greater than that. No moral order whatsoever is possible under these circumstances. We Catholics know this, and because we do know it, all the greater is our obligation to proclaim it.

Fourth, we know that the refusal of virtue as the living out of the truth of things leads straight to anarchy and then on to tyranny. As the Pope says, "If one does not acknowledge transcendent truth, then the force of power takes over, and each person tends to make full use of the means at his disposal in order to impose his own interests or his own opinions, with no regard for the rights of others" (VS 99). This is why John Paul II warns us that, although we have witnessed the fall of those Marxist ideologies underwriting recent totalitarian regimes, we still face the danger of new tyrannies resulting from "*an alliance between democracy and ethical relativism*, which would remove any sure moral reference point from political and social life, and on a deeper level make the acknowledgment of truth impossible" (VS 101).

In the final analysis, as the Pope points out, democracy itself depends upon the acceptance of commonly-shared moral norms.

> These norms in fact represent the unshakable foundation and solid guarantee of a just and peaceful human coexistence, and hence of a genuine democracy, which can come into being and develop only on the basis of the equality of all of its members, who possess common rights and duties. *When it is a matter of the moral norms prohibiting intrinsic evil, there are no privileges or exceptions for anyone.* It makes no difference whether one is the master of the world or the "poorest of the poor" on the face of the earth. Before the demands of morality we are all absolutely equal. (VS 96)

These moral norms are, in fact, the only guarantee of any kind of social existence. "In the end, only a morality which acknowledges certain norms as valid always and for anyone, with no exception, can guarantee the ethical foundation of social coexistence, both on the national and international levels" (VS 97).

I had the good fortune to visit Walker Percy in October of 1989, a few months before his death. At that time, he made what many might regard as a very surprising comment, that, in his judgment, the Church is in a better position today than she has been for centuries. He believed that the identification of culture and faith in his country, such that most Catholics thought there was no difference between being a good Catholic and being a good American, was harmful for the Church in many ways. Today people can see that no such identification exists and that a choice must be made. Now the Church is on the firing line and that's where she properly belongs.

Many people, theologians and others, have spoken since Vatican II of the Church as a sign of contradiction to today's culture. Nowhere is this more apparent than with regard to the nature of the family and its role in society. There is no question that the faith of the Church is diametrically opposed to the direction in which American society is today moving. The only question is whether or not we as Catholics are prepared to act upon that faith.

Notes

1. Lewis A. Lawson and Victor A. Kramer (eds), *Conversations with Walker Percy* (Jackson, MS: University Press of Mississippi, 1985), p. 178.

2. Robert Nisbet, *Twilight of Authority* (New York: Oxford University Press, 1975), p. 260.

3. The family may provide us with a microcosm of our desperate state, but the catastrophe which awaits us on our present course has many sources across the length and breadth of our society. As Nisbet points out, "...what was present in very substantial measure in the basic works of the founders of political democracy was respect for such social institutions as property, family, local community, religion, and voluntary association, and for such cultural and social values as objective reason, the discipline of language, self-restraint, the work ethic, and, far from least, the culture that had taken root in classical civilization and grown, with rare interruptions, ever since. If we neglect the role of these institutions and these values in the minds of the Founding Fathers, we have omitted the elements on which alone, in their minds, political democracy could be made a reality. If, in their bold view of the matter, a less than arbitrary and powerful political state could be safely contemplated, this was not because man was deemed naturally good and law-abiding, but only because common sense suggested that such institutions as family, local community, and religion, having been for so many thousands of years the universal contexts of human nature, and such ideals as charity, brotherhood, reason, and justice, having been for more than twenty-five hundred years the principal threads of Western morality, would continue indefinitely into the future.... The architects of Western democracy were all students of history, and they had every intellectual right to suppose that moral values and social structures which had survived as many vicissitudes and environmental changes as these had over the two and a half millennia of their existence in Western society would go on for at least a few more centuries.

But in fact they have not. If there is anything distinct about the twentieth century in the West—in addition to the most destructive wars in all human history—it is the condition of moribundity in which we find these self-same structures and values" (*Ibid*, pp. 76-77).

4. As one political commentator in England has noted (and what he has to say is as applicable here as in Great Britain), "By making education compulsory, the state has imposed an obligation which most parents could not discharge unaided; and by compelling parents to part with their children for most of the day, the state fosters the illusion that they have no real responsibility for their offspring." (Roger Scruton, *Untimely Tracts* [London: Macmillan Press, 1987], p. 224).

5. As classicist Richard Graves points out, "Schools do *not* fail. They succeed. Children *always* learn in school. Always and every day. When their rare and tiny compositions are "rated holistically" without regard for separate "aspects" like spelling, punctuation, capitalization, or even organization, they *learn*. They learn that mistakes bring no consequences.... They learn that the demands of life are easily satisfied with little labor, if any, and that a show of effort is what really counts. They learn to pay attention to *themselves*, their wishes and fears, their likes and dislikes, their idle whims and temperamental tendencies, all of which, idolized as "values" and personological variables, are far more important than "mere achievement" in subject matter. The "whole child" comes first, and no one learns that lesson better than the children.... All those thoughtless, unskilled, unproductive, self-indulgent, and eminently dupable Americans—where have they been and what did they learn there? (*The Graves of Academe* [New York: Simon & Schuster, Inc., A Fireside Book, 1981], p. 188).

6. Richard Schickel, *Intimate Strangers: The Culture of Celebrity* (New York: Fromm International Publishing Corporation, 1985), p. 387.

7. Christopher Lasch, *The Minimal Self* (New York/London: W. W. Norton & Company, 1984), p. 208.

8. Philip Rieff, *The Triumph of the Therapeutic* (New York/Evanston: Harper & Row, Harper Torchbooks, 1966), p. 41.

9. Rieff points out that "The best spirits of the twentieth century have thus expressed their conviction that...the new center, which can be held even as communities disintegrate, is the self. By this conviction a new and dynamic acceptance of disorder, in love with life and destructive of it, has been loosed upon the world." (*Ibid*, p. 5).

10. A former student of mine, now in a graduate program in psychology at a state university, told me recently that the professor in her course on abnormal psychology began the semester by saying that, objectively speaking, there is no such thing as abnormal behavior. What is called abnormal behavior is simply the bias of culture, and cultures differ on what is regarded as abnormal.

11. *Ibid*, pp. 24-25. Or, as Walker Percy puts it, "I am not telling you anything new when I suggest that the Christian notion of man as a wayfarer in search of his salvation no longer informs Western culture. In its place, what most of us seem to be seeking are such familiar goals as maturity, creativity, autonomy, rewarding interpersonal relations, and so forth" (*Signposts in a Strange Land* [New York: Farrar, Straus and Giroux, 1991], p. 208).

12. Rieff, *The Triumph of the Therapeutic*, p. 17.

142

13. This sexual individualism has had devastating effects on human relationships As Scruton so rightly observes, we now find ourselves in a situation in which "The unborn child is no longer a human person, attached by indelible rights and obligations to the mother who bears him, but a slowly ripening deformity, which can be aborted at will, should the mother choose to cure herself. In surrogate motherhood the relation between mother and child ceases to issue from the very body of the mother and is severed from the experience of incarnation. The bond between mother and child is demystified, made clear, intelligible, scientific—and also provisional, revocable and of no more than contractual force.... In just the same way the sexual bond has become clear and intelligible, and also provisional, revocable and of merely contractual force, governed by the morality of adult 'consent.' We have suffered a universal demystification of the human body. It has ceased to be the sacred fount of our deepest obligations and become instead a mere organism, obedient to the biological imperatives which govern all living things. Because we know ourselves in another way, however—as free beings, bound by a moral law—we begin to doubt the moral prerogative of the body. It no longer seems possible to us that the merely *bodily* character of our acts can determine their moral value. Hence arises the extraordinary view that the homosexual act considered in itself, is morally indistinguishable from the heterosexual act: for what is there, in its merely physical character, to justify the traditional stigma? (*Untimely Tracts*, p. 205).

14. Rieff, *Triumph of the Therapeutic*, p. 13.

15. Charles Murray, "The Coming White Underclass," *The Wall Street Journal*, Friday, October 29, 1993.

16. Barbara Dafoe Whitehead, "Dan Quayle was Right," *The Atlantic Monthly*, April, 1993, p. 60.

17. As Christopher Lasch points out, "...children have paid a heavy price for the new freedom enjoyed by adults. They spend too much time watching television, since adults use the television set as a baby-sitter and a substitute for parental guidance and discipline. They spend too many of their days in child-care centers, most of which offer the most perfunctory kind of care. They eat junk food, listen to junk music, read junk comics, and spend endless hours playing video games, because their parents are too busy or too harried to offer them proper nourishment for their minds and bodies. They attend third-rate schools and get third-rate moral advice from their elders. Many parents and educators, having absorbed a therapeutic morality and a misplaced idea of egalitarianism, hesitate to "impose" their moral standards on the young or to appear overly "judgmental" (*The Minimal Self*, pp. 188-189).

18. Rieff, *The Triumph of the Therapeutic*, p. 16.

19. Quoted in Alan Dumas, "New Ways to Preach Eternal Truths," *The Rocky Mountain News*, "Colorado People" Section, Sunday, August 1, 1993.

20. Murray, "The Coming White Underclass."

21. Lasch, *The Culture of Narcissism*, pp. 369, 383.

22. And now, it should be noted, we have a judge in Michigan extending the application of this view of freedom, by declaring unconstitutional that state's law against assisted suicides such as those carried out by Dr. Kevorkian on the

same grounds that such a law violates that freedom protected by the Fourteenth Amendment.

23. As regards so-called family diversity, Whitehead notes that, "Family diversity in the form of increasing numbers of single-parent and step-parent families does not strengthen the social fabric. It dramatically weakens and undermines society, placing new burdens on schools, courts, prisons, and the welfare system. These new families are not an improvement on the nuclear family, nor are they even just as good, whether you look at outcomes for children or outcomes for society as a whole. In short, far from representing social progress, family change represents a stunning example of social regress." ("Dan Quayle was Right," p. 77-80).

24. Stephen Carter, *The Culture of Disbelief* (New York: BasicBooks, 1993), p. 105.

25. The fundamental fact which Americans seem incapable or unwilling to acknowledge today is that, as Rieff puts it, "the religious problem is identical with the moral and the moral with the cultural" (Rieff, *The Triumph of the Therapeutic*, p. 212). Or, as James Madison put it, the future of the American civilization is staked not on government, but on the ability of the American people to sustain themselves in accordance with the Ten Commandments of God. That we see unprecedented corruption today in our politicians, in our celebrities and even in the American population as a whole should come as no surprise to us. Increasing reliance on an increasingly-irreligious government to solve problems created by the unwillingness of the American people to abide by the Ten Commandments can result in nothing less. As Scruton rightly observes, "The vacuum at the heart of the impersonal state cannot be filled by the state itself. There is no ideology, no political goal, no scheme for redemption, no 'irreversible shift' or 'final solution' that will return to the political order the personal conscience which has been expelled from it" (*Untimely Tracts*, p. 177).

26. Whitehead, "Dan Quayle was right," p. 58

27. For a stunning example of this, see Fr. Richard McBrien's keynote address, "Re-Imaging the Church in the Year 2000," given at the Future of the American Church Conference ("Reforming the Church/Transforming the World"), in Washington, D.C., September 20, 1991. There Fr. McBrien compared the situation of the Church since 1978 to the coup by the hardliners in the Soviet Union which had just occurred that summer, with one small difference. The "coup" leaders in the Church had yet to be overthrown by any in-house Boris Yeltsin. As McBrien put it, "we Catholics, I submit, have been living these past thirteen years, not three days, through a prolonged, slow-motion coup of our own against the reforms of Pope John XXIII and the Second Vatican Council." McBrien cited an unnamed Catholic editor who had written that there is a "new left" in the Church which now "dominates the fields of liturgy, religious education, justice and peace offices, campus ministry, Catholic higher education, much popular spirituality and the discipline of theology as a whole." McBrien was happy to agree that this group includes himself and does indeed dominate all of the above. He did, however, disagree that he and his group represent the left, condemning the "lamentable effort to evict the church's most active mem-

144

bers from the center." McBrien received a standing ovation from the more than 1,000 Catholics crowded into the ballroom of Omni Shoreham Hotel to hear his talk. Even more applause greeted the remark of Mr. Tim Ragan, who had introduced McBrien's talk, when he said at the end of it, "Somehow as I was sitting there, the stage seemed to turn into a tank. Did you get that feeling? Yeltsin couldn't have done better. It's amazing that we look to Russia for signs of how to determine the future of the church."

28. The sad fact of the matter is that our families are under attack today not because they are strong, but because they are weak. As Nisbet points out, "There is seldom a major attack on institutions and values until well after processes of decline and erosion have begun. By a strange law of social behavior, decline actually causes attack. Let a government, economic enterprise, or church reach a certain point of enervation, the result of random causes or tidal forces of history, and it is virtually certain that some kind of assault will be mounted on it. As Tocqueville pointed out in his classic study of the French Revolution, it was not the Revolution that brought down the monarchy; it was the steady decline of monarchy, and all that went with it, that brought on the Revolution" (*Twilight of Authority*, p. 80). In like fashion, the family in recent decades has invited attack because of its fragility. To cite Nisbet again, "It is not 'sexual immorality' that weakens the family; it is a weakening of the family that generates what we call 'sexual immorality.' Similarly, it is necessary to see the radical phases of women's liberation not as cause, but as reflection of the diminished significance of marriage and family in our time." (*Ibid*, p. 81).

29. Paul Johnson, *Enemies of Society* (London: Weidenfelt & Nicolson, 1977), p. 245. Nisbet agrees. Pointing out that Protestantism and Judaism as well have suffered an enormous decline in our society in their ability to inspire respect, command authority and provide community, whereas the Catholic Church had been able to maintain in liturgy and sacrament a much stronger influence in the lives of its people, Nisbet warns, however, that, "Vatican II changed that, though we cannot be sure at this juncture exactly how much. If the Roman church, by virtue of the acts of this momentous council, goes the way of the Protestant churches, if escalating secularism is accompanied there as it has been in he Protestant faiths by loss of visible community and authority in the vital sphere of faith, then one more wall of the political community will have been weakened. Religions like Christianity and Judaism were once both strong in the authority of the sacred, and in this fact lay their internal strength and also their extraordinary value to the whole idea of the political community, together with its liberties and rights, in Western society" (*Twilight of Authority*, p. 89).

30. Walter Williams, "It is really a matter of morality," Creators Syndicate, Inc., 1993.

31. Murray, "The Coming White Underclass."

32. *Idem., A Year with Mary* (New York: Catholic Book Publishing Co., 1986), pp. 77-78.

Chapter 10

POPULATION AND ENVIRONMENTAL CONCERNS CONFRONTING THE FAMILY

Arthur J. Dyck, Ph.D.

Science does not have a distinguished record when it comes to assessing population growth. Throughout the first half of the twentieth century, there were scholarly treatises depicting child-bearing and child-rearing as burdens, some expressing the fear that people would soon have so few children that the very survival of the human species was at stake.[1] And, ironically enough, predictions of an ever diminishing population were being made at the very time that the post-World War II baby boom was beginning and death rates in many parts of the world were coming down, fueling population growth.

It did not take very long for some academics to spawn a whole new literature and a new fear. The new fear was evident enough in the titles of some books published in the late 1960s and early 1970s, such as *The Population Bomb, Famine 1975,* and *World Population Crisis: The United States Response.*[2] Once again, academics led the way in yet another of history's ironies, one I experienced firsthand when in 1965 I became a member of a newly formed, heavily endowed, Center for Population Studies at Harvard University, under the leadership of its School of Public Health. What was ironic was that a great deal of money, energy, and scholarship was being generated at the very time when the *rate* of population growth in the world was beginning to decline.[3] Indeed, according to a recent United Nations' medium projection, the world's population will stabilize, that is, attain replacement level fertility rates (about 2.1 children per woman) shortly after 2200.[4]

As a member of the Center for Population Studies, I was expected by many, not all to be sure, to have a particular point of view. This was especially true of visitors to the Center. I recall a man from Sweden who asked to see me not long after I had joined the Center. He described with great enthusiasm how Sweden was leading the way in the population and birth control movement by introducing sex education and birth control information into its schools. "Of course," he said, "we are teaching the students all of the options." I replied, "Good, then you are also teaching abstinence." He looked at me in amazement. "You must be joking," he said. "No," I said, "how could I be? You told me you taught all of the options." With his eyes blazing, he turned, and stomped out of my office without a word.

To their credit, many of my early colleagues at the Center for Population Studies were genuine scholars who were critical of the crisis literature and the simplistic idea that family planning programs, by themselves, address the kinds of social, economic and moral issues involved in trying to reduce population growth. Indeed, a more scholarly approach yielded data and discovered literature that indicated the benefits of population growth. And, it was soon evident to a number of us that many problems blamed on population growth were being falsely understood.[5]

The crisis orientation to population growth died down from about the late 1970s until more recently. I see some signs of its revival presently. But the push for controlling population growth and government sponsored family programs for the purpose of bringing down birth rates has never seriously waned. Academics with this orientation are represented in significant numbers in the American Public Health Association and the Population Association of America; they are also found in foundations, planned parenthood organizations, and the United Nations, particularly its Population Division. I want to deal with what I consider to be a morally problematic orientation toward population issues, particularly toward the family, found among these population experts.

The topic allotted to me for this essay is its title: "Population and Environmental Concerns Confronting Family Rights and Duties." The thesis of this essay is that the well-being of populations and the protection of their environment are congruent with what constitutes responsible familial behavior and respect for familial rights. That population and environmental concerns are perceived as "confronting" family rights and duties stems from a realistic assessment of certain widespread, highly questionable analyses of population problems and environmental degradation, and the population policies advocated and pursued on the basis of these suspect analyses. I will begin, then, by exposing faulty views of the relation between population growth and human well-being. Then I will turn to the views found in population policy advocacy and certain legal policies, which combine to undermine families as procreative units and as significant decision makers within their communities. I will conclude with a sketch of what a just population policy would look like.

Population Growth and Human Well-Being:
The Environment

With respect to environmental problems, the truth of the matter is that current population policies will not by themselves solve any environmental problems. This is true for at least two reasons: (1) a declining population will not as such reverse behaviors responsible for environmental abuses and degradation; (2) population growth rates are declining and will foreseeably continue to do so.

1. *Population policies and environmental problems.* Current population policies promoted by the United States and the United Nations, and adopted in a number of countries, seek to bring about a reduction in birth rates.[6] If, then, these policies are successful, growth rates will decline and populations will stabilize at replacement levels. But if existing population policies expect to reverse environmental abuses and degradation by a decline in birth rates, unrealistic declines in national populations would have to occur. The late Roger Revelle, the first Director of Harvard's Center for Population Studies, has done the necessary analyses demonstrating how absurd it is to claim that programs to bring down birth rates will contribute to the solutions of significant environmental problems. Revelle has calculated how few people there would have to have been in the United States in 1965 to keep environmentally problematic practices at the level they were in 1940:

> Other things being equal, the number of automobiles and the amount of gasoline and paper consumed would have remained about constant over the quarter century if our population had declined from 133 million people in 1940 to 67 million in 1965. To maintain a constant flow of sulphur dioxide in the air from electric power plants, the population would have had to decrease to only 40 million people. Presumably, the amount of nitrogen fertilizers would not have increased, if all but 17 million Americans had remigrated to the homes of their ancestors. Only 17 million people in the country would use the same amount of nitrogen in 1965 as we used in 1940. The national parks would have remained as uncrowded in 1965 as they were in 1940 if our population during the interval had gone down

from 133 million people in 1940 to 30 million in 1965, instead of going up to 195 millions as, of course, it actually did.[7]

The point of Revelle's analysis is that environmentally deleterious behavior, what Revelle called "our filthy habits," and our affluence, grow much faster than our population. And, if there are no changes in behavior that degrade the environment, environmental degradation grows as affluence grows. Furthermore, if, as many population experts assert, decreasing population growth will increase affluence, then policies designed to accomplish that are policies that will actually increase environmental deterioration, unless, of course, environmentally deleterious behaviors are appropriately and sufficiently changed. And so the ironies persist. India, with a population program and declining birth rate, is expanding its industries. And, yes, already I have listened to a special segment on National Public Radio expressing alarm over the growth of heavily polluting manufacturing plants in India. Obviously, environmental problems have to be addressed directly and urgently. It is environmentally abusive behavior that should be curbed. Promising to cure or ameliorate environmental ills through population control contributes to false hopes for what can be accomplished by decreasing population levels. Fortunately, there is an increased awareness that environmental abuses require direct action, and environmentally responsible behavior is being encouraged.

In our legitimate concerns for the environment, we should not neglect the heart of the matter. Good stewardship of the environment is something we do, not only for our own good, but especially for the good of our children and their children. Strong family ties and loyalties support every effort to keep the earth a beautiful and bountiful place for our offspring. The Christian affirmation of the goodness of God's creation and of God's command to replenish it, is a solid, realistic basis for sound environmental behavior. And that realism must include the procreation and nurture of human life, also in its most dependent, developing forms. Good stewardship is anchored in the recognition that life is sacred and all innocent human life is inviolable.

2. *Population growth is a limited phenomenon.* We know that hunter-gatherer societies have always kept their population levels in balance with their natural resources, as well as with their whole

way of life. Modern societies, until recently, have not had such direct and realistic knowledge of their environmental limits, given the enormous productivity of agriculture, the effectiveness of public health measures, and the benefits of wealth created by technical innovations. But now we have sophisticated methods for ascertaining our limits and capabilities. On the one side, our wealthiest societies and couples have the realistic confidence that their children will enjoy a high life expectancy. On the other side, we can better estimate how far we can go in producing food with the most advanced techniques, and how much arable land is in the world for accomplishing that. But whatever the reasons, the rate of population growth in the world is falling.[8] That rate is falling most rapidly in the wealthiest nations.[9] There is, then, no clear basis at the present time for the argument that population growth is unlimited and therefore something must be done lest the space in the world for human beings, and the resources to sustain them, be irrevocably lost. Population growth, it is estimated, will peak at 11.6 billion around the year 2200.[10]

Population Growth and Human Well-Being: Food Supplies

But the question may be raised as to whether all 11.6 billion people can be adequately fed. The most plausible answer is that they can. However, ignorance, political instability and unjust government can, as they do now, lead to malnourishment and starvation for some.

1. *Population growth and adequate food supplies*. There is no need to dwell on the question as to whether 11.6 billion people on earth can be healthily nourished. They can be. Revelle's estimate that it is technically possible to feed up to 38 to 48 billion is reasonably conservative and has not been seriously challenged to my knowledge.[11] Also, there is no lack of food in the world to feed its people. Why then are there famines and why do people starve?

2. *Famines, starvation and malnourishment are not due to population growth*. We do have scholarly research on famines. B. M. Bhatia

found that, in India, there were famines in the nineteenth century caused by genuine food shortages. But in the twentieth century, famines are attributed to distribution problems and to the tendency for the price of food to rise sharply in periods of relative scarcity.[12] Poor people in India, indeed in any country, starve or are malnourished because they lack money or the knowledge of nutritional requirements. Mass starvation of whole populations occurs when there is civil strife, instability or corruption. Most recently, Ethiopia, Somalia and Sudan demonstrate the ravages of civil war and gross instability. Note that these are relatively sparsely populated areas as compared with the well fed, crowded areas of Hong Kong, Singapore and the Netherlands, for example. To blame famines on the number of people in a given region, with what we know now, would be grossly irresponsible.

Population Growth and Human Well-Being: Economic Development

The question is simple enough: Is rapid population growth a serious obstacle to economic development? The answer, however, is not simple. It does depend, in part, on whom you ask and what statistics you select or develop. Still, we do know some things. The industrialized nations grew immensely in wealth during a period of very rapid increases in their populations. We know also that moderate population growth acts as an economic stimulus. At the same time, there are situations in which a rapid rise in the work force and children of school age can create hardships, such as insufficient jobs and schooling, and a depression in the wages for those who can find work.[13] In short, population growth has had, and can have positive economic benefits; it can also have negative economic effects.

Those who focus on certain adverse consequences of rapid population growth have had considerable influence on United States policy to support family planning programs around the world.[14] The argument used for such support is that family planning programs "cannot make a poor country rich, but they can help make it less poor."[15] But even if we grant that some countries would benefit economically from slower growth, granting that does not answer the question as to what is the most effective way to slow population growth; more importantly, granting that does not answer the question as to what is the most moral way to accomplish that. Population experts agree that it is the more affluent countries with their low death rates and high literacy rates which also have low birth rates, some now below replacement levels.[16] This makes a strong case for economic development as a clearly effective means to slow population growth. For example, better strains of rice and other grains (the green revolution) introduced in India has led to lower birth rates as parents have the income to increase the expectation that their children will survive, attend school and find new economic opportunities.[17]

But many who advocate family planning programs agree that economic development should also be fostered. The United States should spend money on both. That is what the United States has been doing since the presidency of Lyndon Johnson, except for the cutbacks by Reagan and Bush in support for any family planning programs offering abortion and practicing coercion. As noted above, President Clinton has reversed the Reagan and Bush policies. To some, funding family planning programs just seems a self-evident way to increase opportunities, otherwise lacking, for poor people whose governments cannot afford to assist them in this way.

But the debate should not be carried on at such an abstract level. Poor families and their children should not be viewed as obstacles to economic development unless they accept modern methods of birth control and abortions to reduce the size of their families. Rather, the question for governments concerned about economic development and population growth should be "What should be offered to poor families so that they may become self-sufficient enough to plan and provide for their children?"

A Harvard economist, the late Simon Kuznitz, pinpointed the issue in a presentation at the Harvard School of Public Health several years ago: There are those who invest by having children; there are those who invest in their children. Those who invest in their children tend to have the means to help them educationally, medically and in numerous others way essential to their economic and general well-being. Those who invest by having children tend not to have such means. But why have a large family while poor? In some situations, it is a hedge against the possibility of losing a number of children in infancy or soon thereafter. In many countries children are needed to help their parents in their work or as security when the parents can no longer work. But for people in poverty a major reason is to have hope for the future. This outlook is well represented and eloquently expressed by an African American woman I have cited in previous articles. She is responding to the efforts in her area of Boston to reduce births through the introduction of free-standing birth control clinics.

> The worst of it is that they try to get you to plan your kids by the year; except they mean by the ten-year plan, one every ten years. The truth is, they don't want you to have any, if they could help it. To me having a baby inside me is the only time I'm really alive. I know I can make something, do something, no matter what color my skin is, and what names people call me. When the baby gets born…you can see the little one grow and get larger and start doing things, and you feel there must be some hope, some chance that things will get better…. The children and their father feel it too, just like I do. They feel the baby is a good sign, or at least he's some sign. If we didn't have that, what would be the difference from death? Even without children my life would still be bad—they're not going to give us what they have, the birth control people. They just want us to be a poor version of them, only without our children and our faith in God and our tasty fried food, or anything.[18]

This woman has stated the heart of the matter: How can you morally justify offering her birth control when "even without children" her "life would still be bad?" Government expenditures to help her and her family cannot justly be targeted in that way. She laments how the streets take her children out of her hands and away from the Ten Commandments she has tried to teach them. Childlessness for such a woman should not be viewed as a "success." But it is precisely viewed that way by a program that makes birth control methods freely available for the purpose of reducing the number of children born to poor people, and, thus, improve economic conditions for the whole society. This is crassly utilitarian since the poor woman, in this case, recognizes no benefit to her; worse yet, she sees her situation as completely hopeless without children—no different from death.

The whole idea of funding birth control clinics for the poor is misguided as well as unjust. The transition from high to low birth rates in industrialized nations occurred without government programs designed to do that, and without the use of modern contraceptives, since they were not yet invented. Furthermore, it is not simply affluence for a nation as a whole which will assure lower birth rates. The key to lowering birth rates lies in the extensiveness of the distribution of income and of social services. After analyzing considerable data, William Rich concluded that

> developmental policies that focus on participation and increased access to benefits for the population as a whole do seem to produce a major impact on family size. In countries which have a relatively equitable distribution of health and education services, and which provide land, credit and other income opportunities, the cumulative effect of such policies seems to be that the poorest half of the population is vastly better off than it is in countries with equal or higher levels of per capita GNP and poor distribution patterns. The combined effects of such policies has made it possible for some countries to reduce birth rates despite their relatively low levels of national production.[19]

Economic justice is the best and the morally justifiable population policy. Families with decent incomes can and do decide for themselves what to do about family size, and how to help create opportunities for the children they have. And, they deserve better from those governments and professionals who have tended to scorn natural methods of family planning, and to push modern contraceptives as well as abortions.[20] Pope Paul VI had it right in his excellent analysis of the relation between economic justice and population growth. I found it sad when so many in the media, and far too many in academia, dismissed *Populorum progressio* as out of step because of its moral stance on birth control and abortion. There is no reason from a purely scholarly perspective to fail to inform all people, not just Roman Catholics, of the advantages of natural methods of family planning as well as of the risks of modern contraceptives, especially the pill and the IUD. Furthermore, I have seen no evidence that casts doubt on the efficacy of a population policy that lifts families out of poverty and allows them to be productive, self-sufficient and responsible. Then they need no government subsidized birth control programs.

Population Policy and the Family:
Tendencies to Individualize Procreative Decisions

As I have tried to make clear so far, population growth as such provides no basis for diminishing any of the responsibilities and rights of families. But the advocates of family planning do espouse views that tend to undermine the family, specifically married couples, as the unit with the responsibility and right to make procreative decisions. This can and does happen in policies and policy recommendations. Increasingly, family planning is portrayed as an *individual* responsibility and right.

In 1968, at the International Conference on Human Rights in Teheran, it was "parents" who were said to have a basic right to decide freely and responsibly on the number and spacing of their children.[21] Then in 1974, the World Population Plan of Action issued by the Bucharest Conference stated that "All couples and individuals have the basic right to decide freely and responsibly the number and spacing of their children and to have the information, education and means to do so...."[22] In this document, it is asserted that individuals, as well as couples, not only have a right to make procreative decisions, but a right to the means to make such decisions. Notice also that "couples" are not identified as either married or unmarried. What this means is that it is not necessary for an individual to be married to demand, as a basic right, that governments assure the means to avoid having children if and when they desire these means. Indeed, that right is made an explicit rationale for governmentally supported family planning programs designed to reduce high fertility (birth rates): "Involuntary high fertility may infringe upon a person's human right to choose his or her family size."[23] This statement was contained in the "Final Report of the Seventy-first American Assembly" in 1986.[24] This rationale was used to argue that the United States government has an

156

obligation to support United Nations' population programs, as well as non-governmental organizations making contraceptives and abortions available in the so-called developing nations. In this report, family planning decisions are considered to be individual decisions. The participants reached a consensus that the United States government should not withhold funds from countries or organizations that engage in abortion activities where abortion is legal. Regarding "reproductive freedom" as a fundamental human right, a majority of these participants felt that this right should include access to contraception and abortion. To fail to help finance the United Nations Fund for Population Activities and the International Planned Parenthood Federation is regarded as frustrating the exercise of this individual, fundamental right to access to contraception and abortion.

Those who advocate government-financed abortions, wittingly or unwittingly, are prepared to violate the rights of those who are morally opposed to abortions for family planning purposes by forcing them to pay for abortions. Nor are there discussions of the rights of husbands or parents to have a voice as to whether their wives or their children respectively should have an abortion. This literature, supporting the current policies of the United Nations Fund for Population Activities and of International Planned Parenthood, does not explicitly concern itself either with preserving the unity of the family, or with maintaining a marital bond as the locus of procreative decision-making.[25] It should be noted that the literature used by Planned Parenthood for educational purposes thoroughly individualizes procreative decisions, and this applies also to children below the age of eighteen in relation to their own parents.

It is important to emphasize that there are no empirical analyses of population-related problems which provide any basis for legitimating the individualization of procreative decisions. Nor are there any empirical analyses that make government intervention of this kind, or of any other kind, necessary for reducing population growth. As indicated earlier, reductions in birth rates without government programs for that purpose have occurred before, occur now, and are expected in the future. In short, there is no moral justification for policies that would undermine the family structures that have evolved and which have been undergirded by Christian traditions.

The individualization of procreative decisions and the lack of explicit policies to strengthen families permeates American law. This is especially evident, as Professor Mary Ann Glendon of Harvard Law School has amply documented, in the areas of abortion and divorce laws.[26] In contrast to the United States, European countries, to various degrees and in various ways, try to discourage divorce and abortion, and at the same time offer incentives and/or support to those who have children, and to those who remain together in their marriages. America's family policies are implicit, and they strongly tend to weaken families and isolate individuals from one another. Abortion, for example, is depicted as a right to privacy, shielded by law from the scrutiny and advice of loving parents and spouses. The story United States' divorce laws tell about marriage is one Glendon has summarized as follows:

> Marriage is a relationship that exists primarily for the fulfillment of the individual spouses. If it ceases to perform this function, no one is to blame and either spouse may terminate it at will. After divorce, each spouse is expected to be self-sufficient. If this is not possible with the aid of property division, some rehabilitative maintenance may be in order for a temporary period. Children hardly appear in the story....[27]

It is not surprising, given this story, that the United States' divorce rate is high and that divorce is a major source of the increased proportion of children in poverty. The income of noncustodial parents rises; the income of custodial parents, mainly women, declines.[28] To make matters worse, United States' tax laws are such that the deductions for children are small, do not keep up with inflation, and do not help the poor. Child support is not only inadequate, but discouraged, since it is not tax deductible for noncustodial parents. In Glendon's words, "American divorce law in practice seems to be saying to parents, especially mothers, that it is not safe to devote oneself primarily or exclusively to raising children."[29] What a terrible disincentive to finding hope, through investing in your children, and through nurturing their moral, spiritual and intellectual powers. Our laws need to be monitored and changed by an explicit effort to strengthen marriage and families. That would be a policy of family planning in conformity with justice, and which should be at the heart of any population policy. For, after all, population policy should be formulated for the purpose of human survival and well-being. Procreation and nurture by loving, committed parents is absolutely requisite to achieving that goal; so are communities that strengthen rather than undermine such love and commitment.

Strengthening the Family as a Procreative Unit: Toward a Just Population Policy

What follows is a brief overview of the various policies I have been suggesting along the way and a few more concrete suggestions in the United States context.

1. *Develop explicit family policies that strengthen families as procreative units.* With a view to strengthening the family as a procreative unit, tax laws that are unfair to married couples should be changed. Note, for example, that a married couple does not receive as much of a standard deduction as two single individuals. Given the costs of education, particularly higher education, parents should receive a great deal more tax relief to retain their income for helping their children. That tax relief should be increased in a timely fashion to keep pace with inflation. Divorce should be made more difficult, particularly for those who have children. Financial support for one's children should be required of non-custodial parents, but tax laws should facilitate, not penalize, such financial support. Much more realistic amounts of support should be exacted by the courts in divorce cases. Current levels of child support are inadequate to say the least.

Universal health coverage is a necessity if parents are to be encouraged to stay together and to stay out of poverty. To give medical coverage to individual women with children who are not working, while some working individuals and couples (an estimated 25 million, two-thirds of 37 million Americans) are without health coverage, discourages men in low-paying jobs from supporting children they have parented. I am not, however, in favor of any plan for universal health coverage which tries to save money by rationing care or medical innovations. When it comes to providing care, the Good Samaritan had it right. He promised to pay more if more was needed to take care of the wounded one he found on the Jericho road. (If you want to save big money for medical care, reduce vices such as violence, smoking and substance abuse.)

2. *Support family planning through medical and public health services.* Maternal and child health clinics in the United States have helped reduce infant mortality and birth rates among the poor; birth control clinics have been largely subsidies for the middle class. There is no reason for the United States to support Planned Parenthood in the United States or in other countries; there are, as I have suggested, good reasons not to do so, given their views of procreation and abortion. Why not target the money, in this country and in others, so that those who cannot now assure their health and the spacing of their children, receive help? There is every reason to do that: It is just; it saves lives; it engenders hope; and from all we know, it reduces family size on average, as families try to do more for the children they have.

3. *Support economic development that increases opportunities for the disadvantaged.* Specific policies that open up economic opportunities for the poor, whether through new agricultural products, low-interest or interest-free loans, etc., will work together with health education and care, to strengthen hope in the children families already have. Helping families economically increases freedom. It does not dictate family size or send signals that children are a burden.

Citing Daniel Patrick Moynihan and Alva Myrdal as sources, Glendon asserts that "family policy...makes a difference."[30] As Christians, we acknowledge that we are commanded by God to be fruitful and multiply and replenish the earth. Sound population policies would be in support of that commandment. Justice, in accord with human dignity and human rights, demands no less of us.

Notes

1. See a number of references in Arthur J. Dyck, "The Moral Bonds of the Family," *The Linacre Quarterly* 48:1 (February 1981), 14-22.

2. Paul Ehrlich, *The Population Bomb* (New York: Ballantine Books, 1968); W. Paddock and P. Paddock, *Famine 1975* (Boston: Little Brown and Co., 1967);

Phyllis Tilson Piotrow, *World Population Crisis: The United States Response* (New York: Praeger Publishers, 1973).

3. Paul Demeny, "The World Demographic Situation," in Jane Menken (ed.), *World Population & U.S. Policy: The Choices Ahead* (New York: W. W. Norton & Co., 1986), 27-66.

4. *Population Newsletter #51* (June 1991), 10.

5. See the article and the references in Arthur J. Dyck, "An Ethical Analysis of Population Policy Alternatives," *The Monist* 60:1 (January 1977), 29-46.

6. See "Family Planning for all Families," *The New York Times*, November 29, 1993, p. A16 and "U.S. to Spend more on Birth Control," *The New York Times*, International, Sunday, January 23, 1994, p. 9, for the kinds of programs being supported and the increased amounts of money being given by the Clinton administration.

7. Roger Revelle (Testimony), "Effects of Population Growth on Natural Resources and the Environment," Hearings before the Reuss Subcommittee on Conservation and Natural Resources (Washington, D.C.: U.S. Government Printing Office, 1969).

8. Paul Demeny, "The World Demographic Situation."

9. *Ibid.*

10. *Population Newsletter* #51 (June 1991), p. 10.

11. Roger Revelle, "Food and Population," *Scientific American* 231:3 (September 1974).

12. B. M. Bhatia, *Famines in India: 1860-1995* (New York: Asia Publishing House, 1967).

13. Samuel H. Preston, "Are the Economic Consequences of Population Growth a Sound Basis for Population Policy," and Ansley J. Coale, "Population Trends and Economic Development," in Jane Menken (ed.), *World Population & U.S. Policy*, 67-95 and 96-104.

14. See Jane Menken, "Introduction and Overview," in Jane Menken, (ed.), *World Population & U.S. Policy*, 6-26. See also note 6 above.

15. Samuel H. Preston, "Are the Economic Consequences of Population Growth a Sound Basis for Population Policy," 95.

16. Paul Demeny, "The World Demographic Situation."

17. J. B. Wyon and J. E. Gordon, *The Khanna Study* (Cambridge: Harvard University Press, 1971).

18. Robert Coles, *Children of Crisis* (Boston: Atlantic-Little-Brown, 1964), 368-69.

19. William Rich, *Smaller Families through Social and Economic Progress*, Monograph no. 7 of the Overseas Development Council (Washington, D.C., January 1973), 37.

20. *Reproductive Health: A Strategy for the 1990s*, (New York: The Ford Foundation, 1991) and in the "final Report of the Seventy-first American Assembly," in Jane Menken (ed.), *World Population & U.S. Policy*, 299-41.

21. *Reproductive Health: A Strategy for the 1990s*, 11, n 17.

22. *Ibid.*, 11, n. 18.

23. "Final Report of the Seventy-first American Assembly," 231.

24. *Ibid.*

25. See notes 20-24 for examples of this.

26. Mary Ann Glendon, *Abortion and Divorce in Western Law* (Cambridge, Mass.: Harvard University Press, 1987.

27. *Ibid.*, 108.

28. *Ibid.*, 81-91.

29. *Ibid.*, 111.

30. *Ibid.*, 135 and n 69.

Chapter 11

LOVE AND LIFE WITHIN THE FAMILY: PART ONE

John J. Billings, M.D.

Lyn and I are baptized Catholics and medical doctors. We have been married for 50 years, have 9 children, including one adopted child, 32 grandchildren living here on earth and a few more who have gone before us to meet their Creator, and one great-grandchild. Our knowledge of the problems confronting the family in modern society increased during participation in the Synod of Bishops in Rome in 1980 considering the Role of the Christian Family in the Modern world, and also through working in nearly 100 countries around the world during the past 25 years, spending on average some 3–4 months of each year outside Australia, where we were born. We recognize that having been "incorporated into Christ by Baptism" we share in the way of the laity in "the priestly, prophetic and kingly office of Christ" as the Second Vatican Council has taught us. Those in Holy Orders, the members of religious congregations, those living consecrated lives, and the rest of the laity, all belong to the Mystical Body of Christ.

Lyn and I have always sought to work in close harmony with the Bishops and Priests and count it a special privilege to be here to address those Pastors whom we recognize as the successors of the Apostles.

"All the faithful in any state or walk of life," as the Council recalled, "are called to the fullness of Christian life and to the perfection of love" (*Lumen gentium,* 40). What we wish to do, by example and by our words, is to help married people to live according to God's plan for the married state. This means, in the words of Pope John Paul II "The experience married couples are called to live as their own way of sanctification."[1]

Pope John Paul has recently drawn attention to what he himself has called "a genuine crisis…which has come about within the Christian community itself…. It is no longer a matter of limited and occasional dissent, but an overall and systematic calling into question of traditional moral doctrine" (*Veritatis splendor* 4).

Just at the end of the last century, the anti-Christian German philosopher Friedrich Nietzsche wrote these words: "Christianity is a system. It is a consistently thought-out and complete view of things. If one breaks a fundamental idea within it, the whole thing will fall to pieces."

There are three fundamental links in the chain of Christianity which have been gravely weakened in modern times:

1. The consequences which have flowed from work of the most influential schools of modern Christian Biblical Scholarship.

2. The disintegration of the recognized patterns of Catholic morality, particularly, but not exclusively, sexual morality.

3. The fragmentation of the structure of Catholic worship and piety—the liturgy, the Sacraments, sacramental and pious practices in general, which followed the introduction of the Mass

in the vernacular, and more particularly, the various aberrations which have continued to appear and which, for example, have turned many Masses into a charade. From the centers of Catholic scholarship, the influence flows down through seminaries, teachers' colleges, and through them to teachers in the Catholic schools.

In his address to the United States Bishops on November 14, 1993, Archbishop William H. Keeler,[2] President of the National Conference, said that the real "American Catholic story" is that the Church in the United States grew last year by about a million members, the Catholic schools continue to increase in enrollments, there has been an increase in those beginning theological studies for the diocesan priesthood every year during the past 3 years, the Catholic press has a circulation of more than 25 million, the Catholic hospitals served more than 50 million patients yearly, and more than any other private group in the country they care for the hungry, the homeless and those in greatest need.

He went on to point out the "encircling gloom," the difficulties and challenges that are faced—what Pope John Paul has called the "culture of death" in which there is injustice, discrimination, exploitation, and violence, including elimination of the unborn, the elderly and the disabled.

It is very appropriate for Archbishop Keeler not to give way to pessimism and despair; in fact, we will not be able to solve any of the most serious problems that we face unless we are first able to understand and enunciate them clearly.

We in Australia adopt many attitudes and patterns of behavior, both good and bad, from the United States of America. It is unlikely that the problems which exist within the Catholic Church and in society in Australia are very different from those which exist in the United States.

During the past 20 years, the number of those people who have publicly identified themselves as Catholics throughout Australia has grown quite rapidly, so that Catholicism is now numerically the largest religious body in Australia. However, the percentage of those who go to Mass weekly has fallen far more rapidly. In 1970, it was reliably estimated that 60% of those who identified themselves as Catholics went to Mass every Sunday. By 1986, in the Melbourne archdiocese, only 26% went to Mass each week, and in 1993, the figure was 20.5%. In just 20 years, the regular attendance at Sunday Mass has fallen by two-thirds, and is continuing to fall.

There is to a large extent a disintegration of the Catholic hospitals and schools. In some of the Catholic hospitals, morally objectionable practices occur in the use of modern reproductive technologies and surgical sterilization, the latter sometimes described as "uterine isolation," which is simply a euphemistic term for tubal ligation. In the schools, even those charged with the teaching of religion are not always Catholics, and those who claim to be Catholic are inculcating opinions which contradict the teaching of the Magisterium of the Church.

In the United States, there is reliable evidence that not more than 1% of Catholic doctors publicly declare their loyalty to the teaching of the Church regarding the regulation of births, and refuse to cooperate with the provision of contraception, sterilization and abortion; it is unlikely that the situation in Australia is any different. The moribund state of most of the Catholic medical societies does not say much for the remaining 99%. The once honorable profession of medicine has deserted its traditional ethic, to a large extent as a result of greed and the tolerance of abortion, and at the same time, the Catholic doctors have ceased to exercise the influence for good which once did so much to elevate ethical standards in medical practice.

Utilitarian and consequentialist theories of moral relativism have had a pernicious influence on the whole of society. One can see that these modern errors are to a large extent the same as the first sins ever to be recorded: the rejection of legitimate authority is an echo of the *non serviam* (I will not serve) of Satan and his cohorts, and the demand for personal freedom to decide what is good and what is evil takes us back to the Garden of Eden.

The primacy of conscience has never been an authentic teaching of the Catholic Church. Conscience is ultimately subservient to truth. For the past 20 years, the teaching most usually imparted in most Catholic secondary schools has been that in matters of morality, and in particular, sexual morality, the final authority is the person's own conscience. It is said that the Church's most serious moral teaching should always be respectfully and prayerfully considered, but the person's own conscience is the final "decider" as to the course of conduct which he ought to pursue. This is the substance of the concept of the "informed conscience" which represents in fact the privatization of morality.

One has had the experience of a Catholic couple asking for guidance after it had been recommended by their doctor that the wife should be sterilized, and when the couple consulted a priest about the matter, they had been told "to follow their conscience." The poignant questions asked by the husband were, "What should our conscience be telling us? What is the teaching of the Church?" It should surprise no one that insisting upon the inviolability of the personal conscience has ended with disbelief in all moral absolutes. Then there is very little difference between what Catholics and others believe, not merely in the matter of contraception, but of pre-marital sex, abortion and homosexual practices.

Meanwhile, as reported in a national newspaper, *The Australian*, on December 24, 1993, the latest figures show that 43% of marriages in Australia can now be expected to end in divorce or separation within 30 years, and the corresponding figure in the United States is 54%.

I remember a good Catholic priest expressing the opinion that, seeing that God has created every individual human being, He speaks to each one of them, and it would be difficult to believe otherwise. We can also see that in various non-Christian religions and schools of philosophy what seems to be an influence of the Holy Spirit. These good opinions should not lead us to conclude, as the rejection of moral absolutes does, that one religion is as good as another, as good as the religion which is to follow Christ.

A new book by Zbigniew Brzezinski,[3] former National Security Adviser to President Jimmy Carter, argues that moral and cultural disintegration is the real cause of the demise of the West. America in particular will not retain its role as leader of the free world if it does not seek a return to some moral sanity: "Unless there is some deliberate effort to re-establish the centrality of some moral criteria for the exercise of self-control over gratification as an end in itself, the phase of American preponderance may not last long, despite the absence of any self-evident replacement."

Brzezinski also says, "The role of religion in defining moral standards has also declined, while an ethos of consumerism masquerades as a substitute for ethical standards."

When Pope John Paul II visited Denver, Colorado, in August of 1993, for the World Youth congress, he spoke to President Clinton and told him that the United States can no longer be looked upon as the country most able to defend human freedom, when it will not defend the life of the conceived child. One can add that surgical sterilization may be appropriate to a domestic or farm animal, but is an insult to a human being. Every man and woman who has been subjected to direct sterilization knows that a very important part of his/her whole organism has been destroyed. The widespread incidence of direct sterilization will certainly have a demoralizing effect upon the whole community which will become more and more evident as serious challenges present themselves to the nation.

The scientific evidence is incontrovertible that the individual human life begins as soon as the sperm cell penetrates the ovum, and that individual human life continues, even if from that single cell monozygotic twins develop. The humanity of Christ began in a single cell within the womb of the virgin Mary, and that single cell contained His full humanity and His Divinity. To use an embryo as a pure object of analysis or experimentation is to attack the dignity of the person and the human race.

There is no such thing as a victimless crime. A woman once said plaintively, when informed that the serious ill health that she was experiencing was the result of the ingestion of contraceptive medication, "But I wasn't taking it for contraception," as if the ill effects are an expression of Divine wrath. The corrupting influence of contraceptive and sterilizing practices, and even more of abortion, on the conjugal relationship are widespread amongst those Catholics who are "acting in good conscience." Not least amongst the prophetic utterances of the Encyclical *Humanæ vitæ* were the warnings issued by Pope Paul VI of the grave consequences of methods of artificial birth control. "Let them consider," he wrote, "first of all, how wide and easy a road would thus be opened up towards conjugal infidelity and the general lowering of morality."

It should not be difficult to perceive that the use of drugs to contracept, sterilize or abort is bad science, and can never be otherwise. The drug is being used in a way that is wrong in principle, in that the effect intended can only be produced by the serious disruption of an important and complex biological system. It is inevitable that such use of drugs will produce serious harm to many individuals and will not continue to be used in medical practice in the long-term.

The full story of the harm and the fatalities that have resulted from chemical contraception will eventually be revealed. Already many pharmaceutical firms have withdrawn from the market. Even by now Pope Paul VI and the Catholic Church would be the subject of vociferous ridicule if the Holy Father had not reaffirmed the unchanging teaching of the Church.

One medical scientist, who is not at all well-disposed towards natural family planning, was recently quoted in the *British Medical Journal* thus:

> We can reduce, but by definition we can never remove all the risks from any systemic method. Without fear of contradiction during the next 100 years, one can say that no chemical, steroidal, non-steroidal or antigenic can be devised which, whether given to women or men, whether administered pre-coitly or post-coitly or whether used by the oral, nasal, retinal, cutaneous, sub-cutaneous, rectal or vaginal routes will be totally free of all risk. Anything that gets into the bloodstream must be capable of causing harmful effects somewhere, yet the scientific establishment have so far concentrated overwhelmingly on these very systemic methods...the search for the impossible, a risk-free systemic method.[4]

One can add that he need not have modestly restricted his prophecy to the next 100 years.

Although our brief is to consider the scientific and psychosocial aspects on methods of regulating births, particularly upon the individual, the matters we have raised have a political significance and implications for the whole fabric of society. Respect for human life is itself the seamless garment on which the whole structure of the family depends, and as G. K. Chesterton[5] wrote, along with the quoted comments of Brzezinski, "There is no basis for democracy except in a dogma about the Divine origin of man."

In St. Luke's Gospel, Our Lord rebuked the lawyers when He said, "Alas for you lawyers also because you load on men burdens that are unendurable, burdens that you yourselves do not move a finger to lift" (Luke 11:46). Those bishops and priests who do not arrange for the teaching of natural family planning to be available to everyone within their pastoral care are worthy of the same condemnation. Blessed John Henry Newman wrote that England lost the Faith through the cowardice of the laity. It may be said in the future that widespread loss of Faith, both in Australia and the United States, and all the Western world, resulted from the cowardice of the clergy.

We had the good fortune to develop in Melbourne, Australia, a modern, scientific, simple, highly effective, natural method for the achievement or the spacing of pregnancies. It is truly a universal method because it is understood and used successfully by illiterate couples living in extreme poverty, is acceptable to people of all cultures and religions, or no religion at all, and is applicable in all the varied circumstances which may be encountered during the course of the woman's reproductive life. Not being a contraceptive, that is, not being against the child, not distorting the act of sexual intercourse, not depending for its effect upon the suppression or destruction of fertility, nor of course the destruction of the conceived child, it is appropriate to the dignity of the human person. Because it acknowledges the dominion of God in the creation of all human life and never acts to obstruct His creative intent at any particular time, it enables married couples to live at peace with their conscience. Because it imposes a gentle discipline whereby the husband and wife express their love for one another in a paschal way, that is, by self-discipline, sometimes amounting to a difficult sacrifice, they manifest a love which is truly like that which Christ has for His Church.

Our work around the world has taught us that husbands everywhere will accept their role in cooperating with the application of the method, once they understand what is required of them. We have come to understand the goodness that exists in the heart of every human person, truly made in the image of God. We have seen families grow in peace, fidelity, happiness and love when they have decided to live according to God's plan for married people, a plan which restores the child to the center of love and concern within the family. The rights of the child may be summarized in its right to be loved.

It cannot be argued that any method of regulating births has had more intensive scientific research to verify its basic principles and guidelines than the Billings Ovulation Method. We have worked in close collaboration since 1963 with Professor James Brown,[6] an endocrine chemist of the Melbourne University Department of Obstetrics and Gynecology and Professor Henry G. Burger,[7] Director of Prince Henry's Medical Research Institute at Monash University, Melbourne. During the past 15 years we have also collaborated closely with Professor Erik Odeblad,[8] Director, Department of Medical Biophysics, University of Umea, Sweden; his brilliant studies on the physical properties of cervical mucus have made a unique contribution to our knowledge of the role of the cervix in human reproduction. More recently, Dr. Thomas Hilgers of Omaha, Nebraska, has undertaken very beautiful and informative ultra-sound studies with his colleagues at the Pope Paul VI Institute for the Study of Human Reproduction, at Omaha, Nebraska, U.S.A. Field trials in different parts of the world are now consistently revealing a method-effectiveness of 99-100% in the application of the guidelines for the postponement of pregnancy, and there is no method of contraception or sterilization which is capable of producing a better result. Some information about modern, scientific natural family planning was included in an article by Dr. R. E. J. Ryder[9] of Newcastle in the British Medical Journal of September 18, 1993.

When Pope Paul VI produced the Encyclical *Humanæ vitæ*, many people said that it would all be different when he died. Now that Pope John Paul has produced the Apostolic Exhortation *Familiaris consortio*, and more recently, the Encyclical *Veritatis splendor*, people are again saying that it will be different if we wait until we have a new Pope. The result of the waiting will be that those people will die and we will all die, and we will have a new Pope (not necessarily in that order), and the teaching of the Catholic Church will be the same. The battle will be long and the situation may become worse before it becomes better, but as the historian Arnold Toynbee wrote, situations are never determined by majorities, but

171

what he called "creative minorities." What will decide the issue is what the Church composed of the Catholics remaining loyal to the Magisterium actually believe, that being a Catholic means to follow Christ and to be loyal to His Vicar on earth, who governs the Church with the authority given to Peter at Caesarea Philippi (Matt 16:17-19), and that, under God, is what we propose to do. The teachers and scientists involved in natural family planning, and the Catholic doctors, will succeed in their vocations if the bishops and priests give them the help they need.

Notes

I acknowledge with gratitude the generous assistance given to me by Mr. B. A. Santamaria, Editor, *AD2000*, Melbourne, Australia.

1. Pope John Paul II. Address given to participants in a Congress on November 26, 1993, celebrating the 25th anniversary of *Humanæ vitæ* sponsored by the Pontifical Council for the Family and the Institute for Studies on Marriage and Family, Rome.

2. Archbishop William H. Keeler. *L'Osservatore Romano*, December 1, 1993, pp. 8-9.

3. Zbigniew Brzezinski. *OUT OF CONTROL: Global Turmoil on the Eve of the Twenty-First Century*. Macmillan.

4. J. Guillebaud, "Present and Future Trends in Contraception." *British Journal of Family Planning*, 1988, 13:2-8. Quoted by J. Kelly in Letters to the Editor, *British Medical Journal*, 1993, 307:1357.

5. G. K. Chesterton, 1922. *What I Saw in America*.

6. J. B. Brown, et al. "Correlations Between the Mucus Symptoms and the Hormonal Markers of Fertility throughout Reproductive Life." Appendix to *The Ovulation Method*, 7th Edition, by John J. Billings. Advocate Press, Melbourne, 1983.

7. E. L. Billings, J. J. Billings, J. B. Brown, and H. G. Burger. *Symptoms and hormonal changes accompanying ovulation*. Lancet, 1:282-4, 1972.

8. E. Odeblad, "The Cervix, the Vagina and Fertility." Appendix to *Billings Atlas of the Ovulation Method*, 5th Edition, 1989. Published by the Ovulation Method Research & Reference Centre of Australia, North Fitzroy 3068, Australia.

9. R. E. J. Ryder, "Natural family planning: effective birth-control supported by the Catholic Church," *British Medical Journal*, 1993; 307:723-6. See also Editor's Choice and Letters to the Editor, *British Medical Journal*, 1993; 307-1351 and 1357-60.

Chapter 12

LOVE AND LIFE WITHIN THE FAMILY: PART TWO

Evelyn L. Billings, M.D.

Your Excellencies, thank you for inviting me to speak about our work which has occupied some 40 years, although during the first 10 years I was more occupied with looking after our own brood and only began to help John in the early 1960s. It is true to say that the inspiration for the development of this method came from a belief in and the love of the Church teaching, as well as the faithfulness of the people. This provided the impetus to work scientifically with scientists who were also dedicated to the goodness of Providence, one a United Churchman, Professor James Brown, and the other a Lutheran, Professor Erik Odeblad of Sweden. This work opened up such a wealth of proof for the method that our joy in teaching spread to many thousands of others who have worked all around the world ever since. At the same time, we have seen a great upheaval in the Church where the most precious articles of our Faith are the ones which have been most assiduously questioned and attacked by many, including clergy, theologians and ethicists. Perhaps these people wish to prove themselves right by demonstrating their unassailability, for if they fall there is nothing, and we fall also. The big problem has been that while the intellectuals go about their business of testing revealed truths, there are those who listen and glean excuses for their own preferred various patterns of behavior which are often disastrous both for themselves and even those that they truly love. The distress has been felt far and wide as many have followed along the paths of uncertainty. We know that truth will prevail in the end, but in the meantime we struggle against untruths.

Sexual behavior offers an outstanding example of the consequences of departure from revealed truth as is seen in the various social ills of our time.

There are many who cannot or will not relate the directives of the Papal documents *Humanæ vitæ*, *Familiaris consortio* and *Veritatis splendor* to the natural sexual lives of ordinary men and women. They see the injunctions as theoretical formulations far removed from reality. We have had long experience with armchair theorists and "what ifs" whose attitude of pessimism is common to them all. The most infrequent and most unrealistic scenarios are proposed, including mental defectiveness, uncooperative husbands, alcoholic husbands, cultural practices, perilous health conditions, and many others in order to theoretically disprove the overall applicability of natural family planning.

Persuasion to depart from truth in matters of sexuality is supported by strong physical inducements, hormonal in origin, which it is argued are undeniable components of human nature and must not be denied. It is true to say most surely that human nature is at its most perfect when it operates not by hormones, but by free will governed by intelligence and influenced overall by love. Many are the stories we can tell how the practice of natural regulation of

174

fertility has resulted in restoration of harmony and happiness for couples and families in trouble. The method, by providing the means of effecting solutions to severe problems, provides also the conjugal strength necessary for true love. We learned this as time went by. The method came to be seen as containing an inherent goodness which worked on the good in human nature and perfected it in marriage.

Sexual love is by no means exclusively physical. That statement should go without saying. It is within marriage in the context of the family that the full truth of this can be seen. It is only when constraints are imposed by fidelity and by the resources of the family that sexual love reaches its full maturity, just as a tree yields its best fruit after several years of nurture and pruning, leaving behind the wild uninhibited growth of its early years. When I first began to work in natural family planning in Melbourne in the early 60s, 10 years after John had begun with Fr. Catarinich as marriage counselor, I used to see sexual love expressed as total abstinence for several years as couples approached the problematical years of the climacteric when they could no longer rely on the regular behavior of the woman's cycles. The Church ruling against contraception was not questioned. Physical sexual practices were given up, if not joyfully, at least willingly and dutifully and lovingly. There were few who were not prepared to welcome any child which came along, and so it was not uncommon for children who were called "after-thoughts" in those days to arrive 10 years after the others, bringing with them great love and a rejuvenating influence on the parents, who were on the point of entering retirement and were now obliged to keep going in order to provide for the new demands with consequent unexpected benefits to everyone.

As attitudes towards physical sexual relationships changed within the community and sexual relationships became the great *sine qua non* of relationships between men and women, married or not, such attitudes to "after-thoughts" changed. They became unacceptable as sexual intercourse took pride of place. To accommodate this attitude, the woman was physically manipulated to become readily available, and at the same time, the impediment of childbearing was removed—done in several ways, hysterectomy, sterilization by tubal ligation, medication, various barrier devices.

It became totally unacceptable for many to deny themselves the gratification of sexual pleasure and contraception became widely acceptable. While women welcomed this change in attitude as a great relief from burdensome childbearing, men welcomed it as a sexual liberation. Thus regard for the child became weakened, and then even changed to a hostility towards the child.

At the same time, the requirement of a perfect child became commonplace and medical technology provided amniocentesis, chorion villus sampling and selective abortion to fulfill this "right." Childlessness was no longer tolerated, and when adoption became unacceptable and indeed unpopular, assisted reproductive services became available, together with the ensuing well-known destruction demanded of simultaneously conceived siblings—all this to accommodate the newly perceived right of adults to parent a perfect child. This child's right became secondary to science and society. The powerful physical expression of married love, created for mutual comfort and happiness, by denying its fruitfulness became sterile self-service. Love for spouse and child were weakened, and men and women now hid from God. Churches were depleted.

Minds were closed to service, love and duty. The chaste spousal relationship between St. Joseph and his virgin wife were seldom referred to. This seemed no longer appropriate or relevant to modern thinking or living, and there were those who even doubted its veracity. Attempts were made to deny this most holy chastity, thereby removing the example of the deepest human spousal love known to the world ever, now or to be—an example so valuable because it contains all the essentials of love, fortitude and kindness that are the essential ingredients of all human marriages, perfected in service to God.

Mary and Joseph were given the Christ Child, and Mary, human motherhood. St. Joseph was given the enormous privilege of foster fatherhood of God's son, and together they were asked to maintain their virginity in order to proclaim that this child was no other than God's Son. They were called the Holy Family. All this was possible only through the spousal love given to them by the Father—that love which included love and fidelity to Him. In full realization of it, how powerful their love must have been, and how fitting a love to embrace the Son of God, a human love to nurture the Heavenly Son who is Love in a human family. What happiness must have reigned in their home!

It is only rarely that husbands and wives are asked to live thus for more than a brief span of time, yet in all marriages from time to time this is required due to circumstances of illness or absence. The growth of such deep spousal love between them, as exemplified by Mary and Joseph who lived dutifully and lovingly, enables couples to be happy in difficult circumstances and reject the persuasion of artificially induced infertility which rejects the child as an impediment to happiness in the most pernicious philosophy of our day.

Modern natural family planning, and particularly the solution to pre-ovulatory infertility which has been the contribution of the Ovulation Method, has meant that no matter how difficult circumstances are, no long periods of abstinence are ever required for the avoidance of conception. There is one circumstance where total abstinence is required of couples, and that is if one member of the couple is carrying the HIV virus. There is no way which is reliable of protecting the uninfected member, save by complete abstinence. If death is to be a consequence of sexual intercourse, then in charity sexual intercourse should be given up for the sake of the uninfected member. And if there are children, also for their sake. The healthy parent must stay well in order to look after them. It is then that love for the beloved is seen as all-powerful in duty, service and elimination of self. It is then seen that the example of the Holy Family provides the needed inspiration for perseverance. The practice of natural fertility regulation equips a couple to accept any sacrifice depending on their strong love. It ensures their fidelity, and thereby protects the family in many ways, including the physical health of husband and wife.

As the word contraception proclaims, it is an act against conception—against the initiation of new life. As said before, it is one of the most, if not the most pernicious practices and philosophy of our time. It is a ruthless philosophy that cares not how the child's existence is prevented—by prevention of the joining of the gametes, or destruction of the embryonic life which comes into existence with the joining of the gametes.

The whole contraceptive enterprise has resulted in a miserable failure. The whole thrust of the newest medications is towards destroying early life. Reproductive health also is a casualty and results not only from the drugs and devices used, but also from sexual aberrations and promiscuity. One hears the spurious argument "but people choose contraception lovingly and caringly, and they get by all right." One only has to look at all the unhappy marriages to know that there are many who do not "get by all right." The child especially does not "get by all right."

It is through the child that society will be restored to health and truth. The child demands service, not expedience. He demands duty, not denial and neglect. He demands love.

Teaching the youth has become an essential part of the work that is done because of the pernicious influences in society on malleable minds and the lack of parental guidance due to confusion, practice of double-standards, inability to confront society and even willingness to conform to society to the extent of giving their daughters the pill and taking them to an abortion clinic to rid themselves of their own grandchildren, or even expelling their children from their home, being unable to cope with or control the bad behavior of children who are thereby displaying their anguish and misery.

It is a prerequisite that all our teachers should love babies and welcome them all. For a long time, natural family planning was thought of as a Catholic method of freeing the physical relationship from childbearing in order to preserve the unitive aspect of marriage. The Ovulation Method was criticized particularly because there were more children among its users than among users of other methods. The total pregnancy rates were quoted as "failures" of the method, especially by organizations like International Planned Parenthood who are concerned mainly with reducing numbers of people. Our methodology was shown to respect the wishes of couples wanting a large family. It was also shown that these couples were happy! Indeed, the love and generosity engendered by the use of the method was responsible for the seeking to have the child as an expression of that love. Furthermore, it has been demonstrated in all societies and peoples that it is not possible to use the Billings Ovulation Method as a contraceptive. If the fertile phase of the cycle is regarded merely as a time of prohibition, there will be dissension. If it is regarded as a time of fertility and possibility of conceiving, it will be treated with responsibility, and this is what engenders generous consideration and love.

The teaching is individual one-to-one addressing the specific needs of each couple, refusing no one no matter how unpromising or off-putting the problem seems to be, remembering how Our Lord came for the sick, not for the healthy. It is the policy of our teachers that no one is left untaught. Some come with an ingrained anti-child attitude and an intention never to have a child. Their purpose in learning the method is to benefit from its healthy naturalness. They do not, however, see their own unnatural attitude to the child which confronts the liberal philosophy of the Ovulation Method. So we talk to them, and the reasons which are often unfounded for denying the child become clear. We teach them the method, and in many cases the generosity and love that the method engenders between them works in time a change in attitude, and they then decide to bring a child into an atmosphere of happiness that they did not imagine possible. Many of these couples have come from contraception. If we did not teach them, where would they go? Some have come unrepentant from abortion, intending to repeat this in the future if pregnancy occurs. These couples indeed pose a challenge to the teachers. Often they lack consideration for each other and discipline for themselves, and sometimes this does result in pregnancy, and sometimes they will abort again. We take them back. They come even though they know that abortion has no part in the Ovulation Method. If we had refused them, they would have finally resorted to sterilization with all its ensuing ills. In many cases, the couple will have imbibed the loving strength of the method from the teacher, and together they will reject abortion as their love and confidence in each other grows. Sometimes we think that all we have done is not enough if abortion follows and we have failed, but I do not think that if we offer what we have we will fail forever. Who knows when the seed will germinate? We are only the sowers. We cannot discount the soil, rain and sun. We cannot always see the end of the gathering into the barns. We must always believe that Our Lord who came for the sick comes still. All we know is that since we learned not to be daunted by seeming impossibilities that the work has prospered, certainly as far as methodology is concerned, but also in marriage and other relationships as well with the young and untaught, poor and rejected. There is a huge family of teachers now around the world, 1,500 in Nigeria, 3,000 in Argentina, 600 in France, 800 in Italy, to name a few. Teachers everywhere will record the same successes of a return to family stability. Over 50 million couples are using the Billings Ovulation Method world-wide.

There is plenty of encouragement to be had from the Scriptures from Genesis onwards. In Genesis we are told that a man joins himself to his wife and they become one body. "I have acquired a man with the help of the Lord," Eve said when Cain was born, conceived by union with Adam. Therefore, "in the beginning" there was no contraception and God was credited with the gift of the child. Yet the seeds of rejection and rebellion had been sown. "I will not serve" was Satan's war-cry, and with this he infected Eve who did what was forbidden by God, and drew her husband Adam into the snare, who has many times treated her very badly in later history.

Woman in the feminist movement, in her search for justice and freedom from the power of man, instead of finding equality with him and in aiming for a reversal of power, has lost it. This loss has come about through denial of her femininity by removal of her fertility and denial of the child. "I will not serve." Woman's true power comes through her intactness, her integrity which includes her fertility and childbearing potential. This renders her capable of loving maternally, whether married or not, whether childless or not. Maternal love is unique among all human loves, and she shares a holiness and spirituality with the Mother of God, who brought forth the Son in human form. To relinquish that is indeed a great loss and is a mystery which is hard to explain but a treasure to be taught and held. It contains a paradox where to serve is to find freedom, explained only by the power of love, which yearns to serve the beloved.

Encouragements are many in the precepts given, and the consequences plain if they are not followed. Psalm 81 tells us:

Rescue the weak and the poor;
Set them free from the hand of the wicked.

Unperceiving, they grope in the darkness
And the order of the world is shaken.

We are all weak and poor and unperceiving. Bishops have the power to ignite the torch, and free us from the hand of the wicked, and restore the order of the world.

Once when in the Philippines we were talking to a newly consecrated bishop, he told us that before the event he had been talking to Mother Teresa and he asked her if she had any advice for him. She said, "Yes. Be a happy bishop." There are many things to make bishops happy, even if responsibility weighs heavily and burdens are many. The first words of St. John's First Letter contain a good recipe for happy bishops. You know it well. Like all good things, it bears repeating, especially as it ends with these wonderful words of St. John, "We are writing this to you to make our own joy complete." So bishops were meant to have the happiness spoken of in this passage of St. John's Letter:

Something which has existed since the beginning,
that we have heard,
and we have seen with our own eyes;
that we have watched
and touched with our hands:
the Word, who is life —
this is our subject.
That life was made visible:
we saw it and we are giving our testimony,
telling you of the eternal life
which was with the Father and has been made visible to us.
What we have seen and heard
we are telling you
so that you too may be in union with us,
as we are in union
with the Father
and with his Son Jesus Christ.
We are writing this to you to make our own joy complete.

Give to us, who are the poor and unperceiving, the truth. Then we will possess the freedom to fulfill the yearning which alone satisfies love.

Chapter 13

THE CATHOLIC ETHIC IN HEALTH CARE REFORM: MARGINALIZATION, HOMOGENIZATION OR INTEGRATION

Sister Margaret John Kelly, D.C., Ph.D.

While the topic of this presentation, "The Catholic Ethic in Health Care Reform: Marginalization, Homogenization or Integration," appears quite complex, it is only minimally reflective of the challenge our nation and our Church are facing at this moment. We can gain some little insight into what we will experience over these next months, and possibly years, of debate if we turn the clock back to 1935 with the controversy over social security, or to 1965 with the impassioned implementation of Medicare and Medicaid legislation. I qualified insight with "some little" because the issues are more complex and the interests more diverse in this legislation than in the two previous cases. The Clinton Health Security Plan is considered by some a panacea and others a fiasco because of its flawed financing and cumbersome bureaucracy. Other proposals evoke the same mixed response. We can indeed expect the next year of federal and state legislative activity in health care to be controversial, energetic and polarizing.

Times of transition are, true to Chinese crisis symbol, always times of danger as well as opportunity. Health care reform is not an exception, and for the Church, the stakes are very high. We are not only facing one of the most critical questions of distributive justice: "What health care benefits must a society and/or its government assure its people?" but this debate on health care reform may determine the future of Catholic health care institutions operating with a distinctive mission, as well as determine the ability of the Church to influence in this area of ethics where it has long standing competence.

As downsizing and regional integration occur, Catholic facilities (now well over one thousand hospitals, long term care facilities and services) may have to decide if they will be providers of health services, but compromised in their Catholic identity, or if they will continue to be visible participants in the mission of the Church. Health care providers and the greater Church will be tested on the Vatican II mandate to "penetrate and perfect" the secular order. That is why this presentation has been entitled "marginalization, homogenization or integration." At the conclusion of this health care reform debate, the greater part of the Catholic ministry could be forced to the sidelines, could become indistinguishable from the secular health care providers, or best case, could continue to retain its well-earned respected place as a major provider of health and medical services with a distinctive Gospel character and Church identity. In short, the choices for Catholic institutions seem to be elimination, comprised integrity or renewed identity. The challenges facing the bishops, as teachers, are the effective articulation of the church's coherent, consistent ethic as it illumines health care delivery and the preservation of the right of religious groups to sponsor services for the public.

The seriousness of the issue for church institutions has been complicated by a subtle orientation drift from ministry to corporation within Catholic health care itself, and a diversity of views on the role of Church institutions. Other non-church factors complicate the situation further: the complex nature of health care delivery, the fiscal implications of an industry which now absorbs 1/7th of the troubled U.S. economy, and the confusion created by our current health policy vacuum.

The United States has not in the past, nor does it in the present, have a consistent, coherent national health policy. It is a truism that when philosophical direction is lacking or when a program or policy does not have a well thought out, convincing human and societal rationale, economic considerations assume priority. Despite the rhetorical emphasis on health security for all, the current imperative in health care reform seems to be principally economic, try as many do to give it a more noble slant or PR spin. Unfortunately, rather than addressing some basic philosophical issues, reform is focusing on technical issues of structure and financing. However, many of the concepts and proposals are very consistent with our Church social justice perspective which calls for universal access, reasonable coverage and responsible use of resources.

This stress on technical issues rather than on philosophical underpinnings seems to be traceable to our current lack of consensus on the nature and rights of the human person, and more directly, the role of society and government in advancing human development and solidarity. A similar situation will occur when legislators tackle welfare reform at a later date. The well-reasoned Catholic ethic (capital c and small c) could well be the integrating force to cut through the various secular disciplines required to develop a sound philosophical approach to health care and welfare reform: philosophy, politics and government, economics, sociology, anthropology, history, technology, and communications.

Presidential Commissions

The lack of a national health policy and this current technical emphasis over the philosophical is surprising because past presidential commissions on health policy have focused on philosophical questions, and even the Clinton task force began with value statements. The Eisenhower Commission declared the right to medical care before Pope John XXIII articulated it in "Pacem in terris." The President's Commission for the Study of Ethical Problems in Medicine and Biomedical and Behavioral Research, formed in 1979 and dissolved in 1983, urged strongly that efforts be made to identify the universal ethical principles that should inform health care decision-making in this nation. Currently, President Clinton's Health Security Plan Task Force has identified fourteen value statements which "reflect fundamental national beliefs about community, equality, justice, and liberty":

1. Universal access

2. Comprehensive benefits

3. Choice of providers, plans and treatments

4. Equality of care

5. Fair distribution of costs

6. Personal responsibility

7. Inter-generational justice

8. Wise allocation of resources

9. Effectiveness

10. Quality

11. Effective Management

12. Professional Integrity and Responsibility

13. Fair Procedures

14. Local Responsibility[1]

In recent months, it has been often said about other administration proposals that "the devil is in the details." Nowhere is this truer than in the details and implications of the Clinton plan, but also in other reform proposals. Before details can be carved out, the undergirding philosophical convictions about the individual person, society and government need to be articulated. Experience tells us that unless the nation has reached consensus on the philosophical underpinnings of a bill, legislative proposals are doomed to long debates and many accommodations, if not failure.

When we compare President Clinton's "Ethical Foundations of Health Reform" with the values proposed by the United States Bishops and the Catholic Health Association, there is much similarity in the ideal of social justice, particularly in universal access, basic coverage and stewardship. But there are also many areas where definitions are required, much greater specification is demanded, and knowledge from a variety of other disciplines needs to be accessed.

Bishops' Conference

It would be helpful at this point to review our U.S. bishops' statements and CHA's value orientation to identify some specific ethical issues which the Church must be prepared to study rigorously and present cogently in the debate. To search out the relevant perspectives of the U.S. bishops on health care reform we could reach all the way to 1919 and "Social Reconstruction," but we will begin with 1981. In the pastoral, "Health and Health Care," the United States bishops identified the following principles:

1. Every person has a basic right to adequate health care which flows from the sanctity of human life and the dignity that belongs to all human persons.

2. Pluralism is an essential characteristic of the health care delivery system of the United States.

3. The benefits provided in a national health care policy should be sufficient to maintain and promote good health as well as to treat disease and disability.

4. Consumers should be allowed a reasonable choice of providers, and public policy should ensure broad consumer participation in planning and decision-making.

5. Health care planning is an essential element in the development of an efficient and coordinated health care system.

6. Methods of containing and controlling costs are essential.[2]

In stating their position several times over the past year, the U.S. bishops presented eight basic criteria for evaluating the strengths and weaknesses of health policy proposals. They are:

1. Respect for life.

2. Priority concern for the poor.

3. Universal access to comprehensive health care.

4. Comprehensive benefits.

5. Pluralism of providers and respect for religious and ethical values of consumers and providers.

6. Equitable financing based on ability to pay and avoidance of financial barriers.

7. Cost containment and controls.

8. Quality.[3]

If we, as Church, are to participate well in the debate, we will need to articulate clearly and present convincingly philosophical points 1, 2 and 5 because these are critical to the identity and integrity of health care delivery under Catholic sponsorship. Point 2 (priority concern for the poor) will be more easily achieved because of the Clinton emphasis on universal access, than will points 1 (respect for life) and 5 (pluralism and freedom of conscience). There is both logic and symbolism in always placing respect for life in the human person first in the catalogue, particularly when some thinkers in a Faustian/Promethean spirit, suggest there is a need to redefine human personhood.

Catholic Health Association

The Catholic Health Association introduced their health policy programs by identifying the values that they would judge or develop proposals by. These appear in the book, *HealthCare Reform in the Making*, which Bill Cox of the CHA Washington Office has so graciously provided for each of our participants here.

They are:

1. Health care is a service to people in need, not a commodity.

2. Every person is the subject of human dignity with the right to basic, continuing and comprehensive health care.

3. Health policy must service the common good.

4. There is a special duty to care for the poor.

5. There must be responsible stewardship of resources.

6. The system must have a simple structure (easy access, minimal administration, streamlined financing).[4]

In the evolution of their reform proposal, CHA developed in 1990 and re-issued in 1992 nine principles, the fourth of which was Freedom of Conscience. In recent testimonies before Congress, CHA representatives have explicitated access for the undocumented which is excluded from the Clinton proposal, exclusion of abortion coverage, and the inclusion of a conscience clause as also essential.

Consensus Issues

While we can see some philosophical agreement among the three sources (Presidential Commissions, U.S. Bishops and CHA), each of whom is concerned with universal access, comprehensive benefits, quality (although it is hard to define and measure quality), and stewardship accountability, we also realize that cultures and convictions will collide when we come to the specifics of some bioethical issues from abortion to euthanasia, genetic engineering to resource allocation, and freedom for the more morally restrictive conscience, whether it be personal or institutional.

Rights language, strong in Church statements, is avoided in the Clinton plan and other proposals, although "access" to care is "guaranteed." The language of rights had been used from the time of the Eisenhower Commission and actually was the philosophical basis for the Medicare and Medicaid legislation. In the 1983 President's Commission on Ethics publication "Securing Access to Health Care," the language shifted from the individual's right to health care to the "societal obligation" to assure care was available.[5] This shifts the emphasis from rights inhering in the individual person to the responsibility of the undefined collective body with its competing demands. This is a subtle but substantive shift. The balancing of the rights of the individual with the common good is critical to these discussions, whether it be questions of access or allocation, right of conscience or right of privacy.

Historical Overview of Policy Issues

Before we go into some of the specific ethical issues and their impact on marginalization, homogenization or integration, let's review quite briefly some of the historical events which have led us to this present moment. Some trends will sensitize us to past flaws, and others will warn us of future trouble-spots.

After World War II, health care in this country burgeoned, benefitting greatly from the military scientific knowledge which was converted easily into medical technology. In addition, the GI Bill of Rights for veterans provided the opportunity for many to enter higher education and professional schools, so by the mid-1950s, an expanding personnel pool was in place. The New Society emphasis of the 1960s led logically to the passage of Medicare and Medicaid which within just a few years showed the inadequacies of the financial projections of these two programs for both the federal and state treasuries. This experience was repeated in the understated estimates for coverage for renal dialysis which came under the purview of Medicare. These experiences, as well as the general distrust of government, make many wary of the number-crunching being done today in Washington and in state capitols, and the ultimate effect of health care reform on the national debt.

Because of run-away costs, the 1970s witnessed a major move toward health planning and cost controls and a failed Nixon proposal for a national health program. The imposed regulatory efforts, with their complicated administrative structures and systems, achieved an unforeseen effect. They rallied a large corps of very creative lawyers and accountants who managed to outmaneuver or circumvent each of the imposed regulations so that reimbursement for services, which was at the time retrospective, continued to escalate, and the corporatization of health care was secured.

In the early 1980s, an antidote for such escalating costs and corporate innovations was administered through the Prospective Payment System which assigned a specific payment for each of almost 500 diagnostic groups rather than paying for the actual services rendered to an individual in a hospital. Based on the law of averages, the system did provide for outliers and regional differences, but the effect was mixed with some hospitals closing while others profited greatly from the new system. This system contributed to the reduced length of hospital stay, the transfer of many services to outpatient areas, some cut-backs on defensive medical testing, and even to charges of "patient dumping" and "premature discharging."

Costs continued to escalate. Managed care programs increased as employers saw these as a way to cut spiraling health insurance costs and to involve employees through choice and the imposition of co-payments and deductibles. Previously, in most first dollar insurance arrangements, the financing and the delivery of care were controlled by separate entities, and thus were not interfaced until after service had been received. With this new approach of managed care, financial accountability and clinical responsibility were merged in the same organization, usually a Health Maintenance Organization. This system obviously has an inherent moral tension and requires a great integrity on the part of the providers/insurers because patient needs are balanced against the fiscal stability of the organization. In the fee-for-service model, the physician also could be motivated to test and treat the patient more intensively because of economic incentives. In managed care, the physician is not only encouraged, but required, to provide only necessary care because there are economic penalties for unnecessary or inappropriate care. Motivation for the less scrupulous shifts from overtreatment to undertreatment and the happy medium remains elusive. The success of some plans notwithstanding, one still has to wonder if totally integrated financing and delivery systems in general do not present serious conflicts of interest in the same way that retrospective reimbursement and physician participation in joint ventures, even with strict referral and disclosure controls, do. While one wants to be optimistic about the goodness of individuals, one must also profit from experience and not be naive. The movement toward merged delivery and financing systems requires conscientious oversight to protect patients from their right of access to the confidentiality of their records.

Dr. Relman, the former editor of *The New England Journal of Medicine*, and others warned constantly in the 1980s about the Medical-Industrial complex, the commercialization of health care and its dehumanizing effect on health care. They reminded us that health care is a unique consumer good, if it is a consumer good at all, and it certainly must not be a commodity. In the 1980s, the profit-motive had enticed many for-profit companies into what had been almost exclusively the province of not-for-profits and civic entities. Almost overnight the for-profit hospital systems and related companies became the darling of Wall Street. While some for-profit hospitals and long term care companies have failed, acquisitions, merger-mania and consolidation in that sector continue.

Physicians became major players in the commercialization of health care. In addition to fulfilling their traditional role of health care professionals in the spirit of Hippocrates, in the 1980s, physicians became entrepreneurs and hospital competitors. They set up laboratories, diagnostic centers, emergency centers, rehabilitation and other services formerly offered by hospitals only. Because the physician is so critical to managed care, there is now almost a frenzied move toward hospitals and other groups buying up medical practices and developing organizational structures with physicians. This needs careful study to assure that prudent financial standards of preserving assets and avoiding undue risks are adopted. This is not to say that managed care and joint ventures with physicians cannot be effective planning strategies. However, it is necessary to observe that there are many ethical questions intrinsic to both designs. The clients' and the patients' needs must remain the central focus of health care delivery.

Furthermore, cost-shifting (technically known as price-discrimination) to the private insurers and self-responsible payers reached new heights over the past seven years as group discounts were negotiated through managed care contracts and with government purchasers. It was cost-shifting which made business enter the group lobbying for health insurance reform, if not health care delivery reform. The cost of administration, much of it attributable to insurance and oversight activities, has been among the fastest growing components of total health care expenditures in the U.S. and is approximately 8% of costs today, although some commentators feel it is higher.[6] The CHA document shows graphically the effects of these movements in health care which now absorb one-seventh of the economy. While this amount is generally thought to be too high, I am unaware of any objective criteria (other than the experience of other nations) to determine what is an appropriate percentage when so many health and medical services are being provided.

No wonder this decade of the 1990s is the Decade of Health Care Reform and that the chief driving force appears to be economics. The decade opened with the passage of the Patient Self Determination Act and a bustle of activity in living wills, advanced directives and court decisions on patients in a persistent vegetative

192

state. While many opine that these activities have had little effect on clinical practice and economics, this past year has witnessed the lowest annual increase in health care costs in 20 years, even though it is still well above the level of inflation.

Readiness and Challenges to Reform

While there is no question that some reform is necessary to assure that all those values and principles mentioned above are reflected in the emerging U.S. health policy, the task of reforming health care is complicated by many factors operative at this time. These range from demographics of the country to expectations of the public, and each has ethical implications.

Demographically, our aging population is contributing substantially to increased health care costs because it is both logical and well documented that persons over 65, primarily because of chronic illnesses, consume much higher percentages of resources than younger persons. This has caused some philosophers like Daniel Callahan and politicians like former Governor Lamm of Colorado to suggest age as the criterion for eligibility for some procedures. CHA reported that a very small proportion of the public (just 10%) accounts for 70% of health expenditures, with just 1% of the people accounting for 10% of the total costs.[7] Much of this expense occurs at the extremes of the life-spectrum.

The many social causes contributing to the rising medical costs do not seem to be sufficiently acknowledged or remedied in the current reform proposals. We may be providing an economic solution to what is in large part a social problem. Increasing violence, drug use and adolescent pregnancy, with their related costs, are major contributors to the current situation of escalating health care costs, and will not be affected by the various reform proposals. Cocaine admissions to hospitals are increasing. It is impossible to assess now the long-term costs of the learning defects and medical problems which generally accompany the children born of chemically addicted mothers and fathers or of teenage mothers. Another discouraging observation is that advanced on the front page of the

New York Times on January 2[8] which declared rather unambiguously that the emphasis on healthy life-styles which marked the 1980s has totally passed and we are into a physical indulgence era. This vogue, if lasting, bodes ill. We are all familiar with the estimates of the impact on health care costs of unhealthy life-styles, especially substance abuse, obesity, lack of exercise and poor nutrition.

Technology is a two-edged sword for hospitals as it improves productivity but decreases inpatient utilization and adds costs. It is projected that technological advances will cause hospitals to close, with some commentators suggesting that one-third could close within this decade. Medical technology adds to the rise of overall costs, even though many types of technology do in fact reduce the cost of specific diagnoses and treatments. Technology has given us an increasing ability to treat disease and trauma that just a decade ago would have meant death for the individual. Because of the uncertainty of some of the results of these aggressive treatments, however, proposals and protocols are now being proposed to limit these sophisticated interventions at both ends of the life spectrum. Again, the motivation appears to be heavily economic and needs to be put through the ethical screen as well. There is much more emphasis on quality of life rather than sanctity of life. Both terms need a great deal of definition and nuancing. The church has sound principles, much experience and collective wisdom here, particularly in regard to end of life treatment decisions and care of the dying.

Much of the confusion marking discussions on the necessity and efficacy of various treatments, as well as on the general topic of health policy, emanates from the multiple interest groups who are or will be affected by changes in the status quo. While the CHA model rightfully places the person at the center of its design, in reality, insurance companies, physicians, AARP, attorneys, urban hospital administrators, the for-profit owners and managers of health systems, union worker retirees, and a host of others jostle for that center place. They come to the discussions with varying expectations and often conflicting demands. In addition, the role of state and local governments needs to be integrated into national policy development, but the states are moving ahead and develop-

194

ing their own plans according to their diverse situations. Cities like Washington, DC, New York, Miami, and Los Angeles confront the issue quite differently from Little Rock, Memphis, Portland Maine, and Main Line Philadelphia. There is a need for subsidiarity, but giving states the power to determine their own system of health benefits has the potential to create the inequity problems experienced by welfare systems as more generous states draw more people and intensify fiscal allocations for those states. Less generous states can continue to shortchange their residents as we saw in the unconscionable Medicaid eligibility standards established by some states. Businesses may avoid or select states to operate independent upon tax benefits and health insurance requirements so the Clinton demand for some minimal standards is necessary. Seven states have already initiated health care reform, and their experience, while limited, can be very instructive as national reform is hammered out.[9]

Personnel issues, in terms of supply and distribution, also present ethical concerns in health care reform. It is an unfortunate truism that in general, services and workers follow monetary rewards rather than human need. While the gate-keeping function in both the prevention and intervention model is most logically assumed by a family practice physician, at the present moment we have over 70% specialists whose services are much more highly compensated than the family practitioner. While the reform plans call for a reversal of this proportion, we will have much difficulty moving from our present point of over-specialization and poor physician distribution because of the debts accrued by medical graduates as well as by the economic motivations of both practitioners and students. Will vanity-inspired cosmetic surgery continue in metropolitan Los Angeles and New York while children in Mississippi fail to get immunizations, and mothers in rural New York do not have access to pre-natal care because of the unavailability or disinterest of physicians? Who has the responsibility to control personnel resourcing, and how is such allocation done with equity when 80% of the current medical students express a preference for specialization and minority and poor students will be most dependent on scholarship aid? This could become an issue of distributive justice if the availability of optional services, even if they are not reimbursed, precludes the provision of basic service. It is interesting to note that Derek Bok, the former president of Harvard, in his recent book *The Cost of Talent*, suggests that many of our economic problems will not be resolved until we get control of skyrocketing salaries, and health care as a labor-intensive industry is not exempt from his charge. Physicians tend to be targeted most in this issue, and yet they account for only 10–15% of the nation's expenditures. Recent reports of top executive salaries within both the not-for-profit and the for-profit systems call for scrutiny. Malpractice premiums and awards also contribute to escalating costs and must be studied from the ethical perspective. The recent award of $89 million to the family of a California woman who died from cancer and who had been refused coverage for a bone marrow transplant suggests that this is still a major issue to reckon with. On that point, the Clinton proposal continues to allow for 1/3 of the liability settlement or award to be assigned to the attorney, but it does allow the states to impose lower limits if they wish. Insurance reform is a critical element to the achieving of justice in health care reform.

Finally, the expectations of the public present a very serious challenge to health care reform from the appropriateness and economic perspectives. People want to reduce costs, but our instant/microwave society demands immediate relief from pain and suffering, settles for nothing less than total cure, and is highly intolerant of slowness and failure, each of which is inherent to the human condition and inescapable in the situation of human sickness. This is why the use of the word Security in the PR surrounding the Clinton Plan is feeding into this American refusal to admit, not to mention accept, limits and poor results. Even within our own Church where we are given constant reminders of transcendence and the passing of this life, there is sometimes a vitalistic resistance to terminating treatment and initiating palliative care. All of us need a healthy dose of realism about perfectionism and eternity if any real reform is to occur.

Basic Conflict in Health Care Reform

With that very quick historical overview of efforts at health care reform, and that quick survey of some primary challenges, let's turn to a conflict which is central to Health Care Reform discussions. DeTocqueville, many decades ago, identified the central issue of American socio-political-economic life when he described our innate struggle to relate liberty and equality, individual rights with the common good. DeTocqueville is proven correct when we apply his observation to the ethics of health care reform. Traditionally, there has been an ambivalence about health care being a social good or a consumption good with much discussion about whether it should be, like education, considered a government responsibility or if it should be considered a benefit of employment. As an employment benefit, insurance or the lack thereof creates great inequality of coverage, unfairness in taxation benefits, as well as "job-lock," and perpetuates a system designed for a bygone day where the father of the family was the principal wage earner. The current suggestion of substituting households for families as the base unit of coverage raises other questions in terms of relationships and family responsibility. The desire for low premiums for the majority has created the unbelievable and unconscionable situation where the sick and unhealthy individual is either excluded from insurance coverage or must pay higher rates through experience rated systems rather than community rated insurance premiums. Portability of coverage and elimination of pre-existing condition exclusions require immediate attention. This ambivalence of public/private, common good/individual good will probably continue to express itself in reform efforts. At the present, we have in fact a public and private system for both delivery and financing. Some ethicists feel that because of administrative ease and monetary savings, a single payer system would be most just and cite Canada's system as an example of this, but others label this "socialistic." It is important to note that a single payer system does not imply a state-owned, socialist system as in England, although even there, there are private institutions. The single payer system seems to provide the best answer to the troubling question which relates the philosophical and financial elements: How should the financial risk of a generally non-predictable and sometimes catastrophic cost experienced by an individual be fairly allocated within society?

Ethical Challenges for Church Leadership and Catholic Institutions

As we have been looking at the principles articulated by the United States Bishops and the CHA, as well as the values undergirding the Clinton proposal, and have quickly overviewed the context in which health policy is currently being discussed, it must be apparent that health care reform is rife with ethical challenges for all, but particularly for religiously-oriented providers and Church leadership. While I have tangentially alluded to many of these issues as I sketched the historical and current situations, I will now limit the discussion to what seems to be the most critical if the Church, as moral force and health care provider, is to remain integrated and not be marginalized or morally homogenized after this process of restructuring is completed. Even if health care reform is not legislated over the next year and a half as projected by the Clinton administration, these ethical issues will still be with us, just because of the fiscal consequences, the increasing social implications, ongoing technological advances, already established expectations, and of course, the deteriorating financial situation of our country.

Examination of Corporate Consciousness

But, before that we must consider three other points if rigorous ethical analysis is to be conducted and if ethical leadership is to be exercised by the Church. First, it is important that there be consensus about the meaning of the Catholic identity of an institution or service. Surprisingly, this is still an area where unanimity at times seems distant. The publication and promulgation of the revised *Ethical Directives* could be an important step in moving toward a national consensus. Secondly, the role of the bishop in regard to some of the efforts of developing integrated delivery networks or managed care networks must be clarified. It may be advisable to consider national or regional or state conference guidelines to provide some political consistency and clout, even though in the implementation there may be need for accommodation to the diverse situations in which the Church finds herself. And, finally, a point which really precedes in logic the two just presented: Is there a need for Catholic health care at all, or can other agencies provide the service as well as the Church agencies can?

Because I am convinced there is a need for Catholic Health Care, and I am even more convinced that the coherent view of the human person, the family and society held by the Church, and which is eminently commonly sensed can contribute greatly to the resolution of many of our current challenges if it can be "packaged" and "marketed" effectively, let me present just a few of the ethical challenges I think we will be facing as we enter more deeply into the heath care debate. Because I believe each of these needs a great deal of theoretical analysis as well as practical application, which requires much greater expertise and specialization than I can offer, I am just going to raise ten cluster issues which I feel are most pressing for you as Church leaders. This listing is not going to include some ethical issues which are interesting and very important, but not intimately related to Catholic identity but still should be raised in philosophical discussions:

—Should for-profits be involved in the provision of a necessary human service like health care?

—What are the implications of health care as a consumer good or a social good?

—What are the components of a basic health plan which should be available to all?

—Is a single payer system the most equitable and to be preferred?

—Is freedom of choice in providers an essential component of a just system?

—Should health insurance be tied to employment status?

—How does one determine what is a reasonable and appropriate amount of the gross domestic product to be allocated to health care?

—Is a plan like Clinton's which invests so much power in the executive branch of government and in regional alliances opening up the possibility of corruption and conflict of interest, as well as discrimination against religious groups?

Those are the central questions, but the listing is not exhaustive because of the essential complexity of personal situations and systemic availability.

Specific Ethical Clusters

Let me now outline some ethical cluster areas which seem to require careful study and attention as health care reform efforts proceed. The preservation of our institutional "moral capital" may need more attention now than the preservation of our financial capital. The issues are complex and decisions will reverberate down the decades because collusion and cooperation are frequently hard to distinguish.

1. PLURALISM. Much time will have to be spent on articulating well the right of church organizations to exist within this reformed system, and to exist in a manner which allows them to retain their integrity. Fortunately at this time there are some very fine and serious books being published on constitutional rights and on the role of values and beliefs in society and political life. Written by both Catholics and others, these may be establishing a healthy readiness among many thinkers within the country. Some even suggest that as the 1980s were the decade of the law and economics, the 1990s may be the decade of the law and religion. A definition of, and a rationale for, pluralism needs to be presented in a manner which will convince the public not only of the value of pluralism, but also

its absolute necessity. The question of a Catholic facility maintaining a strict denominational ethic while serving a diverse community in a pluralistic society and being reimbursed for service at times by public monies will be raised again even without our Church agencies, and needs a carefully articulated response which educates Catholic providers on pluralism and freedom of conscience. This is a profoundly complex question, but the answer needs to be expressed in simple, convincing terms. It is so essential because it is the basis for our first amendment rights and our insistence on the conscience clause.

2. CHURCH PROPERTY. In justice to the Church, it is also very important that every institution clarify its position in regard to Church ownership of property. Father Frank Morrissey in a *Health Progress* article, has noted that this is important for some congregational sponsors who may have mingled the assets of their religious institute with their apostolic works, but also for other separately incorporated institutions, to assure that alienation of property is understood and that the claims of the Catholic sponsor are respected in joint ventures and mergers, etc.[10] There has been a great deal of talk in some Catholic circles about sponsors of Catholic services moving from a position of control to one of influence. This may be necessary, but it could also be a bit naive from the long-term perspective. Experience has shown that in difficult situations in the rough and tumble business world, influence is frequently limited and easily lost unless backed up by legal or financial control. The resources of the health care ministry have been built up over many years and that cannot be lost sight of from the justice perspective, as well as from the ministry perspective.

3. CONSCIENCE ISSUES, INSURANCE. Medical procedures that violate our conscience will trouble us if they are included in the insurance provided for our large pool of Church employees or if they are included in any overall pooled insurance to which we contribute. These proscribed procedures need to be identified and excluded, and in some clairvoyant way, the unknowns must be anticipated. Science is moving so fast that

many other medical procedures and experiments could be joining very soon the proscribed list of abortion, assisted suicide, euthanasia, and in vitro fertilization which is excluded in the Clinton plan. In this decade, the Genome project and reproductive technologies will present many ethical questions we have not even imagined at this time. We will not want to pay for some services for our own employees, and this will require negotiations for exclusions and much explanation to employees, many of whom do not share our value system. This will be a problem under either a mandated employer tax for individual employee coverage or an overall tax pooled to provide universal insurance coverage. Recent attempts by the administration to loosen abortion restrictions and public health advertising initiatives by Health and Human Services are not encouraging and highlight the need for conscience protection.

4. CONSCIENCE ISSUES, SERVICES. As providers of health and medical services begin to collaborate so that they will be able to offer comprehensive services regionally, several other challenges to Catholic authenticity will surface in the area of toleration, material cooperation and scandal. Our ethical posture will not allow us to offer some services in Catholic sponsored facilities, and this most probably will make us less desirable in collaborative arrangements, unless we can with consummate marketing skill, make our ethical position an added value to our service. Some of the questions which will surface are:

a. How can a Catholic facility distance itself both legally and financially from those who provide proscribed services? This question needs to be answered in terms of shared resources, collaborative management of organizations, and representation on the board of a network. There is no question that formal cooperation in abortion or euthanasia is not possible, but are the rationale for and the guidelines governing material cooperation clearly articulated and communicated? How is scandal to be prevented when promotional materials list in the membership of a regional health plan a Catholic hospital along with the local family planning center or the

202

in-vitro clinic, or a suspect death with dignity hospice. The chief executive officer of the Catholic hospital or system or its sponsor may be invited to serve on the board which determines policy for the service network. Does this presence provide an opportunity to bring Catholic values to bear and perhaps to influence overall policy, or does it compromise the Church? Are the bookkeeping systems such that it is clear that the Catholic participant in the network is not profiting financially from, or contributing to, any immoral or unethical services? Are any referrals made within the network by the Catholic facility which advance immoral practices and procedures?

5. LEADERSHIP. Because the Church has a cadre of respected leaders in health care, it will probably be necessary to suggest the conditions under which a Catholic could serve in leadership roles nationally or state-wide or regionally if proscribed services are included in the guaranteed benefit package? While in the Clinton Task Force Report, a brief description of each service provided in the basic package is described, "Family planning services" and "Pregnancy-related services" are merely named.[11] Catholic social service agencies and schools may also be affected by some aspects of the sex education programs urged by some political leaders.

6. RATIONING. If resources continue to decline while expectations continue to rise, a system of explicit rationing may well be required. What are the criteria which the Church will put forth as most consistent with the dignity of the person and the responsibility of the human community? Is the major problem with the Oregon plan its discriminatory basis as applied to public insurance, or its foundation in cost-efficiency? We need also to reflect on the meaning of "tiers of care" and consider whether the Church should in some cases deliberately opt for those locations and services which might be "redlined" and provide a reasonable level of care for the poor and disadvantaged, particularly Hispanic Americans who have the highest uninsured rates, and the African Americans who have the highest incidence of several disease entities. Would such a step in

the long term weaken our goal of universal access and basic necessary care for all, or would it be a positive step and witness of our commitment to the poor and vulnerable? Because so many government programs, including Medicare and Medicaid, have been eroded over the years, it is important to maintain a healthy skepticism, but not cynicism, about the commitment to the disadvantaged in a time of fiscal constraint.

7. GLOBAL AWARENESS. We also have to raise the important question of how these issues of access at the personal and national levels affect the global situation. Should the U.S. and other first world nations continue to advance technologically while basic needs are not being met throughout the world, or is health care to be considered a strictly national issue so that great gaps between nations can continue to be tolerated?

8. PUNITIVE TREATMENT. How do we support personal responsibility and universal access and still effectively influence those who recommend punitive treatment of not only drug abusers, but also the children of welfare mothers who exceed the permitted number of offspring or babies born with AIDS and the many other categories within "undesirable life styles?" This question of deserving and undeserving will intensify as the Genome project advances and the carriers of many diseases will be identified. Furthermore, how will the information gained from these advances in testing impact the basic freedom of individuals in terms of privacy and confidentiality?

9. FAMILY AND SOCIETAL OBLIGATIONS. Intergenerational conflicts over financial responsibility for social security for the senior citizens may surface. The controversial means-testing and eligibility standards for Medicare may also be proposed seriously. Have we, as Church, articulated a convincing rationale on the Church's teaching on private property, family obligations, and social responsibility so that we an contribute positively to the education on and resolution of this painful issue? The Church's teaching on ordinary and extraordinary means has a great deal to offer in the area of medical futility and clinical necessity, but also in terms of social and familial responsibility in this age when four or five generation nuclear families and

blended families are quite numerous. Another aspect of this issue is to determine whether a dollar amount or percentage of income standard should be set to establish what is a reasonable limit on out-of-pocket health care expenses for an individual and a family. It is still not clear if co-payments and deductibles threaten the elderly and the poor and are ultimately counter-productive at some economic levels.

10. EDUCATION AND COMMUNICATION. From the educational and public relations perspective, do we have in place diocesan or regional communication and educational systems that can provide for a well thought out and carefully expressed Catholic position on ethical issues generated by health care reform proposals? New ethical questions will continue to arise from both scientific advances and public expectations. Diocesan ethics committees need to relate closely with the institutional committees and seek to relate to parishes. Teachable moments will be many and they cannot be lost. Periodic "application seminars" on the new *Directives*, if and when they are approved, would be extremely helpful, particularly when the greater number of our health care providers do not have an adequate education or formation in philosophy or moral theology.

Finally, political trade-offs in these areas may be necessary. In legislation where less than the desired can be achieved, particularly in areas where the Church ethic is not accepted by the majority of Americans, should the Church agree to the less or hold out for the best? It is the traditional question of should you accept a half-loaf when a full loaf is needed, or should we abandon the good in search of the perfect? Father Philip Keane, S.S., has developed an interesting response to this in his book *Health Care Reform: A Catholic View*, in which he cites Cardinal O'Connor's three criteria for approving abortion legislation: first, no better bill is feasible; second, the bill is better than the existing legislation; third, the bill does not preclude further reform in the future.[12]

Conclusion

The current political climate and the economic situation of the nation seem to demand that some type of health care reform occur. While the outcome is uncertain, the need for the Church's preparation for and practical participation in the debate is quite certain. Health care is a basic requirement of society, as well as one of the most prominent services within the Church. Leadership in health care has the potential to exert great influence on the moral and social consciousness of the nation. When Pope John Paul II spoke to Catholic health care leaders on his visit to the United States in the late 1980s, he made that point strongly. He also challenges the bishops in *Veritatis splendor,* 116, to be vigilant about Catholic doctrine and Catholic institutions. Because the major life-issues are played out in the health care arena, and our Catholic health care system is currently a great resource of the Church, let us make every effort to avoid marginalization and homogenization so that the Catholic ethical perspective, as well as the various services and institutions, may be a gospel leaven in society and a light for policy developers.

Notes

1. *The President's Health Security Plan*, The White House Domestic Policy Council, (New York: Times Books, 1993), pp. 11-13.

2. *Health and Health Care: A Pastoral Letter of the American Catholic Bishops* (Washington, DC: United States Catholic Conference, November 19, 1991), pp. 17-19.

3. "Resolution on Health Care Reform," *Origins* Vol. 23: No 7, (July 1, 1993), pp. 98-102.

4. *Health Care Reform in the Making*, (St. Louis: Catholic Health Association, 1993), p. 2.

5. *President's Commission for the Study of Ethical Problems in Medicine and Biomedical and Behavioral Research, Securing Access to Health Care: A Report on the Ethical Implications of Differences in the Availability of Health Services*, (Washington, D.C.: U.S. Government Printing Office, 1983), pp. 7-10.

6. D. Himmelstein and S. Woolhandler, "Costs Without Benefit: Administrative Waste is U.S. Health Care, *New England Journal of Medicine*, (February 13, 1986), pp. 441.45.

7. *Health Care Reform in the Making*, p. 44.

8. *New York Times* (January 2, 1994), p. 1.

9. Ann Markus, *Health Care Reform and Access to Health Care*, (Washington, D.C.: George Washington University, 1993), pp. 1-20. Miss Markus provides a side-by-side analysis of the Clinton plan with those developed in Florida, Minnesota, Vermont, Washington, Colorado, Oregon, and Hawaii.

10. Francis Morrissey, "Church Law's Role in Collaboration," *Health Progress*, (November, 1993), pp. 24-25.

11. *Health Security Plan*, p. 25.

12. Philip Keane, *Health Care Reform: A Catholic View*, (New York: Paulist Press, 1993), p. 170.

References

American Health Policy, ed. by Robert Helms, (Washington: American Enterprise Institute, 1993).

Carlin, David. "Paying for Abortion," *America*. November 20, 1993, pp. 6-10.

Epstein, Arnold. "Changes in the Delivery of Care under Comprehensive Health Care Reform," *New England Journal of Medicine*. November 28, 1993, pp. 1672-1676.

Ethical Issues in Healthcare Marketing. (St. Louis: Catholic Health Association, 1990).

Graig, Laurene. "An International Perspective on U.S. Health Care Reform," *Health of Nations*. Washington, DC: Congressional Quarterly Inc., 1993.

Griese, Orville. *Catholic Identity in Health Care*. Boston: Pope John Center, 1988.

"Health Care: Ethical and Religious Issues," *Chicago Studies*. November, 1988, Volume 27; Number 3.

Health Care Reform in the Making: Improving the Clinton Legislation. St. Louis: Catholic Health Association, 1993.

Keane, Philip S. *Health Care Reform: A Catholic View*. New York: Paulist Press, 1993.

Kelly, Margaret J. (ed.) *Justice and Health Care*. St. Louis: Catholic Health Association, 1985.

Malone, James. "Criteria for Evaluating Health Care Reform," *Origins*. April 14, 1992, pp. 23-24.

Markus, Ann. "Side by Side Analysis of the Clinton Plan and Seven State Plans," *The Intergovernmental Health Policy Project*. George Washington University, November, 1993.

McMillan, Elizabeth. "Joint Ventures: A Risk to the Ministry's Moral Capital," *Health Progress*. April, 1987, 54-57.

Morrissey, Francis, OMI. "Church Law's Role in Collaborations," *Health Progress*. November, 1993, pp. 24-29.

O'Donnell, Thomas. *Medicine and Christian Morality*. New York: Alba House, 1991.

"On Health and Health Care," *Origins*. December 3, 1981, p. 402.

Reinhardt, Uwe. "Whether Private Health Insurance? Self-Destruction or Rebirth?" *Frontiers of Health Service Management*. Volume 9, Fall, 1992, pp. 5-31.

Roberts, Marc. "Health Care: Your Money or Your Life," *America*. December 4, 1993, pp. 6-9.

Search for Identity: Canonical Sponsorship of Catholic Healthcare. St. Louis: Catholic Health Association, 1993.

Setting Relationships Right: A Working Proposal for Systemic Healthcare Reform. St. Louis: Catholic Health Association, 1992.

. Starr, Paul. "The Framework of Health Care Reform," *New England Journal of Medicine*. November 25, 1993, pp. 1666-1672.

The President's Health Security Plan. New York: Times Books, 1993.

PART THREE:
LEADERSHIP TASKS IN
PROVIDING EXCELLENT EDUCATION
FOR FAMILIES TODAY

Chapter 14

MINISTRY TO FAMILIES AND EDUCATION IN FAMILY LIFE

The Reverend Monsignor John G. Woolsey

There is an increased focus on the topic of the family these days—from a sociological and political perspective, as well as from a theological one. This attention has been generated by the long acknowledged relationship that exists between family and society. A United States senator from New York recently used the term "deviancy downward" when referring to current society, and he does not hesitate to link this societal malaise to the fragmentation of the family. The Holy Father, Pope John Paul II, leading the Catholic Church along this sentiment, reminded us on the occasion of the opening of the International Year of the Family, that the breakdown of the family erodes the base of society's values and poses risks for all mankind. Because of the relationship between a healthy society and a healthy family, the fundamental purpose of the Family Life Office quite obviously then is to reinforce the quality and stability of marriage and family life.

While the picture does at times appear to be bleak and the facts and figures regarding family life are discouraging, there is hope. Indeed, it is our belief that the Church can be and must be the source of hope in today's culture. It is a challenge—and one that we must address.

Herein are some thoughts as to how a Diocesan Family Life Office can address the current family crisis. Diocesan family life educational programs can and do have a positive impact on marriage and family life in today's society.

The essential question that needs to be addressed therefore is—how does the Church and/or the Diocese *reinforce* and *nourish* the family—since it is indeed the fundamental cell of a civilized society. Herein lies the primary challenge and task of a Diocesan Family Life Office—not exclusively, but substantially. This challenge and this task is guided by one underlying, necessary principle and we point that out here: all diocesan programs and services must consist of an appropriate blending of sociological and theological thought regarding family life.

With regard to the sociological: The programs and services must be consistent with sociological evidence. These programs and services must be relevant to the time. In current society, that means developing and implementing programs that address the family from the perspective of *relationships*—because it is precisely healthy, meaningful relationships which serve as the "glue," the determining factor, for successful, functional family life. The purpose here is not to delve into the sociology of the family—that may be left to the sociologists. The purpose of this paper is to indicate to every priest and diocesan worker that a family life program must be cognizant of the current sociological status and needs of the family.

With regard to the spiritual or theological: The incorporation of the spiritual dimension into the family life programs is really what characterizes and distinguishes the Family Life Office. This is pre-

212

cisely where Church leaders can make a contribution. It is what justifies the existence of a Diocesan Family Life Office. The family is not simply a construct of social scientists; it is a spiritual reality instituted by God. To leave God, and all that is associated with a belief in God, out of the picture, is to invite disaster. That is precisely why there is now a deluge of condom distribution programs, the promotion of a homosexual agenda, the blatant display of sexually explicit materials in our school systems, and a plethora of violence and sex on T.V. The fact that family life originates with God is basic to a discussion of family, but it is a belief and concept sadly omitted in contemporary discussion. In secular contemporary public form, the words "sacred," "sacramental," "vocation," "made in the image and likeness of God," "sacrifice," are hardly ever heard, and this is the reason why we need Family Life Offices. These offices must always incorporate and stress the spiritual element of marriage and family life. This is what will make the difference.

The resources regarding the spirituality of family are many and varied. There has been a recent surge in efforts to develop a "Theology of the Family." Most notable of the sources are the documents of Vatican II, the 1979 working paper, "Role of the Christian Family in the Modern World," which became the basis for the 1980 Synod on the Family, *Familiaris consortio*, and a host of pastoral letters published by local conferences of Bishops. Again, it is not the purpose of this paper to discuss the theology of the family, but to stress that the primary function of a Family Life Office is to integrate the spiritual dimension into all its programs. The concepts and thoughts presented in documents and pastoral letters must become reality for the people of the Diocese, for each family in the parish. The directives from the pages of books must be transferred into the minds and hearts of people.

The one document, however, that deserves special mention, at least for those of us in the U.S., is the "Plan for Pastoral Action for Family Ministry" developed by the U.S. Catholic Conference's Commission on Marriage and Family Life. For all practical purposes, this document served and continues to serve as the blueprint for Family Life Offices—calling for the development of structures that will "facilitate marriage and family life." It is from this perspective then, acknowledging the sociological, and stressing the theological, that a Family Life Office launches into its task of developing and implementing "programs" and "support groups" that address marriage and family life and breathe into them sound Christian morals and practice.

The following is a brief resumé of some of the programs:

Marriage Preparation: This should be a primary program. If a diocese could provide only *one* program, then it should advocate marriage preparation. If a Diocese were evaluating family life programs, then the very first one to be evaluated should be the marriage preparation program. This is so because when all is said and done, the well-being of the family is directly contingent upon the well-being of the marriage. Following upon the principles, both sociological and theological, there is much that can be said to young couples vis-à-vis a happy, successful, fulfilling marriage. We do know, as a matter of fact, that certain sociological traits and characteristics contribute to happy, viable marriages. For example, positive attitudes regarding marriage, the ability to disclose and communicate, the recognition of sexuality as an expression of love, do indeed contribute to a happy, successful marriage. But in accordance with that basic principle, the significant determining factor for a successful marriage is a recognition of marriage as a spiritual vocation—a sacred calling. Too often couples are simply unaware of, and do not understand, the rich theology of marriage. As "shepherds of the flock," we have incalculable insights that may be shared with them regarding the spiritual vocation that is theirs as spouses and parents of children. Tears have fallen from the eyes of young men and women as they listen to and reflect upon the beautiful spiritual calling that God is extending to them. It would be tragic indeed if young people should be deprived of these truths.

One other comment regarding Marriage Preparation. It must never be expected to "do it all"—other factors are involved and critical to one's formation, such as family experience, cultural influences and faith development. A *Marriage Enrichment Program* for newly married couples can be an excellent follow-up component for marriage preparation. It is a well-known fact that the first 5 to 7 years of marriage are critical in establishing stability. Thus a significant contribution to family life can be made by helping secure the marriages of young couples through the enrichment programs.

The formula—sociological and theological—continues to be carried out in all our family enrichment programs and support groups. This may be briefly illustrated with examples of other programs.

Parent Education Programs: There are many parent education programs available in our society—and while they can be good in techniques, they fail to identify parenting as a vocation. They fail to speak of children as made in the image and likeness of God— they fail to mention faith and prayer, or to speak of the family as a domestic Church wherein are included values and insights that truly make for good parenting. How can one conduct a program for the *divorced*, and *separated* or conduct a support group for the *widowed* and *bereaved*, or teach an *NFP* program, without speaking of God, faith and commitment and vocation? How can you help a woman who has destroyed the life of her child through abortion if one operates in a moral vacuum—without understanding the sacredness of life or the real terms of forgiveness and reconciliation?

With regard to all of the programs and services, the Family Life Office serves as an "extended family"—providing meaningful relationships to the members of the Church family. It is in this "caring" and welcoming context that the Church, through its programs, provides a positive evangelizing influence on the members of God's family as a whole, and upon married couples and their families in particular. In the minds and hearts of our people, the outreach through these programs and services can make "all the difference in the world."

Once again, it must be stressed that while a diocesan program must be sociologically sensitive and realistic, its purpose above all is to convey the rich spiritual treasures of our faith. This is what "we" as Church are called to do; this indeed is what "we" are supposed to do best; and this is precisely what our people are looking to us for. We have to give strong support to the establishment and implementation of diocesan sponsored programs as a way of ensuring that our theology and spirituality is accurately transmitted in a uniform and systematic way. Local parishes and local regions are not to be excluded; on the contrary, their support and reinforcement is critical to the ultimate success of the programs. Is there hope for our people? Yes, indeed. Let us provide that hope through our diocesan family life programs.

Two final comments:

1) In these days, it is important that the Family Life Office serve as an advocate in the public square regarding such issues as sex education, condom distribution and family life legislation. We must make our presence felt in the secular arena.

2) A word about structuring, staffing and financing a Family Life Office. All of this is said with a profound awareness that each diocese is different—each has its own "flow chart," and each one faces varying financial pressures.

Nevertheless, to the extent that it is possible:

a) A separately funded office with a full-time Director is basic.

b) Programs are to be prioritized. It is better to have one or two well-run and well-organized programs than to have a multitude of programs without direction or purpose.

Staff should be recruited according to budgetary and priority needs. For greater efficiency, it is recommended that professional or professional-type people be recruited to coordinate the implementation and ongoing supervision of programs and support groups.

Whenever and wherever there is a challenge to the preservation and imparting of spiritual and cultural values, it is always a big and critical challenge, and one we must not fail to address.

We are God's family. God's family needs our help and support. If we as the Church do not respond—then God only knows. Our families become the targets of secularistic and materialistic agendas.

Chapter 15

REALISTIC MARRIAGE PREPARATION

Ralph Martin

The growing number of annulments, and the still larger number of failed Catholic marriages which have resulted in divorce and remarriage without annulments, raise troubling questions about the adequacy of our marriage preparation.

In the years following the Second Vatican council, while there have been many positive developments that bode well for the future, there nevertheless has been a substantial weakening of faith, morality and mission among North American Catholics. The sharply rising percentage of Catholics who have been divorced or legally separated is particularly striking. In roughly a ten-year period from the early 1970s to the early 1980s, the proportion has risen from one in every seven Catholics ever married to one in every four. While the percentage of those ever married who have been divorced and separated in the general population rose by 50% in this ten-year period, the percentage of divorced and separated among Catholics rose by 90%. As a result, the percentage of the divorced and separated among Catholics ever married is higher today than was the percentage of the divorced and separated in U.S. society as a whole a decade previously.[1]

While the "blame" for these failures cannot justly be placed solely on the marriage preparation process (many other factors both in the Church at large and the wider culture play an important role), the marriage preparation process is certainly an indispensable element for an improvement in the situation in the future.

While obviously the question of what constitutes adequate matrimonial consent plays an important role in the success of sacramental marriages and continuing efforts to adequately assess its presence in proposed marriages is important, I would like to focus on another element critical to the success of sacramental marriage, one that is often not given adequate attention, namely the presence of faith.

From my own experience, and from conversations with many priests and lay-people engaged in marriage preparation, it is clear that many couples who want to have a "church wedding," are seriously ignorant not only of the distinctiveness of Christian marriage, but even more fundamentally, seriously ignorant of the gospel and of the Christian life. Some priests have told me that up to 80% of the couples approaching them seeking a "church wedding" are already living together.

It's clear that marriage preparation in these increasingly frequent cases must consist of more than a compatibility profile and a check to see that the proper sacramental certificates are in order, as important as these elements are. Faith adequate enough to ensure a reasonable chance of success in Christian marriage can no longer be presupposed in many cases, even if the couples have been baptized. While canon law concerning marriage is understandably focused on whether the partners are baptized or not, baptism itself today is certainly not an adequate indicator that the couples entering marriage have a reasonable chance of succeeding in Christian marriage. And our obligation as a Church, particularly as pastors, is not only to ascertain that the marriage is valid, but that assistance is given "by which the married state is preserved in its Christian character and develops in perfection" (Canons 1063, 1064). This includes "personal preparation for entering marriage, so that the spouses are disposed to the holiness and the obligations of their new state...so that by faithfully observing and protecting their conjugal covenant, they may day by day achieve a holier and a fuller family life" (Canon 1063). Canon Law is clearly not advocating a minimalist approach to marriage preparation.

Many couples desiring to receive the sacrament of marriage have been *sacramentalized*, but neither *evangelized* to a basic Christian conversion nor adequately *catechized* to know even the fundamentals of Christian faith.

Dr. Peter Kreeft, professor of philosophy at Boston College, speaks of the serious ignorance of the very basics of the gospel present in his Catholic college students, oftentimes products of the "best" Catholic high schools. These are the same students, many of whom a few years after graduation, seek to be married "in church."

> The gift of God comes into us by faith, through us by hope, and out of us by the works of love.

> That is clearly the biblical view, and when Protestants and Catholics who know the Bible discuss the issue sincerely, it's amazing how quickly they come to agree with each other on this, the fundamental point.

> But many Catholics still have not learned this thoroughly Catholic and biblical doctrine. They think we're saved by good intentions, or being nice, or sincere, or trying a little harder, or doing a sufficient number of good deeds. Over the past 25 years I've asked hundreds of Catholic college students the question: If you should die tonight and God asks you why he should let you into heaven, what would you answer?

> The vast majority of them simply don't know the right answer to this, the most important of all questions, the very essence of Christianity. They usually don't even mention Jesus!

Until we Catholics know the foundation, Protestants are not going to listen to us when we try to teach them about the upper stories of the building. Perhaps God allows the Protestant-Catholic division to persist not only because Protestants have abandoned some precious truths taught by the Church, but also because many Catholics have never been taught the most precious truth of all: that salvation is a free gift of grace, accepted by faith.[2]

The reason why the issue of faith is so important right now is that with increasingly little societal support of the basic Christian life, not to mention Christian marriage, it is appearing more and more impossible for many couples to live Christian morality, particularly as it applies to Christian marriage. And as Divine Revelation indicates, for the "natural" man it is impossible: only the "spiritual" man is able to live what is essentially a spiritual life (1 Cor. 2:12-16). Christian morality requires Christian spirituality in order to be successfully lived. The foundation of Christian spirituality is faith in the person of Jesus and all that He teaches, and the communication of faith must be at the heart of any adequate marriage preparation program. This truth is becoming increasingly well articulated in documents like *Veritatis splendor*, and the new *Catechism of the Catholic Church*.

Dimensions of Faith

Let's consider now some of the aspects of faith that it is important be communicated.

One meaning of the Scripture's teaching on faith is faith as in the "deposit of faith," that body of truths revealed by God (2 Timothy 1:13-14, 2:2; Jude 3). A primary meaning of faith in this sense is faith as a knowledge of truth. This is the meaning of faith we have primarily in mind when we talk about passing on "the faith," or teaching "the faith." Obviously, as essential as "propositional" faith is, it is not enough. "Even the demons believe" (James 2:19) but are lacking both obedience and trust, and so they tremble.

Another meaning given by Scripture to faith is faith as in "the obedience of faith" (Romans 1:5, 16:26). Faith in this sense is that knowledge of truth which has implicit or explicit in it a call to obedience. Another well-known formulation of this would be "faith without works is dead" (James 2:17). Or, as Jesus said: "If you live according to my teaching, you are truly my disciples; then you will know the truth, and the truth will set you free" (John 8: 31-32). There is a clear implication in the scriptural teaching that it is indeed obedience to the truth that is revealed that unfolds a deeper understanding of that very truth.

A third and perhaps most common use of the word faith in scripture is faith as trust. "Blest is she who trusted that the Lord's words to her would be fulfilled" (Luke 1:45).

The basic thrust of Jesus' whole message is to *trust* in him, and in the Father.

> If God clothes in such splendor the grass of the field, which grows today and is thrown on the fire tomorrow, how much more will he provide for you, O weak in faith! It is not for you to be in search of what you are to eat or drink. Stop worrying. The unbelievers of this world are always running after these things. Your Father knows that you need such things. Seek out instead his kingship over you, and the rest will follow in turn (Luke 12:28-31).

It is clear when we consider the biblical picture of faith and discipleship that many couples approaching marriage are approaching their lives and marriages in a way that the scripture indicates is characteristic of unbelievers.

The kind of faith that Jesus is calling us to is faith in the goodness of God, the power of God, the truthfulness of God, and most of all the personal love of God for each one of us in every aspect of our lives and needs. He's calling us to the kind of surrender and abandonment (conversion) that is only possible when we know who God is.

It's the kind of faith that Job had when he was able to say that he would trust in God "even if He slay me" (Job 3:15).

It's the kind of faith necessary for Catholic couples as they face the inevitable difficult temptations and trials of married life.

As a Church we've tended to stress most strongly the first and second dimensions of faith, that of "propositional" faith and its moral requirements, perhaps because we've been living with a "Christendom" mentality where saving faith was presupposed. But today, in a rapidly de-Christianizing environment, the dimension of faith as trust and surrender to a God who is personally encountered and known in the person of Christ, in the power of the Holy Spirit, is essential. I believe that the new *Catechism of the Catholic Church* makes this very clear.

Sometimes all three meanings are implied when scripture refers to faith. "Indeed, this is the will of my Father, that everyone who looks upon the Son and believes in him shall have eternal life" (John 6:40).

A fourth dimension of faith that scripture talks about is what might be called charismatic faith; faith that works wonders, moves mountains, releases the power of God in signs and wonders.

In any event, faith is clearly presented in scriptures as our lifeline to God. Faith is what inaugurates, sustains and deepens our relationship with God. As vital as the oxygen line is to the deep-sea diver, so is faith to our life with God, so is faith to the success of Christian marriage.

It is clear that serious deficiencies of faith are present in many couples seeking a "church wedding." One Archdiocesan office of Family Life decided to ask the Marriage Tribunal what they were finding in marriages that were seeking decrees of nullity. The major theme cited was a lack of fundamental Christian faith and knowledge. And this is certainly the experience of many pastors in North America whom I have talked with regarding their experience with marriage preparation.

There are deficiencies in belief and knowledge (the deposit of faith); deficiencies in moral adherence (the obedience of faith); and deficiencies in living relationships with Christ in the Church (the trust and abiding of faith). One response to this situation is to not face it, to remain silent about the real truth of Christian marriage, and to hope for the best. But this is a response of the "flesh," of despair, of fear. Or perhaps simply from the unfortunate situation of so many overworked and overburdened priests. And we will reap its fruits in the annulment, divorce and remarriage statistics of the future. We've been given, not a spirit of fear, but a spirit of power, of love and of self-control (2 Tim. 1:7). I believe the Spirit is already pointing us along the path to a solution, the need for a new evangelization.

222

The Importance of the "New Evangelization"

With increasing frequency Pope John Paul II has called for the entire Church to devote its energies to a "new evangelization," new in ardor, methods and expression. In "Mission of the Redeemer," he declares:

> God is opening before the Church the horizons of a humanity more fully prepared for the sowing of the Gospel. I sense that the moment has come to commit all of the Church's energies to a new evangelization and to the mission *ad gentes*. No believer in Christ, no institution of the Church can avoid this supreme duty: to proclaim Christ to all peoples.[3]

Like Paul VI before him, John Paul II has made it clear that vast segments of the Catholic people need to be re-evangelized. The American bishops, as have other bishops' conferences, have endorsed a plan of evangelization that calls for each parish to orient each and every activity and organization towards this new evangelization.

> These goals assume that an evangelizing spirit will touch every dimension of Catholic parish life. Welcome, acceptance, the invitation to conversation and renewal, reconciliation and peace, beginning with our worship, must characterize the whole tenor of our parishes. Every element of the parish must respond to the evangelization imperative—priests and religious, lay persons, staff, ministers, organizations, social clubs, parochial schools, and parish religious education programs. Otherwise, evangelization will be something a few people in the parish see as their ministry—rather than the reason for the parish's existence and the objective of every ministry in the parish. The spirit of conversion...should radiate through the action of all Catholics so that the call to conversion is experienced and celebrated as part of our way of life.[4]

Fr. Avery Dulles, S. J., has pointed out how significant this shift in our approach as a church is.

> The majority of Catholics are not strongly inclined toward evangelization. The very term has for them a Protestant ring. The Catholic Church is highly institutional, sacramental, and hierarchical in its structures. Its activities are primarily directed toward the instruc-

tion and pastoral care of its own members, whose needs and demands tax the institution to its limits. Absorbed in the inner problems of the Church, and occasionally in issues of peace and justice, contemporary Catholics feel relatively little responsibility for spreading the faith.[5]

Fr. Dulles points out that missionary activity in predominantly non-Christian lands was seen as the job of a specialized few, and that in predominantly Christian lands "mission" for Catholics was in bringing Protestants to see the truth of the claims of the Catholic Church.

In predominantly Christian territories Catholics showed no lack of interest in convert-making, but again the thrust was not evangelical; the gospel was hardly at the center. This apostolate was mainly directed to showing, against Protestants, that Christ had founded a hierarchical Church, which was to be accepted as the organ of divine revelation. The focus was more on authority than on content. Catholics were instructed to believe whatever the Church taught precisely because it was Church teaching.[6]

Fr. Dulles cites the significance of Vatican II in refocusing the Catholic Church on the gospel and on evangelization.

Vatican I used the term "gospel" only once, and never used the terms "evangelize" or "evangelization." Vatican II, by contrast, mentioned the "gospel" 157 times, "evangelize" 18 times, and "evangelization" 31 times. When it spoke of evangelizing, Vatican II seems generally to have meant what the kerygmatic theologians meant by the term: the proclamation of the basic Christian message to those who did not yet believe in Christ.[7]

Fr. Dulles then traces the development of this more evangelical focus in the post Conciliar writings of the Popes and concludes with this remarkable summation:

In my judgment the evangelical turn in the ecclesial vision of Pope Paul VI and John Paul II is one of the most surprising and important developments in the Catholic Church since Vatican II.... While both popes have notably broadened the concept of evangelization, they have retained the main emphasis of the earlier kerygmatic concept. For them, as for the kerygmatic theologians, the heart and center of evangelization is the proclamation of God's saving love as shown forth in Jesus Christ. Where the name of Jesus is not spoken, there can be no evangelization in the true sense.... All of this constitutes a remarkable shift in the Catholic tradition. For centuries evangelization had been a poor stepchild. Even when the term was used, evangelization was treated as a secondary matter, the special vocation of a few priests and religious. And even these specialists were more concerned with gaining new adherents for the Church than with proclaiming the good news of Jesus Christ. Today we seem to be witnessing the birth of a new Catholicism that, without loss of its institutional, sacramental, and social dimensions, is authentically evangelical.... Catholic spirituality at its best has always promoted a deep personal relationship with Christ. In evangelizing we are required to raise our eyes to him and to transcend all ecclesiocentrism. The Church is of crucial importance but is not self-enclosed. It is a means of drawing the whole world into union with God through Jesus Christ.... Too many Catholics of our day seem never to have encountered Christ. They know a certain amount about him from the teaching of the Church, but they lack direct personal familiarity.... The first and highest priority is for the Church to proclaim the good news concerning Jesus Christ as a joyful message to all the world. Only if the Church is faithful to its evangelical mission can it hope to make its distinctive contribution in the social, political, and cultural spheres.[8]

I might add that only if the Church in its marriage preparation programs approaches them in an evangelistic manner will we have well grounded hope of improving the current situation of attempting to celebrate a sacramental marriage for what many pastors acknowledge are "baptized pagans." This raises questions of sacrilege and scandal. Marriage preparation, like other forms of sacramental preparation, must be rethought and reconciled from an evangelistic point of view. We can no longer presuppose faith in any of its dimensions, but must be prepared to start at the beginning with as effective a proclamation of the gospel as possible. We must begin to train marriage preparation teams that are able to "speak the truth in love," starting with the basics.

Speaking the Truth in Love

Faith comes through hearing the Word of God (Rom. 10:6-14) spoken in love and the power of the Holy Spirit (1 Cor. 2:1-5). Effective marriage preparation programs must be designed to lead people to know and encounter the person of Christ and at least begin the process of conversion, appropriation of the power of the Holy Spirit, and participation in the sacramental life of the Church which gives us the power to live the high calling of Christian marriage.

The waiting period that many dioceses have established for couples seeking to be married in the Catholic Church needs to be seen as an evangelistic window of opportunity that must be well used. Balancing what's needed with what's realistically possible to ask from people in this situation, much can be learned from what has been successful in bringing nominal Catholics to conversion in various renewal programs and movements in the contemporary church.

The judicious use of weekend retreats or days of renewal that focus not just on the specifics of marriage but also have an evangelistic focus can be powerful instruments. If these weekends though are sponsored on a diocesan wide level, and have no connection to the local parish where the couple is being married, they are more limited in their effect. Building a team of couples living a dedicated Christian life as married couples to assist with the marriage preparation can be very effective. Introducing couples to the practice of the Sacrament of Penance and celebrations of the Eucharist with a faith environment can be important evangelistic moments. Proving follow-up opportunities after the wedding, such as small group sharing, special retreats for young married couples, short courses that go into more depth on topics of interest, can also be helpful. But whatever the means, the important thing is that the truth of the gospel be spoken in love, in the power of the Holy Spirit. What are some aspects of this truth that need to be incorporated in an effective marriage preparation program?

1. The truth of the gospel. What it means to be a sinner saved by grace, through faith. Who Jesus is and what he's done for us

through his death and resurrection, the gift of his Spirit, the reliability of his promises. The reality of heaven and hell. The need for saving faith to issue in good works if it is real. The need for repentance, faith and life in the Holy Spirit in the Church. Those close to the preparation of the new *Catechism of the Catholic Church* acknowledge that they needed to make a conscious effort to avoid our Pelagian tendencies and put the proper Biblical emphasis on the grace of God. This certainly seems to be one of the things that the Spirit is clearly saying to the Church today.[9]

2. The call to holiness. The life of Christian morality. The grace and reliance on Christ that makes it possible.

3. The Church as the body of Christ. The sacraments as participation in the life of Christ.

4. Our mission as Christians to be salt and light.

Besides the basics of Catholic Christianity, presented in an evangelistically effective manner, the basic truths about Christian marriage need to be presented clearly.

1. Marriage is a great gift of God, whose purpose is established by God.

2. Christian marriage images the greater reality of the union of Christ with the Church.

3. Life-long fidelity. The intention not to embrace life-long fidelity makes Christian marriage impossible (unity and indissolubility).

4. Essential openness to children. The intention not to have children makes Christian marriage impossible.

    —the truth about the moral regulation of birth (*Humanæ vitæ*)

    —the importance of effective instruction in natural family planning[10]

5. The grave difficulty of sustaining Christian marriage without an active relationship with Christ and participation in the Church. Many couples have been sobered by the failure of

their parents' marriages and the high divorce rate in society and are highly motivated to discover how to live their marriage in such a way that divorce is unlikely. This predisposition can be built on in our marriage preparation programs.

6. The grave difficulty in raising children "in the discipline and instruction of the Lord" (Eph. 6:4b) without an active relationship with Christ and participation in the life of the Church. Again, many couples are afraid of raising children and would welcome some of the helpful Christian child rearing literature that is available today.

Even though these are difficult matters to teach clearly in today's climate, it is ever more important to do so. There is no hope for the human race or for Christian marriage if the whole truth of Christ is not taught clearly no matter what the opinion polls might currently say.[11] And if the Pastors of the Catholic Church don't give a clear sound of the trumpet, who will?

The Need for Witnesses

It's important that everyone involved in marriage preparation be living a faithful Christian life, loyal to the teachings of the Church. Personal witness to the truth of the gospel and the truths of Christian marriage are indispensable in successful communication of faith. From the Bishop to the Director of Family Life to the Pastor to Associates, to Deacons to couples involved in marriage preparation, everyone needs to regularly witness to the importance of Jesus for them personally—"He's my savior, he's my Lord, I depend on him for the strength to live the life he's called me to." Married couples need to specifically witness to the importance of their faith in Christ and dependence on him in their relationship as couples and their responsibilities as parents.

The Need for Patience

Patience is a powerful quality. The Romans conquered the world through patience, the saying goes. The task before us is great, but if we tackle it a step at a time and do not denigrate small steps and small beginnings, little by little an environment in a parish, in a diocese can change, one by one faithful and faith-filled couples and priests can be found, and one by one couples preparing for marriage can be led to encounter the person of Christ and appreciate his great gift of Christian marriage.

Is there Hope?

If we're realistic, the task before us is very difficult. Some of those responsible for preparing couples for marriage today may not be very faithful or faith-filled. Others may be so overworked that doing one more thing may truly be impossible. And we may not know where we can find enough faithful and faith-filled priests and lay people who have the gifts, interest, time, wisdom, and courage, to seriously invest in preparing couples for marriage. And sometimes the climate in a particular parish or diocese itself is very problematic. But I believe that if we're willing to admit the difficulty of our situation, the impossibility of the task, humanly speaking, and turn to God in our need, he will help us. But if we pretend the situation isn't that difficult or that "business as usual" will do, things will only get worse.

> The Amen, the faithful Witness and true, the Source of God's creation, has this to say: I know your deeds; I know you are neither hot nor cold. How I wish you were one or the other—hot or cold! But because you are lukewarm, neither hot nor cold, I will spew you out of my mouth! You keep saying, 'I am so rich and secure that I want for nothing.' Little do you realize how wretched you are, how pitiable and poor, how blind and naked! Take my advice. Buy from me gold refined by fire if you would be truly rich, buy white garments in which to be clothed, if the shame of your nakedness is to be covered.

Buy ointment to smear on your eyes, if you would see once more....
Be earnest about it, therefore. Repent! (Rev. 3:14-19)

Could it be that the humiliating disclosures of recent years, whether it be the distressing indications of the polls about what Catholics really believe and how they live, or the tragic scandals that are still unfolding, contain in them an invitation to us by the Spirit to repent? To turn from any "business as usual" mentality, to turn from any unwillingness to face the facts, the facts of our grave difficulties as a church, the facts of the great power and salvation available to us, now, only in Christ.

If I close heaven so that there is no rain, if I command the locust to devour the land, if I send pestilence among my people, and if my people, upon whom my name has been pronounced, humble themselves and pray, and seek my presence and turn from their evil ways, I will hear them from heaven and pardon their sins and revive their land. (2 Chron. 7:13-14)

Over the past few years John Paul II and other major Church leaders have expressed sorrow and repentance for various unfortunate actions that we as a Church have been at least partially responsible for.

Cardinal O'Connor, in speaking recently of the great trials and purification "by fire" that the Church is going through spoke of the heartfelt repentance that is needed. "It is long since time to get down on our knees, to beat our breasts, to ask God's mercy."[12]

As Fr. Benedict Groeschel, C.F.R., Director of Spiritual Development for the Archdiocese of New York, has pointed out, there is a need not just for individual repentance when appropriate but also for institutional repentance.

In addition to the individual, communities in the Church, societies that consider themselves Christian and the whole Church herself, must constantly repent and believe again with new fervor the Good News of salvation brought and proclaimed by Our Lord Jesus Christ.[13]

Fr. Groeschel goes on to speak specifically of the humiliation and embarrassment the Church is going through as a result of the clergy sex-abuse scandals.

More than any time in the past 200 years, the Catholic Church in the United States is filled with pain.... Since I believe deeply in the mercy of God, and know that he painfully punishes his children only to correct them, I suspect that the present humiliation may have some beneficial effects. It could lead to a real reformation of our moral practice as a Church, and to a thorough examination of our moral teaching, from kindergarten to doctoral studies.... We could make better use of all this suffering by putting our house in order.[14]

It is encouraging to see John Paul II, and the Church as a whole, taking responsibility to acknowledge Church failings, not touching on its infallible teaching authority of course, but significant nonetheless, whether it be mistakes made in the Galileo case, in contributing to the breaking of the unity of Christians, or "dark spots and shadows" in the evangelization of the new world and the treatment of the native Indians, or acknowledging Catholic involvement in African slavery.

The Church is human, but unlike her head, Jesus, not without sin.

THE GALILEO CASE

It is in that historical and cultural framework, far removed from our own times, that Galileo's judges, incapable of dissociating faith from an age-old cosmology, believed, quite wrongly, that the adoption of the Copernican revolution, in fact not yet definitively proven, was such as to undermine Catholic tradition, and that it was their duty to forbid its being taught. This subjective error of judgment, so clear to us today, led them to a disciplinary measure from which Galileo 'had much to suffer.' These mistakes must be frankly recognized, as you, Holy Father, have requested.[15]

THE DISUNITY OF CHRISTIANS

In this one and only Church of God from its very beginnings there arose certain rifts, which the Apostle strongly censures as damnable. But in subsequent centuries much more serious dissensions appeared and large communities became separated from full communion with the Catholic Church—for which, often enough, men of both sides were to blame...their (the Catholic faithful) primary duty is to make a careful and honest appraisal of whatever needs to be renewed and done in the Catholic household itself, in order that its life may bear

231

witness more clearly and faithfully to the teachings and institutions which have been handed down from Christ through the apostles.

For although the Catholic Church has been endowed with all divinely revealed truth and with all means of grace, yet its members fail to live by them with all the fervor that they should. As a result the radiance of the Church's face shines less brightly in the eyes of our separated brethren and of the world at large, and the growth of God's kingdom is retarded... St John has testified: 'If we say we have not sinned, we make him a liar, and his word is not in us' (1 Jn. 1:19). This holds good for sins against unity. Thus, in humble prayer we beg pardon of God and of our separated brethren, just as we forgive them that offend us.[16]

African Slavery

These men, women and children were the victims of a disgraceful trade in which people who were baptized, but who did not live their faith, took part. How can we forget the enormous suffering inflicted, the violation of the most basic human rights, on those people deported from the African continent? How can we forget the human lives destroyed by slavery?

In all truth and humility this sin of man against man, this sin of man against God, must be confessed....

From this African shrine of black sorrow, we implore heaven's forgiveness. We pray that in the future Christ's disciples will be totally faithful to the observance of the commandment of fraternal love which the Master left us.[17]

These words and actions regarding our responsibility for the tragedy of the Reformation, the Galileo case, African slavery, and the treatment of Indians in the new world needed to be said. In a rare interview at the end of 1993, John Paul II indicated that it was time to make a general examination of conscience as a Church:

Certainly at the end of this second millennium we should make an examination of conscience: where we are, where Christ has brought us, where we have strayed from the Gospel. It is a subject that would undoubtedly require a deeper analysis.[18]

Could it be that a season of repentance is beginning that as we acknowledge our sin and desperate need for God Himself, could lead to a "New Pentecost" for the Church, that will make possible the success of the New Evangelization? Not just as it pertains to marriage preparation, but in a much wider way as well?

If each of us at this gathering, and far beyond, truly hear "what the Spirit is saying to the Church" as we near the end of the twentieth century, and respond to it with repentance and faith, we will truly see the glory of God.

May it be so.

Notes

1. Joseph E. Davis & Kevin Perrotta, "Finally, Figures on Divorce among Christians," *Pastoral Renewal*, April 1984, pp. 120-122.

2. Peter Kreeft, "Luther, Faith & Good Works," *National Catholic Register*, November 10, 1991. p. 8. Emphases mine.

3. John Paul II, *Mission of the Redeemer*, 3.

4. National Conference of Catholic Bishops, *"Go and Make Disciples,"* (November 18, 1992). Part II, p. 12.

5. Avery Dulles, S.J., *John Paul II And The New Evangelization*, (New York: Fordman University, 1992), p. 3.

6. *Ibid.*, pp. 3-4.

7. *Ibid.*, p. 4.

8. *Ibid.*, p. 13, pp. 16-17

9. Cardinal Daneels has pointed out how profound the tendency in us is to resist the truth that we can't save ourselves, even partly.

"Today, the doctrine of grace is no doubt the most neglected concept in theology and in practical Christian life. The fact that we are not able to save ourselves, even partly—that we are entirely dependent on the gift of grace from God—is a stumbling block for many. They find it difficult to understand that grace does not eliminate our freedom and our autonomy; on the contrary, it is their very foundation. The dream of a person who is self-sufficient is apparently ineradicable. However, the very essence of faith is to accept the idea of our dependence on God." Cardinal Godfried Daneels, *Christ or Aquarius? Exploring The New Age Movement*, (Dublin: Veritas Publications, 1992) pp. 38-39.

In order to avoid the danger of a Pelagian moralism the new *Catechism of the Catholic Church* emphasizes strongly, in its introduction to Catholic moral teaching, the absolute need to depend on the grace of God in order to live the moral teaching of the Church.

Archbishop Jean Honore, Archbishop of Tours, France, and closely connected to the development of the new catechism, frankly admits that an earlier draft of the catechism was justifiably criticized for not making clear that Christian morality was not just a matter of "virtuous conformity," but required a radical dependence on the grace of God.

"Indeed, while the Catechism succeeded in expressing the call to follow the Gospel and aim at perfection, it did not show (or at least not sufficiently) that this quest can only be accomplished by the baptized with the help of the gratuitous grace that heals and absolves them from sin and supports them along the way. In brief, because it had not been stated fully or with sufficient clarity, it was not immediately obvious that whatever Christians do in the order of salvation and holiness, they do not do alone, but only with divine assistance. In their effort to grow in virtue, all Christians, even the greatest saints, are justified and saved sinners. By failing to emphasize the prevenient action of the Lord's grace and the inner presence of the Spirit, the Catechism was in danger of omitting one of the most basic conditions of moral action according to the Gospel. A conscious effort had been made to avoid the trap of casuistry. That of moralism was narrowly avoided. The draft could be said to have retained a Pelagian tone that still had to be corrected." Archbishop Jean Honore, "Catechism presents morality as a lived experience of faith in Christ," *L'Ossservatore Romano*, English Language Edition, May 12, 1993, p. 10.

As Cardinal Ratzinger put it when speaking of the new catechism's treatment of moral teaching: "This section of the text is not a list of sins but is aimed at illustrating how moral living is constituted within a Christian perspective. Morality thus becomes a very simple thing; it is friendship with the Lord, it is living and journeying with Him." Cardinal Ratzinger/Andrea Tornielli, "Testimonies In the Pagan Age," *30 DAYS*, No. 11-1992, p. 29.

10. The Couple to Couple League has developed effective pre- and post-marriage instruction programs in NFP, that my wife and myself as well as many other couples that we know have found very helpful. They've also just published an excellent short book on what it means to be a Catholic Christian and enter a Catholic marriage, which would be very useful to give couples approaching marriage. Information is available by contacting their headquarters in Cincinnati, Ohio.

11. Pope John Paul II, *The Splendor of Truth*, 5, 30, 114, 115, 116, 117.

12. Peter Steinfels. "Inquiries Pledged On Abusive Priests," *The New York Times*, July 2, 1993, A1, A7.

13. Fr. Benedict J. Groeschel, C.F.R., *The Reform of Renewal*, (San Francisco: Ignatius Press, 1990), p. 28.

14. Fr. Benedict J. Groeschel, C.F.R., "Making Sense of the Scandal," *The Catholic World Report*, November, 1993, pp. 43, 46.

15. Cardinal Paul Poupard, "Galileo's Case is Resolved," *L'Osservatore Romano*, English Language Edition, November 4, 1992. p. 8.

16. Decree of Ecumenism, 3, 4, 7.

17. Pope John Paul II, "From this African shrine of sorrow let us implore heaven's forgiveness," *L'Osservatore Romano*, English Language Edition, March, 4, 1992, p. 2.

18. John Paul II, "The Gospel never ceases to be sign of contradiction," *L'Osservatore Romano*, English edition, November 17, 1993, p. 7.

Chapter 16

WHATEVER IS TRUE IS OURS: HELPING PHYSICIANS, LAWYERS AND UNIVERSITY LEADERS SUPPORT FAMILY IDEALS

John E. Murray, Jr., J.D., S.J.D.

On April 15, 1993, the United States Senator from New York, Daniel Patrick Moynihan, spoke to a group of 800 Civic leaders comprising the Association for a Better New York City. Moynihan was celebrating the fiftieth anniversary of his graduation from Benjamin Franklin High School in New York City. He compared the New York City of 1943 with the New York of 1993. In 1943, there were 44 homicides committed with guns. In 1993, the number was 1,499. In 1943, there were 73,000 people on welfare. In 1993, New York City recorded one million welfare recipients. In 1943, three percent of babies were born out of wedlock compared to 45 percent fifty years later. How did New York become a society filled with social pathologies? Moynihan's response was clear and direct.

> The decline of our social institutions is more importantly the decline of the family, those small platoons without which a society of this size cannot function. There are parts of the city where families have disappeared and the social chaos that comes in the aftermath of the inability to socialize young males is all around us and growing worse.

This message was not well received by many of the civic leaders in the audience. Senator Moynihan should not have been terribly surprised by these reactions. Thirty years earlier he was accused of racism when he worried aloud about the decline of the black family in America. As to this recent analysis, one religious leader said that Moynihan's statements were the product of nostalgia and lost innocence. Another questioned Moynihan's sobriety. The Mayor of New York City and a New York Congressman were among those who concluded that Moynihan had discounted the corrosive effects of racism, drugs, AIDS and guns in his analysis.

Moynihan is well aware of the corrosive effects of these and other pathologies in our society, but he sees them for what they are. They are effects, not causes. His audience was particularly disappointed in his failure to even mention how more federal money might be made available to New York. That is what they wanted to hear. Instead of telling them what they wanted to hear, he told the truth: the basic cause of all of these pathological effects is the decline of the family.

The decline of the family, the basic social institution upon which all other societal structures depend, became inevitable in the twentieth century because it was in this century, our century, when the concept of freedom became not only the highest value, but the only value. Absolute freedom mandates the emasculation of all other values. Absolute freedom requires the denunciation of any eternal or natural law, and tolerates positive law only because the state has the power to coerce compliance. Absolute freedom rejects any claim to truth beyond the alleged truth of absolute free-

236

dom itself. Any claim to truth is immediately relegated to the assertion of an opinion or predilection. If freedom is the only certain value, moral philosophy is a joke. It cannot be a discipline because it is nothing more than a collection of individual opinions. Even worse, theology is the quintessential fraud because it promotes religious attachment which is nothing more than a way of coping with our fears or projecting our hopes as part of an infantile psychology.

In this century, we have reached the zenith of relativism and its ultimate end, nihilism. We are surrounded by deconstructionists and reductionists in our philosophy, our literature and our law. There are no universal truths or values. Everything is culturally determined. Any claim to the validity of social or political principles are ideological superstructures generated and maintained by ruling powers. Rationality does not exist because our activities can be reduced to a variety of factors. They may be the product of repressed desires causing us to play roles created in early childhood, or they may be induced by external stimuli or internal biochemical and electrical activity in our brains and current hormone imbalances. The reductionists also claim that our cultural patterns including marriage, religious attendance, childbearing, friendship and suicide cannot be explained by the reasons people offer, but by the needs of society or by self-interested economic calculations.

Not all of these theories can be true. But that does not matter to the reductionist whose sole and exclusive purpose is devaluation—the destruction of human dignity—so that we can all share in the consciousness of lower and lower self-esteem.

Who are these so-called intellectuals who have brought us to this irrational and purposeless concept of life? They include Karl Marx, that intellectually dishonest, anti-Semitic racist who is almost singular in his corrosive influence on society and the family during this century. How could academics be so completely deceived by this outrageous exemplar of lies, infidelity and a progeny of suicide and despair? What would life in the twentieth century have been without the absurd but incredibly influential writings of Sigmund Freud whose theories have been proven to be scientifically baseless? Freud may be singularly responsible for our current no-fault society, where the last scintilla of guilt and personal re-

237

sponsibility must be repressed and any notion of conjugal love as participation in an eternal plan is reduced to autoeroticism or any other act that suggests instant gratification. What are the current effects of the work of B. F. Skinner and his cohorts who would reduce us to higher forms of Pavlovian dogs?

We return to the eighteenth century to find the seeds of modern relativism and nihilism in David Hume who convinced succeeding philosophers that the only reality is what *is*. What *ought* to be is a matter of opinion because it cannot be derived from what *is*. From that moment on, the eternal question, "How shall I live," could have no answer because it was rationally impossible to tell anyone how he or she ought to conduct a life. From that moment on, the advice or counsel much less command of a parent or the Church were mere predilections. Worse, they were patently absurd. The virtuous life became a monument to futility. The theological virtues, the moral virtues and even the intellectual virtues were doomed. The rise of British Empiricism and positivism were inevitable. The ultimate separation between what is and what ought to be was established. What ought to be ought not to be studied because there could be no academic discipline of what anyone ought to do. It is all a matter of opinion. When these efforts proved fallacious, we looked to our philosophers again. But modern philosophers were content to spend their days pursuing the largely irrelevant and counterproductive puzzles of linguistic analysis or furthering the cause of absolute freedom through the despair of atheistic existentialism. We had arrived at the certainty that not only is the search for truth quixotic, but that truth does exist.

Suddenly, in 1988, then President of Harvard University, Derek Bok, sounded a clarion call. The last years of his long Presidency were devoted to his remarkable discovery that Harvard had failed to promote the moral growth of its students. After nearly two decades of his presidency, he was appalled to discover that Harvard students were graduating with the belief that one view of morality was necessarily a matter of opinion. He insisted that there were certain immutable values and the education of Harvard students should recognize these values. There is no empirical verification that Bok's views have taken hold. There is even reason to believe that, had Bok promoted his views before being chosen as

President of Harvard, he would not have been chosen. It is important to recall the rumors circulating at the University of Chicago when President Robert Maynard Hutchins declared the overriding importance of metaphysics in the curriculum. Rumors claimed the secret baptisms of Hutchins and his cohort, Mortimer Adler, who, according to the rumors, could be seen kneeling at a nearby Catholic Church. The dogma of Roman Catholicism might be tolerated, but not its metaphysics. That would be too dangerous.

We should not entirely discount the aphorism that the anti-Semitism of society becomes the anti-Catholicism of the university, even in some so-called Catholic universities. Nor should we assume that we have overcome the widespread belief that phrases such as "Catholic intellectual" or "Catholic university" are oxymorons. We live in an age which has been educated to believe that man is autonomous, that any "morality" is, at best, a human morality, that man, alone, has absolute freedom to determine what is good or evil, that man, alone, will create his own values and truth will be found exclusively in these freely created values. Thus, the only truth is freedom because only freedom is truth. When the Church teaches that what is truly good and what is truly evil is not a decision of man but of God, that man's freedom is not unlimited but man is called to accept the moral law given by God who alone is good and knows perfectly what is good for man, the teaching of the Church is diametrically opposed to the ordinary religion of this age. Any suggestion that there is a natural moral law with God as its author is likely to be greeted with a cruel reaction. Any suggestion that, through his reason, man does not establish but merely participates in the eternal law, causes a similarly harsh reaction. Such suggestions are treated harshly because the proponents of absolute freedom, relativism, nihilism and the like do not understand it, or, in the vernacular, they just don't get it. The Church and its educational apostolate, particularly Catholic universities, have failed in this quintessential teaching. That is why *Veritatis splendor* is the most important teaching of the twentieth century.

Even some theologians criticize the teaching of the Church regarding contraception, direct sterilization, autoeroticism, pre-marital sexual relations and artificial insemination on the footing that the morally negative evaluation of these acts fails to consider man's character as a rational and free being and the cultural conditioning of moral norms. "In their view man, as a rational being, not only can but actually must freely determine the meaning of his behavior."[1] The last four decades of the twentieth century are a testament to the absolute freedom of man to determine the meaning of his own behavior as if the human body were "a raw datum devoid of any meaning and moral values until freedom shaped it in accordance with its design."[2] What has this absolute freedom wrought?

While New York may be a particularly effective illustration of the pathologies of our time, virtually any other urban center and many rural areas of the United States are grist for this mill. The remaining superpower in the world leads the industrialized world in crime, divorce, violent deaths of children, child abuse, abortion and incarceration. We have seen a 500 percent increase in teenage pregnancy rates since 1960 and a 500 percent increase in violent crime. Divorce rates have quadrupled. Our children no longer face the threat of nuclear holocaust, but they are twice as likely to be murdered and three times as likely to commit suicide as were their parents. We have not even begun to consider the calamity of 400,000 cocaine or crack babies born each year because these children will never be able to shoulder the burdens of life without complete assistance from a society with neither the means nor the will to render such assistance.

In just two years, 1991 and 1992, firearms killed 60,000 Americans—more than the total number of U.S. soldiers killed during the sixteen-year Vietnam War. Handguns, alone, account for the overwhelming majority of gun deaths each year and the fastest rise in handgun deaths is occurring among our children. In the United States, every twenty-four hours a handgun is the weapon used in 33 rapes, 575 robberies and 1,116 assaults. Handgun sales continue to rise because we live in a society of fear where the family has been fractured and can no longer preserve, protect, educate and nurture our children. We have two defense budgets in the United States, the popular defense budget to guard against foreign invaders which costs about $300 billion a year, and the domestic defense budget where the direct and indirect costs of crime have been carefully estimated at $425 billion a year.

Thirty years ago, one of every ten families with children was headed by a single parent. Soon, one of every three families in America will be headed by a single parent. We now insist on recognizing the single-parent family as the norm and the two-parent family as nostalgic. Yet, eighty percent of children in psychiatric hospitals come from broken homes. Seven of every ten juvenile offenders come from single-parent homes. Most of the state prison inmates in the United States did not live with both parents while growing up and the majority were born to teenage mothers. As of 1991, these inmates had 826,000 children under the age of 18. One can argue that the real problem is poverty, but the correlation between single parent families and poverty is astonishing. A black child from a single-parent home is 500 times more likely to be poor than a black child from a two-parent family. For children born in 1980, 22.2 percent of white children and 92.9 percent of black children will be welfare dependent before reaching age 18. While poverty is a contributing factor, it is not the cause. Numerous studies conclude that students from poor two-parent families perform at a higher academic level than children from single-parent families.

Absolute freedom is the essential cause for divorce because it allegedly "liberates" the individual who can then, alone, determine the meaning of his or her behavior. It is now clear beyond peradventure, that what may be viewed as freedom for the parent is enslavement for the child and it is enslavement for a lifetime. The effects of divorce do not disappear. One study found that young adults from broken families were twice as likely to have the problems of young adults who grew up in intact families. Another study found that children of divorced parents were 73 percent more likely than the general population to suffer from depression in their adult years. For some of these children, there is only one solution. A recent study reported that divorce was the second leading cause of suicide among young people ages 15 to 24.

Consider the studies of Barbara Dafoe Whitehead, reported in a national magazine, the twenty-two year study conducted by Judith Wallerstein, a California psychologist, or the work of Sara McLanahan of Princeton or Kathleen Kiernan at Cambridge. They arrive at identical conclusions. Children of divorced and single parents are more likely to be poor, to have emotional and behavioral problems, to drop out of school, to abuse drugs and to become embroiled in the criminal justice system. Girls of divorced parents are more likely to have a premarital birth in their teens and boys are more likely to be out of work. Children who lose a parent through death, on the other hand, do not manifest these problems. Even children raised in a family of bickering parents show no ill effects from these surroundings.

Critics of these studies often raise the question of whether children should continue living with parents who are physically or psychologically abusive. The obvious answer is, no. The argument, however, is reminiscent of the pro-abortion critics who invariably begin their defense of abortion by citing incest and rape cases, carefully avoiding the small number of pregnancies resulting from such violence. The National Commission on Children reports that physical or psychological abuse occurs in only ten to fifteen percent of marriages. While that is far too many, it is emphatically not the principal cause of the overwhelming number of divorces. Divorce occurs essentially because one of the partners just "feels like it." The divorcer will be more "comfortable" by dissolving the marriage. Most important, divorce allows "freedom," and since that is the only real value, divorce must be desirable.

If the single parent family augurs such unfortunate probabilities, why not solve the problem through remarriage? Sarah McClanahan of Princeton found that children whose parents remarry after divorce still seem to do at least as badly at school and in their personal lives as children of single parents. Many other studies point to the even greater lack of success of second marriages which may expose children to additional traumatic effects through a second divorce.

In our society where guilt and personal responsibility are anathema, it is almost as easy to secure a divorce as it is to procure a federal gun dealer's license because we have no-fault divorce. Though a University of Chicago study has recently labeled no-fault divorce "a failed experiment," it remains as another species of the commitment to absolute freedom. It is another manifestation of our general commitment to a complete no-fault society. How can there possibly be any fault ascribed to any conduct in a society where the only value is absolute freedom and only the actor determines the meaning of his or her behavior? We assiduously avoid describing any conduct as "wrong" because we operate on the conclusive presumption that we cannot know what is "right" with only one exception, the right to absolute freedom.

We characterize the right to absolute freedom in various ways. We indulge any number of euphemisms to communicate the mainstream philosophy of the United States and much of the world. We have developed an entire vocabulary to facilitate our workaday philosophy. We make folk heroes of those who "march to their own drummer." We insist that every person is entitled to pursue a self-determined "lifestyle" which, of course, means that the sole judge and jury of the meaning and effects of that behavior will be the actor, himself. Parents defend the deviant behavior of their children by characterizing that behavior as "sexually active." "Children will be sexually active, won't they?" When does one hear a parent using more precise language such as, "My children will fornicate, won't they?" "Fornication" will not be used because it suggests actions which are evil, wrong, sinful and irresponsible—conduct that departs from a standard. We cannot tolerate such characterizations in our no-fault society of absolute freedom where there are no standards except absolute freedom.

Many other precise characterizations have disappeared from our common dialogue. We insist on characterizing sexual intercourse by a married person with someone other than a spouse as "an affair," or, at worst, "infidelity" rather than "adultery." We never hear "adultery," and even "infidelity" is quickly disappearing because it imports a standard of conduct that is opposed to the autonomous standard which is the only standard. When the President of the United States was accused most recently of "an affair" and simultaneously suspected of some nefarious business dealings, the media consensus was absolutely clear that the charges of "infidelity" were insignificant. Dishonesty in marriage is acceptable, but dishonesty in business is unacceptable. Of course, the ultimate manifestation of dishonesty is dishonesty with the media—the cover-up—which will be fatal. Thus, the only problem for our President is not whether he lied to his wife, but whether he lied to the press.

The apotheosis of the absolute freedom standard is cloaked under a so-called right which has been the obsession of this society during the latter part of this century—the "right of privacy." This "right of privacy" is the cloak under which we justify still another holocaust of the twentieth century, the abortion holocaust. The more fundamental justification, however, is clearly stated in the pronouncements of our Supreme Court which, as recently as 1992, issued the following directives:

> Constitutional protection of the woman's decision to terminate her pregnancy derives from the Due Process Clause of the Fourteenth Amendment. It declares that no State shall 'deprive any person of life, liberty or property without due process of law.' The controlling word...is "liberty."

> Men and women of good conscience can disagree, and we suppose some always shall disagree, about the profound moral and spiritual implications of terminating a pregnancy.... Some of us as individuals find abortion offensive to our most basic principles of morality, but that cannot control our decision. Our obligation is to define the *liberty* of all, not to mandate our own moral code.

If the Court is not mandating its "own moral code," which moral code is it mandating? The same 1992 opinion removes the last scintilla of doubt:

> The destiny of the woman must be shaped to a large extent on *her own* conception of her spiritual imperatives and her place in society.

A fetus is not entitled to life or liberty because a fetus is not a "person." Beware of governments that take it upon themselves to define who is a "person." For some time in our society, blacks were not persons. In Nazi Germany, Jews and many others were not persons. In the Soviet Union, dissidents were not persons. The Nazi and Soviet holocausts were carried out in secret because the tyrants knew they were destroying real "persons." The reality of abortion is also cloaked in secrecy. It has become common to display surgical procedures on our television screens, but not limb-tearing and skull crushing abortions. Is there any wonder why they are not shown? God forgive us. This is what absolute freedom and the consequent standard of autonomous morality has wrought. The Madonna of our society sells sex and the symbol of our society is the condom. The standards of our society are not those standards of the eternal and natural law reaffirmed by John Paul II; they are the standards of absolute freedom popularized by that congenital liar, Jean-Paul Sartre.

To promote the teaching of the Church with respect to marriage and the family under these circumstances is a massive challenge. If we want even Catholics to assimilate the fact that marriage is not only an indissoluble natural contract but a supernatural covenant between God and the marrying spouses demanding total fidelity, we must do much more than merely articulate this command. If we want even Catholics to understand the purpose of marriage as the procreation and education of children who constitute the crowning glory of marriage, we must do much more than merely issue a directive to this effect. We must provide sophisticated and accessible education to all, particularly our leaders in the professions, including the clergy, not only with respect to the specific teachings concerning the family, but to those teachings that provide the foundation for assimilating the teaching of the family and all other utterances of the Magisterium.

How many Catholics will read, much less understand *Veritatis splendor*? How many Catholic universities will devote themselves to the pervasive teaching of these fundamental truths? How many of our leaders have any significant understanding of natural law and its participation in eternal law? How many of our sisters and brothers are aware of the total commitment of the church to truth as the first loyalty of the mind? How many have any understanding of the fact that faith is the most rational of all acts? How many have any understanding of why faith and reason are complementary rather than contradictory or paradoxical? When we speak of virtue, what is the current understanding of theological or moral virtues? An understanding of prudence, justice, fortitude and temperance is not part of one's DNA. It must be developed. It must be understood. It must be assimilated if there is any hope that the virtuous life will be pursued.

There is massive ignorance about Catholic teaching and it is particularly devastating with respect to matters of sex, marriage and the family. It is not uncommon to hear even a priest or a theologian say that, while he is certainly opposed to abortion, he has his doubts about the teaching of the Church regarding contraception. The courageous author of *Humanæ vitæ* may ask too much of those who have been absorbed by the instant gratification society. How many of these same priests or others assume that the only Roman Catholic alternative to artificial contraception is the "rhythm method" which is so relatively ineffective? How many have ever heard of Natural Family Planning and the non-invasive and totally natural Sympto-Thermal method which even the World Health Organization studied and found at least as effective as invasive and chemically oriented methods of contraception?

Our people *are* being educated—in the monopolistic educational system that refutes all values except the value of absolute freedom, a system which is another devastating manifestation of failure as documented in every comparison between United States' primary and secondary students and comparable students from other countries. Where is the teaching of the Church, the sophisticated teaching that combines theology, moral philosophy, sociology, history, the natural sciences and all other disciplines that will support the directives that we will find in our catechism? Where is the research and scholarship? Where is the monthly periodical issued by the Magisterium that will not appear as a ukase but as premier scholarship based upon pristine research? And, what is Catholic higher education doing to promote this research, scholarship and communication of the true teaching of the Magisterium? Current Catholic periodicals are obsessed with criticisms of the Magisterium. Catholic universities are obsessed with apologizing for their Catholic character which is why *Ex Corde Ecclasiæ* is such a critically important teaching. None of the information I present in this little paper was derived from modern Catholic scholarship, and that is shameful.

The teaching of Jesus Christ through the Magisterium is true. He *is* the way, the truth and the life. Only God can tell us how to live to achieve God, our sole and last end. Together, we must bring this teaching to everyone in a way that leaves no possibility of ambiguity or contradiction and reaches such levels of scholarly and research excellence as to make it impervious to attack. We must build a new kind of cathedral for this modern age, a cathedral of truth. As Augustine said, "Whatever is true is ours." This is the quintessential challenge requiring immense fortitude and the avoidance of politically correct homilies. If we fail to meet this challenge, we are guilty. We are at fault. We are responsible. We cannot hide from the face of God.

In the Spirit that gives life, I thank you for allowing me to be with you today.

Notes

1. *Veritatis splendor*, 47.
2. *Ibid*.

PART FOUR:
VERITATIS SPLENDOR
AND THE
CATECHISM OF THE CATHOLIC CHURCH

Chapter 17

VERITATIS SPLENDOR:
MORAL LIFE AS TRANSFIGURED LIFE

The Reverend J. A. DiNoia, O.P., Ph.D.

Pope John Paul II put his signature to *Veritatis splendor* on August 6, 1993, the feast of the Transfiguration of our Lord. While the encyclical did not become public until October, considerable significance attaches to the date on which documents of this magnitude are actually signed. *Veritatis splendor* is arguably the most important encyclical of this pontificate, and will probably be judged to be one of the most significant of this century. I have a single aim in this paper: I want to argue that the date upon which this great encyclical was signed provides a key to unlocking its meaning, that transfiguration and communion are at its heart.

But I shall begin with a quotation, not from *Veritatis splendor*, but from *Pastores dabo vobis*:

> There are spiritual and religious values present in today's culture, and man...cannot help but hunger and thirst for God. However, the Christian religion is often regarded as just one religion among many or reduced to nothing more than a social ethic at the service of man. As a result, its amazing novelty in human history is quite often not apparent. It is a "mystery," the event of the coming of the Son of God who becomes a man and gives to those who welcome him "the power to become the children of God" (Jn 1:12). It is the proclamation, nay the gift of a personal covenant of love and life between God and man.[1]

In these powerful words, Pope John Paul is trying to get us to see the stunning truth of the destiny to which human beings are called, a truth proclaimed by Christ and a destiny made possible for us by his passion, death and resurrection. Human persons are called to nothing less than communion with the Father, Son and Holy Spirit. To put it as forcefully as possible, Christianity affirms that the triune God could not bring about a more intimate union with created persons than that which has begun in Baptism and is to be consummated in the life to come. Ultimate communion involves nothing less than becoming part of the trinitarian family.

Just as Christ is Son by nature—a member of the divine family of the Trinity in virtue of his being the only Son of the Father—so we human persons are to be sons and daughters by adoption. Our fellowship with Christ and with each other in Him brings us into the divine trinitarian family.

For a variety of reasons, we have lost a sense of the "amazing novelty" of this message. For one thing, we simply take it for granted. For another, our culture inclines us to see all religions as in some sense equally concerned with something vaguely called "the Transcendent" and more or less equally fit to leading people to experience and enjoy it.

One of the overriding objectives of *Veritatis splendor* is to affirm that the Christian moral life makes sense only within this understanding of our calling to "life on high in Christ Jesus" (Phil.

3:14). If we are destined to enjoy ultimate communion with the Father, Son and Holy Spirit—and with each other in them—then we must change. We must be transformed into people who can enjoy this high destiny.

As the encyclical strives to make clear, this transformation will be a conformation: the more we become like Christ, the more surely do we discover our true selves, the unique persons created by the triune God to share in the divine life and to enjoy the family life of the Trinity. A moral life is a life lived in Christ and through his grace. The ultimate aim of a morally upright life is not so much to "please God" by successfully keeping the commandments as to render us fit for the eternal company of the triune God. We become good by seeking the good.

The encyclical makes this clear in the long meditation on the encounter between Christ and the rich young man with which it begins. In response to the young man's question, "What good must I do to have eternal life?" Jesus says, "There is only one who is good. If you wish to enter into life, keep the commandments" (see Mt 19:16-22). Our Lord's teaching here indicates that only by seeking the ultimate good—God himself—can we become good. In other words, he connects keeping the commandments with becoming good. The more we seek the ultimate good through the keeping of the commandments, the more we become good and the more fit we become to enjoy the communion with the triune God that is our destiny. Only in Christ can we discover and become enabled to seek the Good through the keeping of the commandments.

Thus, in the encyclical's first chapter, Pope John Paul II summons us to see the Christian moral vision as a matter of increasing transformation in and intimacy with Jesus Christ. Then, in the second chapter, the Pope takes up some of the fundamental principles of the Christian moral life understood in this perspective. In taking up these topics, *Veritatis splendor* is unique among the documents of the magisterium. There has been a great deal of teaching on specific issues of Christian morality, like sexual and social ethics, for example, but this is the first occasion when there has been a sustained discussion of the most basic principles of the Christian moral life. In effect, the question in the encyclical is not simply *how* to act morally in this or that situation, but the more radical question, *why* act morally at all. The resounding response offered by the encyclical is framed in terms of our destiny in Christ to enjoy communion with the triune God and with each in God.

It is true that in this chapter, the Pope takes up in turn the topics of authentic freedom, conscience, sin, and the nature of the moral act. In part, his concern is to correct certain mistaken ideas about these matters put forward in recent years by some Catholic theologians and popularized among people in the Church. His concern here is not academic, but pastoral: mistaken ideas about these issues can undermine a true Christian moral life. But, more important than what the encyclical denies is what it affirms.

When talking about the big changes that Vatican II has caused in Catholic life, most of us tend to think immediately about changes in discipline and liturgy. In fact, one of the most dramatic shifts occurred in the area of moral theology. After a practically undisputed reign of nearly four hundred years, legalism (and the kind of casuistry associated with it), which had governed a lot of Catholic life and sacramental practice, slipped away without so much as an obituary notice.

The reasons for the powerful hold of legalism in moral theology since the Council of Trent are complex, and could be the subject of a lengthy discussion all its own. The important thing to notice for our purposes today is that legalistic moral theology tended to put matters not in terms of the good and evil but in terms of the permitted and the forbidden. In this style of moral theology, moral norms were viewed more as laws to be enforced and obeyed than as principles for a good life, lived in view of God's invitation to ultimate communion. In a legalistic perspective, happiness is a kind of extrinsic reward for a life lived in conformity to an arduous code of conduct. The framework is contractual rather than virtue-centered and personalist.

The fundamental importance of *Veritatis splendor* is that it embodies a complete rejection of this legalistic moral theology. It seeks to recover and reaffirm a more complete biblical, patristic and authentic Thomistic vision of the whole of the Christian life and to locate the moral good within this vision. According to this vision, happiness is the flourishing of a life lived in seeking the

254

good in order to realize and enjoy personal communion with the triune God and with other persons in God.

A simple example will help to dramatize the nature of this shift away from legalism. If you tell a child to stop eating cookies before dinner, and he asks you why, you have at least two possible answers to give: "I'm your mother, and I told you to stop. I make the rules in this house;" or, you could say, "You'll ruin your appetite." The fist answer is an authoritarian one, a very simplified form of the kind of explanation associated with legalistic moral theology. The second answer appeals in a simple way to what is good and bad for you. The new encyclical exemplifies, at a highly sophisticated and theologically dense level, the second kind of answer.

In its rejection of legalism, the new encyclical is solidly in the tradition of Vatican Council II. That council called specifically for a renewal of moral theology that would restore to primacy the biblical categories of love, grace, discipleship and transformation in Christ.[2] The council thus inaugurated a period of tremendous creative ferment in which a variety of new avenues were explored. The new encyclical reviews twenty-five years of reflection and debate in moral theology and resoundingly affirms the best trends in the ongoing renewal of Catholic theology, and at the same time expresses a series of cautionary notes about certain trends in moral theology that seem to be going in the wrong direction. But the crucial point that must not be lost in the controversy that the encyclical has generated among some Catholic authors is the affirmation that morality only makes sense within the perspective of the call to ultimate communion.

The first Truth here is the truth of God himself, as embodied in the person and teaching of Jesus. If we want to live in the truth, we must be conformed to the Truth who is Christ himself. Our happiness is to be found in seeking and attaining the ultimate Good. Moral goodness in human beings is a participation in the divine goodness.

If we are to enjoy communion with the triune God, then we must become fit for it. Interpersonal communion with God is only "natural" to uncreated persons; for created persons, who are also sinners, such communion is possible only through grace. It is through the grace of Christ and, specifically, through the transformation that this grace makes possible, that we are rendered "fit" participants in the communion of the Father, Son and Holy Spirit.

It is at this point that the central significance of the mystery of the Transfiguration emerges.

We are all familiar with the gospel accounts of the Transfiguration. Matthew, Mark and Luke agree in the basic details: Peter, James and John witnessed a remarkable transformation in the countenance of Christ. The ordinary, dusty Jesus who was their companion and master was transformed before their eyes in a dazzling display of glory. The disciples were at a loss even to describe what they saw. Jesus' clothes became whiter, as Mark's gospel quaintly puts it, than any bleach could make them. In fact, as would become clear to the disciples later, what they saw was not so much a "transfiguration" by which Jesus was changed into something he had not been beforehand, but rather a revelation in which His true nature was exposed to view. For a fleeting moment, the veil that concealed His glory from their sight was removed and they beheld the glory of God's only son.

But we need to go deeper. We need to ask why Christ allowed the disciples to behold His glory. St. Leo the Great can be of assistance at this point. In a sermon on the mystery of the Transfiguration, Leo suggested that there were at least two reasons why Christ revealed his glory to these chosen witnesses.[3]

The first reason, Pope St. Leo suggests, was "to remove the scandal of the cross from the hearts of his disciples, and to prevent the humiliation of his voluntary suffering from disturbing the faith of those who had witnessed the surpassing glory that lay concealed." In other words, when the disciples saw Christ dead on the cross, they would not despair or lose heart. Those who had been to the top of Mount Tabor—according to tradition, the locus of the Transfiguration—would know that beneath the appearance of defeat and death lay the reality of victory and life. Appearances to the contrary notwithstanding, as we might put it, the cross constituted a victory over sin and death, a victory that would be confirmed and made manifest in the Resurrection on the third day.

But, Leo goes on, there was another reason why Christ let his disciples witness the Transfiguration. Not only did Christ want to sustain the faith of his disciples in the face of events that would sorely try it. In the Transfiguration he revealed not only His own hidden glory, but our future glory as well. In short, He wanted to show us what would become of us. "The whole body of Christ," Leo says, "was to understand the kind of transformation that it would receive as His gift. The members of that body were to look forward to a share in that glory which first blazed out in Christ their head." Naturally, from our point of view, we seem to be sinking into decrepitude rather than rising to glory! But, again, appearances to the contrary notwithstanding, "all of us, with unveiled faces, seeing the glory of the Lord as though reflected in a mirror, are being transformed from one degree of glory to another" (2 Cor 3:18).

It is Leo's second reason for the Transfiguration that sheds light directly on the meaning of the encyclical. Let the text of the encyclical speak for itself at this point: "The light of God's face shines in all its beauty on the countenance of Jesus Christ, 'the image of the invisible God' (Col 1:15), the 'reflection of God's glory' (Heb 1:13), 'full of grace and truth' (Jn 14:6). Consequently, the decisive answer to every one of man's questions, his religious and moral questions in particular, is given in Jesus Christ, or rather is Jesus Christ himself..."[4] Moral life—the struggle to become good by seeking the good—finds its ultimate pattern and principle in Jesus Christ. Why? Because in Him, the perfect image of God is found, and it is in being conformed to Him that the image of God in us is made perfect. The Transfiguration signals to us that our transformation must be a conformation. It is this conformation that gives us our entry into the trinitarian family. As we pray in one of the Sunday prefaces: "Father,...[y]ou sent him as one like ourselves, though free from sin, that you might see and love in us what you see and love in Christ."[5]

What must be made clear here is that this conformation does not amount to a mere conformity. The conformation to Christ which is the principle of our transformation is not a mere cloning but the realization of our distinctive and unique personal identities. This must be so, for otherwise the communion to which this transformation is directed could not be consummated. The image of God in us consists precisely in the spiritual capacities of knowing and loving that make interpersonal communion possible. But authentic interpersonal communion presupposes the full realization, not the absorption or dissolution, of the individual persons who enter into it. Thus, if Christ is to be the principle of our transformation, it can only mean that in being conformed to Him, we each discover and realize our unique identities as persons.

This is an astounding claim, and we should pause over it. Consider the following saying of the Lord (I shall quote the saying from Matthew, but in each of the synoptic Gospels it is placed, significantly, just before the account of the Transfiguration): "If a man wants to be my disciple, let him deny himself and take up his cross and follow me. For whoever wants to save his life will lose it, and whoever loses his life for my sake will find it. For what will it profit a man if he gains the whole world but loses his life? Or what will he give in return for his life?" (Mt 16:24-26; cf. Mk 8:34-37; Lk 9:23-25). What Christ is asserting, in effect, is that each person will find his or her true self only by being conformed to Christ.

We only need to consider our ordinary experience to grasp how startling, even outrageous, Christ's assertion is. None of us, whether as teachers, or parents, or pastors—no matter how inflated our conceptions of ourselves or how confident our sense of our abilities—would ever dare say to any of our charges that they will find their true selves by imitating us. Naturally, we do sometimes feel that they would be a lot better off if they followed our example at certain points! But we cannot want any child or student of ours simply to be clones of us. On the contrary, we want them to discover themselves, to become independent and self-confident (even if not, these days, self-supporting!). None of us could say to another person: you will find your true self only if you imitate me.

Yet this is precisely what Christ asserts. In effect, this means that an indefinite number of human persons will find their distinctive identities by being conformed to Christ. A moment's reflection shows us that only the Son of God could make such an assertion. Only the inexhaustibly rich *perfect* Image of God who is the Person of the Son could constitute the principle and pattern for the transformation and fulfillment of every human person who has ever lived.

The encyclical locates the moral life within this all-encompassing mystery of communion and transfiguration.

Since we are persons, and precisely as persons, we must freely embrace the personal communion that is offered to us by the triune God as our ultimate happiness and good. Christ's grace empowers us to do so, but it empowers us to do so freely. The meaning of authentic freedom—a central theme of *Veritatis splendor*—lies here. The encyclical is critical of modern notions of freedom for their exaltation of individualism and autonomy. Christian freedom is not a matter of untrammeled choice, but a participation in God's freedom. In effect, authentic freedom is the God-given capacity to enter in a personal way in the realization of our true happiness. Precisely as persons invited into personal communion, we must freely embrace this invitation, or, of course, fail to. In this way, persons are different from non-personal, or as we usually put it, the non- or sub-rational creatures with whom we share the cosmos. Chipmunks and cabbages cannot embrace their good, or for that matter fail to. Only persons are free to join their hearts and souls to the endeavor to realize their true good—which, as we have seen, is the authentically personal good of ultimate communion.

It follows that, since we are persons, and precisely as persons, our actions count for something. We do not become good, or fail to become good, willy-nilly. Nor do we become good, or fail to become good, once and for all—at least on this side of the grave. No, in each action, and in some actions more than in others, we choose the good, or fail to. And through each action, and through some more than others, we become good, or fail to. In the moral life—which is nothing other than the whole realm of our human actions—something is happening to us. We are growing into fitness, or failing to, for the consummation of our already initiated communion with the Father, Son and Holy Spirit. Christ is the principle and pattern of a gradual transformation—to which we freely and in grace join our efforts—by which this fitness takes hold in us. And, since through his passion, death and resurrection he has already overcome the deadly effect of our failures, he makes it possible for us to rise above them through forgiveness and repentance.

In conclusion, a brief remark about the bearing of the encyclical on the theme of this year's workshop, "Faith and Challenges to the Family."

At the beginning of his message for the 1994 Day of Peace, Pope John Paul II recently stated: "God wished humanity to live in harmony and peace, and laid the foundations for this in the very nature of the human being, created 'in his image.' The divine image develops not only in the individual but also in that unique community of persons formed by a man and a woman so united in love that they become 'one flesh' (Gn 2:24).... This specific community of persons has been entrusted by the Lord with the mission of giving life and of nurturing it by the formation of the family."[6]

There are several references to the importance of morality for family life in the encyclical, but it does not contain a lengthy discussion of the issue. As the passage just quoted indicates, however, the themes that are central to the encyclical also afford a fundamental theological perspective on the family. The family is in a true sense an image of trinitarian communion itself.[7] Indeed, family relationships have provided a persistent inspiration for trinitarian theology throughout Christian history. Our destiny of "life on high in Christ" is in a real sense a participation in the trinitarian "family" life. As we noted above, the language of family relationships plays a central role in Christian understanding of the life of grace: we become the adopted sons and daughters of the Father in the Spirit by becoming brothers and sisters of the only Son. Since the image of God in us is realized precisely in interpersonal communion, our transformation into Christ is always in part experienced within the context of our relationships with other persons in whom grace is similarly at work. In this way, the family is central to both our understanding and our experience of communion and transfiguration.

I have argued in this paper that the principal message of the encyclical lies in this: without the mysteries, morals do not make ultimate sense. In the Christian vision of things, we can understand the significance of human action only within the context of the prior divine action. It is only in the perspective of the divine invitation to ultimate communion and the concrete initiation of this communion in Christ that the full significance of morality can be experienced and understood.

Notes

1. John Paul II, *I Will Give You Shepherds: On the Formation of Priests in the Circumstances of the Present Day*, (Washington, DC: United States Catholic Conference, 1992), paragraph 46, pp. 125-26.

2. Vatican Council II, Decree *Optatum totius*, n. 16 states: "Special care should be given to the perfecting of moral theology. Its scientific presentation should draw more fully on the teaching of holy Scripture and should throw light on the exalted vocation of the faithful in Christ and their obligation to bring forth fruit in charity for the life of the world."

3. Leo the Great, *Sermon* 51, 3-4, 8: PL 54, 310-311, 313. See *Liturgy of the Hours*, volume II, pp. 149-50.

4. *Veritatis splendor*, Washington, D.C.: United States Catholic Conference, 1993), paragraph 4, p. 5.

5. Sundays in Ordinary Time, Preface VII, *The Sacramentary* (New York: Catholic Book Publishing Company, 1974), p. 443.

6. John Paul II, "Message for the 1994 World Day of Peace, *L'Osservatore Romano*, December 23/29, 1993, p. 1.

7. The new *Catechism of the Catholic Church* makes this point explicitly when it states in paragraph 2205 that "[t]he Christian family is a communion of persons, the image and reflection of the communion of the Father and the Son in the Holy Spirit."

Chapter 18

EVANGELIZATION, CATECHESIS
AND THE FAMILY

The Reverend Monsignor George P. Graham, J.C.D., Ph.D.

In the year of Our Lord 1994, the historical situation of the family in the world of today appears as "an interplay of light and darkness."[1] The aim of this presentation is to explore and describe some aspects of this darkness and to point out some of our resources by which we can bring the light into this world of darkness.

Part One

In a recent article in the *New York Times*,[2] Peter Steinfels reported on remarks of President Clinton at a convention of black ministers. The President hoped "the nation might finally confront…the blight of crime, drugs, joblessness and family disintegration."[3] Mr. Steinfels reported on data recently presented by Charles Murray in the *Wall Street Journal*. We are approaching the point where one of every three children will be born to an unmarried mother. The illegitimacy birth-rate among white women is nearing 25%. The single most important social problem of our time is "the emergence of a 'critical mass' of fatherless children. It is the crucial factor in poverty, crime, drugs, illiteracy, the whole snarl of social pathologies…."

In the same article, Mr. Steinfels reminds us of "the marketing edge obtained by blatant sexual appeals, verbal shock tactics, or displays of violence."[4] He also suggests the responsibility of newspapers and television in accepting such advertising. He notes how the entertainment industry seems committed to "the excitement of breaking taboos," and asks whether the industry takes seriously "the possibility that an environment saturated with images of sex and violence might be linked to the self-destructive behavior of a 15-year-old."[5]

But I need not spend any time giving you the sad statistics of marriage in the United States. Those of you who are bishops in the United States are dealing with these figures every day in your pastoral work. My guess is that the numbers are less shocking in other nations in the Western Hemisphere, but that the problems of families in those nations have given the bishops of those nations sleepless nights.

It would be hard to find anyone who would approach these symptoms of the decay of the family and society with the thought that all of them could be explained as the result of decisions of individuals, even of wicked persons. There is a widespread conviction among students of the family that the symptoms of disease of the family today are the result of cultural and ideological factors, a culture of disbelief. Until well into the 20th century, few Catholic students approached the study of family problems and other social problems from the viewpoint of culture. The problem of dysfunctional families was treated by most Catholic students in the United States only as a moral problem rather than a problem of society. The book of Max Weber (1863-1920), *The Sociology of Religion*, was only published in Germany in 1922. The book was not translated into English until 1963.[6] Weber's approach to the sociology of religion had part of one chapter on religion and sexuality.[7] Talcott Parsons in his introduction to the English translation of Weber's *Sociology of Religion* did not consider the relationship of religion and the family as a significant part of the sociology of religion.[8] In 1956, Alphonse A. Clemens complained that the available empirical studies on marriage were poorly done because of improper sampling methods.[9]

Part of the problem seems to be the neglect on the part of sociologists and anthropologists to consider the family, at least, in the Christian world, as so essentially related to the sociology of religion that it deserves a major treatment in that discipline. It seems to me that the role of religion in culture and the effect of culture on religion have to be confronted on the level of theory as well as on the level of descriptive study. In order to develop an adequate understanding of the family from a Catholic perspective, the family must be integrated into the sociology of religion. This insight was reached more than fifty years ago by Luigi Sturzo.[10]

Sturzo wrote:

> The sociologist cannot deny the transformation effected by Christianity, whether he regards it from the historical point of view, or compares Christian societies with non-Christian, or truly Christian societies with those that are Christian in name only or which have degenerated....
>
> It will be said that the sociologist cannot look upon these and analogous facts...as supernatural facts. This, I feel I have the right to challenge. The natural and the supernatural are so intertwined in all social life that, in the concrete of history, it is hard to discern where one is at work without the intervention of the other.[11]

In other words, in order to understand the relationship between the Christian family and society, a more sophisticated instrument will have to be devised than we have available now.

The concept of culture itself has undergone definition followed by redefinition followed by new definition. Clyde Kluckholn, in his book *Mirror for Man*, studied eleven definitions of the word "culture."[12] For our present purposes we may accept Clifford Geertz's concept of culture:

> The concept of culture I espouse...is essentially a semiotic one. Believing with Max Weber that man is an animal suspended in webs of significance he himself has spun, I take culture to be those webs....[13]

Geertz says also: "Culture consists of socially established structures of meaning in terms of which people do such things as signal conspiracies and join them or perceive insults and answer them."[14] He also says "The culture concept to which I adhere...denotes an historically transmitted pattern of meanings embodied in meanings, a system of inherited conceptions expressed in symbolic forms by means of which men communicate, perpetuate, and develop their knowledge about and attitudes towards life.[15]

Where does religion fit into culture? When a sociologist or anthropologist turns towards religion, he does not focus upon religion "as such," as the theologian would conceive it, but upon the relationships between religious ideas and commitments and other aspects of human conduct.[16]

Christopher Dawson, in one of his earliest books, *Progress and Religion*, concluded that every living culture must possess some spiritual dynamic, which provides the energy necessary for the sustained social effort which is civilization. Normally, this dynamic is supplied by a religion...."[17]

At the end of that work, Dawson concluded that:

> The vital changes in civilization are always linked with changes in religious beliefs and ideals. The secularization of a society involves the devitalization of that society, for, as Peguy said, "the passing of a religion is not a sign of progress, but a token of social decay."[18]

In the first volume of his Gifford lectures, *Religion & Culture*, Dawson points out that:

> every being of its nature possesses an innate tendency towards God—the natural inclination to do what is absolutely good.[19]

The family, therefore, as an institution, is not closed in on itself. The family and the other institutions of a particular culture are means through which those culture are orientated towards the good that transcends their own power and knowledge.

The insights of Luigi Sturzo and Christopher Dawson, the pioneers of a truly Catholic social science, help us to see the relationships between religion, understood as the soul of a culture, and the family, as a sacred institution within a particular culture. When the family becomes increasingly dysfunctional, that is, when the family ceases to be the bearer of authentic religious values and the sacrament of God's grace, this must be seen as a sign of the devitalization of the culture and a falling away of the community from the Transcendent Power who rules the universe. When the family ceases to be a way of life which is a way of the service of God, it will become a way of death.

I believe that when religion ceases to be the vital principle of a society, the devitalization of that society is directed by an ideology. Dawson has pointed out that the modern Western world has been increasingly detached from its spiritual roots in Christian culture. At the same time, it has advanced in material and scientific power, and has extended its influence over the rest of the world in a cosmopolitan technological world order.[20]

The United States cannot disassociate itself from the fate of the West. We achieved our independence in the wake of the Enlightenment, and the Enlightenment, as an ideology, was central to our national existence. Dawson points out how this ideology of the Enlightenment took on a different color in America. While in Europe the Enlightenment brought in an age of criticism in which no truth was left unquestioned and the spiritual unity of Western culture was lost, in America the Enlightenment united the whole people in their allegiance to certain common truths.[21]

Nevertheless, the process of secularization has wrought major changes in the American national consensus. These changes may be followed historically through a study of the decisions of the Supreme Court of the United States since the Second World War. These decisions, especially in the areas of religion, education and the family, have created an enormous pressure for moral and intellectual uniformity. The First Amendment, which was intended

266

to secure religious freedom, has become an engine for secularizing the American mind. As Stephen L. Carter has pointed out, American law and politics have trivialized religious devotion. In contemporary American culture, religions are more and more treated almost as fads. People are encouraged to give up religious beliefs when they become inconvenient. "And through all of this trivializing rhetoric runs the subtle but unmistakable message: Pray if you like, worship if you must, but whatever you do, do not on any account take your religion seriously."[22]

Bishops and other pastors have the responsibility of proclaiming the Gospel of Christ to the people of a particular parish or diocese. We have to proclaim the Gospel to people with a particular culture, people whose minds have been shaped by the symbols and patterns of meaning of that culture. This much is true always and everywhere. In the Western world, however, the task is made infinitely more complicated by the presence within our culture of the ideology of the Enlightenment. That ideology may be described as a paganism in rebellion against the Christian inheritance and dependent upon the paganism of classical antiquity, but a modern paganism, emancipated from classical thought as much as from Christian dogma.[23]

This ideology of modern paganism dominates our great newspapers and our television networks. It is proudly embraced by our leading publishing houses, and it has insinuated itself into a commanding role in our educational system. Our people are formed and corrupted by the *philosophes* of the modern intelligentsia. If we are to evangelize and catechize our people effectively, we have to be prepared to deal with this culture and this ideology.

Part Two

We began with words of Pope John Paul II that the historical situation in which the family lives appears as an interplay of light and darkness.[24]

It is time to turn now in a spirit of Christian optimism to point out some of the resources by which we can bring the Light of Christ to the families in the dark today.

We have to become instruments of God as we cooperate with His graces to do the work of evangelization and catechesis. First of all, evangelization.

If we remember that our culture is shaped by the ideology of the 18th Century French Enlightenment, we have to devise a strategy for breaking through the defenses set up by that ideology. Pope Paul VI has pointed out that "Modern man is sated by talk; he is obviously often tired of listening and, what is worse, impervious to words."[25] The strategy for making contact with the people and the families of today will have to be focused on a person, Jesus Christ. If we are to break through the hard shell of secularism and disbelief, we will have to present the living person of Jesus in all the attractiveness of His personality as portrayed in the Gospel.

But there is the rub. The revolution in Catholic biblical studies, which began shortly after the Second World War in Europe, developed rapidly in the United States during the early 1950s.[26]

In a movement that has brought so many benefits to the Church, there have been occasional setbacks. One such negative development was the skepticism about the person of Jesus, most frequently associated with the name of the German biblical scholar and theologian Rudolf Bultmann. Bultmann was one of the scholars who introduced the method of form-criticism in the study of the Gospels.[27] One of his earliest works to be translated into English was *Jesus and the Word*.[28]

In that book, Bultmann said:

> I do indeed think that we can now know almost nothing concerning the life and personality of Jesus, since the early Christian sources show no interest in either, are moreover fragmentary and often legendary; and other sources about Jesus do not exist.[29]

It may well be, as Schubert Ogden holds, that Bultmann's skepticism has been blown out of proportion, and that Bultmann argued for a strict historical continuity between Jesus' own proclamation and the early Church message about Christ.[30]

Nevertheless, the message received by many teachers, preachers and catechists seems to have been that one cannot say anything about the historical person of Christ.

But the message of Bultmann, understood correctly or not, is not the only message to come from modern gospel studies. One of the foremost English proponents of form-criticism was C. H. Dodd. Dodd, who was described by John A. T. Robinson as the front-rank English-speaking New Testament scholar, wrote a beautiful book on *The Founder of Christianity*.[31]

In that book the English scholar pointed out that the Gospels are indeed religious documents; they bear witness to the faith of the Church. But that it is not to say that they are not also historical documents, or that their authors had no interest in the facts. Luke set out "to draw up an account of the events that have happened," in order to convey authentic knowledge about them. Any attempt to make a sharp division between fact and religious interpretation is misguided. "The interest and the meaning which an event bore for those who felt its impact is a part of the event."[32] In the New Testament, God discloses His ways to men especially in what Luke calls "the facts about Jesus."[33]

One sometimes hears theologians speak of "the event of Christ," as if the Jesus of the Gospels was an impersonal flat figure playing a functional role in the story. Dodd, on the other hand, with his imagination nourished by poring over the documents day after day for three quarters of a century, does not look on Jesus that way. Instead, he said that "the reported sayings of Jesus bear the stamp of an individual mind."[34]

A large proportion of the teaching of Jesus

> comes in the form of short crisp utterances, pungent, often allusive, even cryptic, laden with irony and paradox. This whole body of sayings, handed down through different channels of tradition, has an unmistakable stamp. It is impossible to suppose that they are merely the product of skillful condensation by early Christian teachers. They have the ring of originality. They betray a mind whose processes were swift and direct, hitting the nail on the head without waste of words.[35]

The English scholar does not take a simplistic approach to the personal traits of Jesus. He notices the reserve which Jesus maintained and which was characteristic of Him. In spite of His dedication to His mission to set fire on the earth, that mission itself set

Jesus apart from other men. "No one knows the son but the Father."[36]

A ray of light illuminating what went on in the mind of Jesus as He approached His death is given through His prayer: "Father, if it is possible, let this cup pass from me; yet not as I will but as you will" (Mt. 26:29).

C. H. Dodd may be taken as an outstanding representative of users of the form-critical method. A younger scholar, Donald Senior, this time a Catholic, may be taken as a representative of the later development in methodology known as Redaction Criticism. Father Senior did his doctoral dissertation in scripture at Louvain on the passion narrative according to Matthew.[37]

This American Passionist wrote a simple and powerful work in which he presents a Gospel portrait of Jesus.[38]

In the foreword to the revised edition, Father Senior reports that one of the "quiet joys of his life has been the letters and personal comments we have received from readers who discovered in this book what I was hoping and praying they would: at least some hint of the compelling beauty and magnetic power of the biblical Jesus."[39]

This moving portrait of Jesus is not based on a kind of fictional re-imagining of the personality of Jesus.

> The treatment dwells as much as possible on those aspects of the life and message of Jesus that enjoy a high degree of consensus in the interpretations of contemporary biblical scholars.[40]

It is tempting to pursue further the encounter with the living person of Jesus as He is portrayed in his gospels, but this brief hors d'oeuvre is all I have time for in this presentation. I wish only to make the point that our work of evangelization should be focused on the person of Jesus as He appears in the gospels, and that we can do that work without falling into a mindless fundamentalism. We can and should use all the techniques of modern Gospel scholarship, without falling into a despairing skepticism about the person of Jesus.

Our work of evangelization cannot stop with the presentation of Christ. If our culture is shaped by the ideas of the Eighteenth Century Enlightenment, and by the deism and atheism of the *philosophes*, our evangelization must counter their ideology with philosophy. We have to show that what can be known about God is evident, because God made it evident (See Romans 1:19).

It seems that not many people agree with that insight from St. Paul today. There are of course atheists like A. J. Ayer[41] and Antony Flew.[42]

And then there is Hans Kung. Kung holds that:

> In the light of our previous experiences, there is no purely rational demonstration of God's existence that could carry universal conviction. Proofs of God turn out in fact not to be coercive for everyone, whatever may be thought of the "possibility" of knowledge of god as taught by Vatican I. There is not a single proof that is universally accepted.[43]

After rejecting any demonstration of the existence of God, Kung holds that the affirmation of the existence of God can only be justified by a confidence rooted in reality, a trusting commitment to an ultimate ground, support, and meaning of reality.[44]

Kung tries to establish that belief in God may be rationally justified, but he holds also that one can adopt a skeptical attitude, he may choose agnosticism with a tendency to atheism, or he may choose atheism with a tendency to nihilism.[45]

It is not clear how Kung can persist in describing his approach as rational. It seems, rather, to be a profoundly anti-intellectual position. Perhaps the basic problem is that Kung approaches all proofs for the existence of God with the expectation of finding a merely logical chain of reasoning which would be accessible to those who have not appropriated the fundamental insights of a realistic metaphysics.

Nevertheless, despite the widely held rejection by various writers of properly philosophical proofs for the existence of God, our work of evangelization has to be backed up by a sound philosophical grasp of the reality of God. One philosopher who can help us in this regard is Bernard J. F. Lonergan. In his major work *Insight*, Lonergan re-thought philosophy in the light of his insight into the activity of insight. He explains the meaning of insight by a comparison with the ideal detective story in which the reader is given all the clues yet fails to spot the criminal. He may advert to each clue as it arises.

He needs no further clues to solve the mystery. Yet he can remain in the dark, for the simple reason that reaching the solution is not the mere apprehension of any clue, not the mere memory of all, but a quite distinct activity of organizing intelligence that places the full set of clues in a unique explanatory perspective.

By insight, then, is meant not any act of attention or advertance or memory, but the supervening act of understanding.[46]

As Lonergan develops his understanding of insight, he uncovers a basic unity in the whole field of human inquiry. He devotes the first part of *Insight* to a consideration of insight as activity. In this way, he tries to convey an insight into insight.

> Mathematicians seek insight into sets of elements. Scientists seek insight into ranges of phenomena. Men of common sense seek insight into concrete situations and practical affairs. But our concern is to reach the act of organizing intelligence that brings within a single perspective the insights of mathematicians, scientists, and men of common sense.[47]

Such a unification of what is known in mathematics, in the sciences, and by common sense brings Lonergan to a metaphysics implied by insight into insight.[48]

Lonergan's insight into insight leads, step by step, into an insight into being and to the affirmation of God. This affirmation of God is an intrinsically rational act. It proceeds with rational necessity from a grasp of the unconditioned, that is, the virtually unconditioned that consists in inferring God's existence from premises that are true. Here Lonergan distances himself from rationalists like Hans Kung who persist in looking for a purely logical proof, the kind of logical game that one might play with a computer. The philosopher deals with words which are signs, signs which can represent a relevant virtually unconditioned. But grasping that unconditioned, and making consequent judgments, is an immanent act of rational consciousness that each has to perform personally. No one else can perform it for us. Contrary to Kung's philosophical agnosticism, Lonergan holds that the existence of God is known as the conclusion of an argument.[49]

Once one grants that the real is being, and once one grants that being is known by intelligent grasp and reasonable affirmation, then God is a reality.

If the real is being, then one must ask What is being? The answer to that question includes the affirmation of the reality of God.[50]

My point in drawing upon Bernard Lonergan's book *Insight*, a book not even mentioned in Kung's book, top-heavy with bibliographical references, is that we need not feel constrained to deprive our evangelization efforts of the support of a philosophical approach to God. Bernard Lonergan is not the only witness to a living Christian philosophical tradition. One might use with similar purpose the work of Father W. Norris Clarke, whose book *The Philosophical Approach to God* is an unsung work of permanent value.[51]

Before leaving our treatment of evangelization, the contact with the person of Jesus Christ which is necessary to break through the hard shell of the ideology of the Eighteenth Century Enlightenment, it seems helpful to reflect briefly on the importance of the splendor of moral truth which must shine forth in the Church, if our evangelization is to bear fruit. The truth about moral goodness enlightens one's intelligence and shapes his freedom, leading him to know and love the Lord. The recent encyclical letter of Pope John Paul II, *Veritatis splendor*,[52] points out that:

Evangelization is the most powerful and stirring challenge which the Church has been called to face from her very beginning.[53]

The Holy Father points out that evangelization is faced today with a formidable challenge to the proclamation of the Gospel.

De-christianization, which weighs heavily upon entire peoples and communities once rich in faith and Christian life, involves not only the loss of faith or, in any event, its becoming irrelevant for every day life, but also, and of necessity, a decline or obscuring of the moral sense.[54]

The Pope points out that there is an eclipse of fundamental principles and ethical values. There are widespread tendencies towards subjectivism, utilitarianism and relativism. The new evangelization therefore involves the proclamation and presentation of a gospel morality. The new evangelization will show its authenticity and unleash its missionary force when it is lived in the life of holiness of many members of the Church.[55] The vocation of the moral theologian must be seen to be in the service of the Church as a community of faith. Moral theologians have the grave duty to instruct the faithful, and especially future pastors, about all those commandments and practical norms authoritatively declared by the Church.

> Moral theologians are to set for the Church's teaching and to give, in the exercise of their ministry, the example of a loyal assent, both internal and external, to the magisterium's teaching in the areas of both dogma and morality.[56]

It seems clear then that moralists and ethicians doing their scholarly work in communion with the Holy Father and in conformity with the teaching of the encyclical *Veritatis splendor* have a necessary role in preparing the priests, religious and lay persons who are to do the work of evangelization of families today. The remarkable beauty of authentic Christian morality taught and lived will help to break through the skepticism about words in order to allow the Gospel message to be heard and loved.

The work of evangelization is never complete in any of us. Once the proclamation of the Gospel has touched the minds and hearts of the members of families, then evangelization has to continue in and through the catechesis of the Catholic faith. It is thus that one may realize the importance of the new *Catechism of the Catholic Church*. The life of grace is nourished by the truth of the Gospel, and it is the Gospel message that is presented in the *Catechism*. Another paper will draw upon the *Catechism* for a realistic catechesis on the family, a second will present the case for creative realism in adult catechesis. Professor Germain Grisez has already provided an excellent article on "Vocation in Family Catechesis" in the *1992 Proceedings of the Fellowship of Catholic Scholars*.[57] The same volume has an excellent article by Professor Scott Hahn on the importance of scripture in catechesis. Without duplicating their work, therefore, in the time remaining to me, I propose to focus on one element in systematic catechesis, that is, the Mass as a sacrifice.

In the heyday of the liturgical movement in the middle years of this century, the one teaching that united and excited liturgists was the teaching of the Church that the Mass is a true sacrifice. This teaching was central in the Constitution on the Liturgy of the Second Vatican Council.[58] Shortly before the Council, however, theologians such as Hans Kung, who were primarily concerned with ecumenism, lobbied for a deemphasis on the Mass as sacrifice in favor of a presentation of the Mass as a banquet. Their efforts were unsuccessful at the Council, but they were extremely influential in the years after the Council.

The unfortunate thing about this is that the teaching on the Eucharist as sacrifice is the key to motivating active participation in the Mass. Participation can be external or internal. Much has been written to encourage external participation through the use of the vernacular, the increased use of music and singing, the vernacular proclamation of the scriptures, and more frequent Holy Communion. What has been almost lost is the realization that, at every Mass, Christ is our great High Priest. By virtue of our baptismal character we are able to join with Christ and with the ministerial priest at the altar in offering the Eucharistic sacrifice in the Eucharist, the Church, with Mary, is at the foot of the cross, united in the offering and in the intercession of Christ.

At a time when the greatest pastoral problem facing the Church in the United States is the wholesale turning away of the Catholic people from the Mass, it is sad to note that when the Mass is not presented as a participation in the Sacrifice of Christ on the Cross, the Mass then becomes a spectacle, or drama, or, sometimes, a show, and attendance at Mass becomes a passive sitting back to enjoy the music. The new *Catechism* presents the Mass as a Sacrifice, and encourages all the faithful to join with the priest at the altar, and with Christ our High Priest, in offering the sacrifice actively, by joining our minds and hearts with Christ as He offers His gift to His Father.

If the *Catechism of the Catholic Church* is to provide help for families and bring them back to an understanding of the Mass as central in the lives of the families, it will be through the presentation of the Mass as a Sacrifice. Once we begin to proclaim the Mass as a Sacrifice, and participation in the Mass as a joining with Christ in offering His gift to the Father, it will be clear that the Mass is not something you go to watch, but something you go to do.

Nothing is more delightful than the exchange of gifts with someone we love. When our families begin to see the Mass as their chance to give the greatest gift of all to the Father, the gift of His Son, and to receive from the Father His gift in return, His Son,

Jesus, in Holy Communion, perhaps we will see a renewal of faith in the Eucharist and the enrichment of the family through the Eucharist as Sacrifice and Sacrament.[59]

In 1985, Pope John Paul II sent a letter of greetings to the workshop organized by the Pope John Center. In that letter, our Holy Father quoted from *Familiaris consortio*,

> The person principally responsible in the diocese for the pastoral care of the family is the Bishop. As father and pastor, he must exercise particular solicitude in this clearly priority sector of pastoral care.[60]

One may hope that the publication in English of the *Catechism of the Catholic Church* will provide a stimulus, especially for bishops, for the evangelization and catechesis of families in order to lead them to union with Christ.

Notes

1. Pope John Paul II, *The Role of the Christian Family in the Modern World* (*Familiaris consortio*, 1981) Boston: St. Paul editions, 1981) No. 6, p. 18.

2. *The New York Times*, Nov. 27, 1993.

3. Steinfels, p. 9.

4. Steinfels, p. 9.

5. Steinfels, p. 9.

6. Max Weber, *The Sociology of Religion* (1922) trns. Ephraim Fischoff (Boston: Beacon Press, 1963).

7. Weber, *Sociology of Religion* pp. 236-243.

8. Weber, *Sociology of Religion*, p. ix-lxvii.

9. Alphonse H. Clemens, *Marriage and the Family: An Integrated Approach for Catholics* (Englewood Cliffs, N.J. Prentice Hall, Inc., 1957), pp. 343-357.

10. Luigi Sturzo, *The True Life: Sociology of the Supernatural* (Washington, D.C.: The Catholic University of America Press; Paterson, N.J.: St. Anthony Guild Press, 1943).

11. Sturzo, *The True Life*, p. 12.

12. Clifford Geertz, *The Interpretation of Cultures* (New York: Basic Books), 1973, p. 4.

13. Geertz, p. 4.

14. Geertz, p. 12.

15. Geertz, p. 89.

16. Talcott Parsons (1902-1979), in his introduction to Max Weber, *The Sociology of Religion*, pp. xixf.

17. Christopher Dawson, *Progress and Religion* (Garden City, NY: Image Books, 1960), p. 8.

18. Dawson, *Progress and Religion*, p. 185.

19. Christopher Dawson, *Religion & Culture, Gifford Lectures Delivered in the University of Edenburgh in the Year 1947* (N.Y.: Sheed & Ward, 1948), p. 62.

20. Christopher Dawson, *The Crisis of Western Education* (New York: Sheed & Ward, Inc., 1961), p. 181.

21. John Courtney Murray, S.J. *We Hold These Truths: Catholic Reflections on the American Proposition* (New York: Sheed & Ward, 1960), pp. viif.

22. Stephen L. Carter, *The Culture of Disbelief: How American Law & Politics Trivialize Religious Devotion* (New York: Basic Books, 1993), p. 14f.

23. Peter Gay, *The Enlightenment: An Interpretation: The Rise of Modern Paganism* (New York: Alfred K. Knopf, 1967), p. xi.

24. John Paul II, *Familiaris consortio*, No. 6, p. 18.

25. Pope Paul VI, Apostolic Exhortation *Evangelii nuntiandi, On Evangelization In The Modern World*. Dec. 8, 1975. (Boston: Daughters of St. Paul 1796) No. 42, p. 24.

26. See Gerald P. Fogerty, S.J. *American Catholic Biblical Scholarship: A History From The Early Republic to Vatican II* (San Francisco: Harper & Row, 1989) for the controversies which attended the new developments.

27. Rudolf Bultmann, *The History of the Synoptic Tradition* (1921) tr. John Marsh (Oxford: Basil Blackwell, 1963). Bultmann's work was preceded by the studies of Karl Ludwig Schmidt, *Der Rahmen der Geschicthe* Jesu (1919) and Martin Dibelius, *From Tradition to Gospel* (New York: Scribners, n.d.) For a description of the method of form criticism, see Raymond Collins *Introduction to the New Testament* (Garden City, New York: Doubleday & Co., Inc., 1983) pp. 156-195.

28. Rudolf Bultmann, *Jesus and the Word* (1926) tr. Louise Pettibone Smith and Erminie Huntress Lantero (1934) (Reprint ed. London: Collins/Fontana Books, 1958).

29. Rudolf Bultmann, *Jesus and the Word*, p. 14.

30. Schubert M. Ogden "Rudolf Bultmann and the Future of Revisionary Christology" in Edward C. Hobbs, ed., *Bultmann, Retrospect and Prospect: The Centenary Symposium at Wellesley Harvard Theological Studies* 35 (Philadelphia: Fortress Press, 1985), p. 50.

31. C. H. Dodd, *The Founder of Christianity* (London: Collins 1971).

32. C. H. Dodd, *The Founder of Christianity*, p. 27f.

33. Acts 18:25. C. H. Dodd *The Founder of Christianity*, p. 28.

34. C. H. Dodd, *The Founder of Christianity*, p. 37.

35. C. H. Dodd, *The Founder of Christianity*, p. 37.

36. Luke 10:22.

37. Donald Senior, C.P., *The Passion Narrative According to Matthew: A Redactional Study*. (Louvain/Leuven: Leuven University Press, 1975).

38. Donald Senior, C.P., *Jesus: A Gospel Portrait*, Revised and expanded edition (New York & Mahwah, N.J. Paulist Press, 1992).

39. Donald Senior, *Jesus: A Gospel Portrait*, p. 1.

40. Donald Senior, *Jesus: A Gospel Portrait*, p. 3.

41. A. J. Ayer, *Language, Truth, and Logic* (1936) (New York: Dover Publications, n.d.).

42. Antony Flew, *God: A Critical Enquiry*, (La Salle Illinois: Open Court Publishing Co., 1984). This is a revised edition of Flew's book *God and Philosophy* (1966).

43. Hans Kung, *Does God Exist? An Answer for Today*, Tr. Edward Quinn (Garden City, New York: Doubleday & Co., Inc., 1980), p. 533.

44. Hans Kung, *Does God Exist?*, p. 572.

45. Hans Kung, *Does God Exist?*, p. 573.

46. Bernard J.F. Lonergan, S.J., *Insight: A Study of Human Understanding*, (London, New York, Toronto: Longmans Green & Co., 1957), p. ix.

47. Bernard Lonergan, *Insight*, p. ix.

48. Lonergan, *Insight*, p. XI.

49. Lonergan, *Insight*, p. 672.

50. See Lonergan, *Insight*, p. 675.

51. W. Norris Clark, S.J., *The Philosophical Approach to God: A Neo-Thomist Perspective*, ed. Wm. E. Ray (Winston-Salem, North Carolina: Wake Forest University, 1979).

52. Pope John Paul II, *The Splendor of Truth (Veritatis splendor)* (Boston: St. Paul Books & Media, 1993), p. 9.

53. John Paul II, *The Splendor of Truth*, No. 106, p. 128.

54. John Paul II, *The Splendor of Truth*, No. 106, p. 128.

55. John Paul II, *The Splendor of Truth*, No. 107, p. 129.

56. John Paul II, *The Splendor of Truth*, No. 110, pp. 133f. This statement of the encyclical is followed by a citation of the encyclical letter of Pope Paul VI *Humanæ vitæ* (July 25, 1968).

57. Anthony J. Mastroeni ed., *The Church and the Universal Catechism, Proceedings of the Fifteenth Convention of the Fellowship of Catholic Scholars* (Steubenville, Ohio: Franciscan University of Steubenville, 1992), pp. 143-160.

58. See Austin Flannery, O.P., *Vatican Council II, The Conciliar & Post-Conciliar Documents* (Northport, New York: Costello Publishing Co., 1975). No. 47, p. 16.

59. See George P. Graham, "The Mass as Sacrifice in the *Catechism of the Catholic Church*," *Lay Witness*, Vol. 15 No. 2 (Oct. 1993), pp. 1-7.

60. Donald G. McCarthy ed., *The Family Today and Tomorrow: The Church Addresses Her Future*, (Braintree, Massachusetts: The Pope John Center, 1985), p. xii.

Chapter 19

REALISTIC CATECHESIS
ON THE FAMILY

Carl Anderson, J.D.

In his *Introduction to Christianity,* Joseph Cardinal Ratzinger poses the dilemma confronting Christianity in our secular age by retelling Kierkegaard's famous story of the circus clown. In the story a circus arrives at a secluded town and with all the circus performers dressed in costumes and their animals on display they parade through the town announcing the opening of the circus the next day. The circus parade marches through the town and into the nearby forest to set up camp and prepare itself for the big show. Early the next morning, one of the circus clowns puts on his costume and goes into the forest toward the town to practice his act. As he does so he sees in the early dawn that a forest fire is quietly surrounding the town and threatens to destroy it. Still in costume, he runs into the streets of the town yelling for help and awakening its sleeping inhabitants. The townspeople, however, refuse to believe the clown that they are in imminent danger. Instead, they think that his warning is in fact some outrageous, self-serving advertisement for the circus later that day. The more desperate the clown becomes, the more the townspeople laugh at him. The clown, having done his best to warn the townspeople, returns to the circus camp while the town is destroyed.[1]

Cardinal Ratzinger was depicting the problem of the Church in the modern world in a more general sense, but certainly each of us as Catholics has at one time or another been treated as was the main character in Cardinal Ratzinger's story. Perhaps to some extent every Christian throughout history has been so treated. Certainly since the time of St. Paul's appearance at the Areopagus, an appearance which also ended in laughter and derision, Christians have realized the difficulty of presenting the Gospel message. It is interesting that Paul's Areopagus speech is one of only three speeches attributed to Paul in Acts which is recounted in detail. Each speech is to a particular and divergent audience: the Jewish community (13:16-41), the Christian community (20:17-35) and the pagan community (17:23-31). It appears that Luke intended his account of the speeches of Paul to be not merely accounts of preaching in apostolic times, but as paradigms of the Church's method of evangelization of those three differing communities. At the same time, Luke warns us in his account of Paul at the Areopagus of the likely reception the Christian should expect and the profound difficulties in communicating the Gospel message. The philosophical and cultural trends of St. Paul's time were certainly different than those of today, but there are similarities which ring as true now as they did then. And so, like St. Paul at the Areopagus, I would like to begin with an assessment of the cultural and philosophical context of the contemporary task of evangelizing the family.

The cultural context in which the Catholic family now lives is constituted by three defining characteristics: it is *post-Christian, post-Modern*, and *post-family*. To say that Western culture is no longer

280

Christian is to say more than that it is merely non-Christian. It is to realize, as did Henri de Lubac nearly 40 years ago in *The Drama of Atheist Humanism*, that modern atheism is essentially an anti-the-ism—it has consciously rejected the Christian way of life that had once been embraced. As Nietzsche wrote, "It is our preference that decides against Christianity—not arguments."[2] The problem is decidedly larger than one of simply being unable to give intellec-tual assent to the five proofs for the existence of God. Certainly there is a decision against God involved here which surpasses mere intellectual inquiry. But that is also a sort of disassociation of being from truth which in a way makes "proofs" for the existence of God no longer convincing.[3]

Because there is no longer a necessary connection between being and truth, the post-Christian man is willing to give assent only to that "truth" which he has fashioned himself. This separa-tion of truth from being not only discards the objective integrity of the objects with which man comes into contact but also violates the subjective integrity of each human person. As the subjective integ-rity and value of the individual evaporates he or she is easily re-duced to being regarded as merely an instrument to be manipulated as the means to another's ends.

Thus, the post-Christian materialism of modern atheism in Western industrial societies subjects not only truth but human re-lationships to a type of manipulative or technological thinking. If truth, human relationships such as marriage and the family, and even the human person, are in a sense "constructed" according to the technological mind, then they can just as easily be "decon-structed." This deadly alliance between technological manipula-tion and materialism in turn breeds a form of consumerism which can be perhaps most easily seen in abortion and fetal experimenta-tion. But it is also apparent in the commercial exploitation of chil-dren, the sexual exploitation of women, and the tax code's treatment of children as simply another consumer choice.

Paul Ricœur has referred to the fathers of modern secular culture—Marx, Freud, and Nietzsche—as the "masters of suspi-cion," thereby underlining the tactic which they used to confront Christianity.[4] They cast suspicion on the convictions of the Chris-tian not by directly confronting the adequacy of his description of

God. Instead, they maintained that Christianity is not really about God at all but merely a mechanism to project into a future world the tension which individuals cannot resolve in this one in such a way as to inhibit human freedom.

With the collapse of Christianity as the unifying principle of society, philosophers such as Kant and Hegel sought to substitute autonomous reason as the principle of social unity and the autonomous, rational individual became the defining and unifying criterion of modern culture. For example, in choosing the moral good, Kant's autonomous decision-maker was bound to choose as though choosing for everyone similarly situated in society.

In his essay, "The Entry into Postmodernity: Nietzsche as a Turning Point," Jurgen Habermas observes that Hegel sought to establish reason as the unifying principle of modern society at a time when Christianity collapsed as a force of social integration. Having "conceived of reason as the reconciling self-knowledge of an absolute spirit," Hegel placed his "hope in a dialectic of enlightenment in which reason was validated as an equivalent for the unifying power of religion."[5] It might be said, therefore, that the modern rational notion of the self had a sort of logic which displaced the Christian notion of self but did not totally destroy it. From their point of view, Modernity might be seen as only a partial rejection of Christian moral values in that it replaced transcendence (or faith) with immanence (or reason) as its unifying principle.

Thus, there remained an important nexus between Christianity and Modernity, namely a confidence that human reason could ascertain moral principles with certainty and universal application. In short, both the man of faith and the man of reason could readily assent, for example, to the proposition that each person possesses fundamental and inalienable rights. The Enlightenment philosophers may have undermined faith in the certainty of the Christian God, but they replaced it with a faith in the certainty of human reason.

In 1931, the historian Carl Becker made a similar point. Speaking of the philosophers of the Enlightenment, Becker stated:

> They ridiculed the idea that the universe had been created in six days, but still believed it to be a beautifully articulated machine designed by the Supreme Being according to a rational plan as an abid-

282

ing place for mankind. The Garden of Eden was for them a myth, no doubt, but they looked enviously back to the olden age of Roman virtue.... They denied that miracles ever happened, but believed in the perfectibility of the human race. We feel that these Philosophers were at once too credulous and too skeptical.[6]

It is this confidence in human capability which is now no longer accepted.

Modernity's methodology of suspicion once unleashed on Christianity failed to confine itself with the collapse of Christianity. Instead, it turned back upon itself to demolish modern rationalism as well. According to Nietzsche, Modernity must be abandoned precisely because its assertion that reason may find truth is an illusion. This confidence in a reason capable of reaching objective truth becomes for Nietzsche the most dangerous illusion of all because by binding man to an absolute order outside himself it creates the last and greatest obstacle to man's freedom. Nietzsche especially criticized the atheist philosophers who followed the Enlightenment; they may call themselves "free thinking," he wrote, but "they are far from being free spirits: for they still have faith in truth."[7] For Nietzsche the modern attack on God could not end with the attack on the divine Truth. It had of necessity to continue with an attack on all truth since the truly free man could not be dependent upon any absolute outside himself.

We now witness "a fundamental disillusionment about the evolution of modernity...[and] modernism has become a sort of myth."[8] Contemporary philosophy, what some now describe as "postmodernism," has accepted Nietzsche's critique of the foundations of modern rationality and rejected modernity's confidence in reason. In doing so, it has inverted the philosophical premises of modernity and radically changed contemporary discourse by replacing necessity with contingency, universality with plurality, certainty with fallibility, and unity with diversity. According to the post-modernists, what we are now left with is simply the conditioning of a particular cultural heritage. "Truth" has application only within a particular culture and cannot be extended outside that society. To attempt to do so is only another form of cultural imperialism by one lifestyle choice over another. In this new system, "truth claims" become meaningless, all that is important is to recognize that what some may call truth or objective moral law is really just a certain cultural or lifestyle bias toward one set of narratives of our life experience.[9]

Contemporary morality has, in a sense, retained the shell of the Enlightenment morality, but emptied it of its contents. What remains is the insistence that "morality is autonomous action, the making of our own moral laws."[10] But what has changed is the new insistence that human rationality no longer provides a principle of unity for the development of common moral principles and social institutions. Gone is Kant's autonomous moral individual acting as would every rational person in his or her circumstances and therefore acting consistently with universal moral norms. It is no longer a question of honoring a right to disagree among ourselves regarding certain human and social values. Instead, it is the contention that agreement is impossible, but not even desirable. Or as the United States Supreme Court recently put it in *Planned Parenthood v. Casey*, it is up to each person to determine for himself "the concept of existence, of meaning, of the universe, and of the mystery of human life."[11]

The third leg of this triad supporting contemporary culture is the revolutionary change in the social, cultural and legal standing of marriage and the family. In the twenty-five years since the promulgation of *Humanæ vitæ*, the traditional laws regarding marriage and divorce, family support systems, the relationship between parents and children, and those of children born outside of marriage which had existed for centuries have been dismantled or radically rearranged. Abortion and no-fault divorce are the most obvious examples of this transformation, but, just as importantly, society during the last quarter century ceased to recognize marriage as an institution that conveyed a special status or one which was assumed for life. In doing so, courts and legislatures dismantled the complicated network of legal, economic and social supports which had maintained the institution of marriage and the family based upon it as unique institutions. Through new laws which facilitated divorce and blurred distinctions between marriage and cohabitation and those which stripped marriage of any special legal or economic benefits, society not only changed the expectations of couples regarding marriage, but they changed the institution of marriage itself.[12]

The old tradition, based for the most part upon Christian presumptions, was family oriented. By discouraging divorce and making it difficult to obtain the old system supported self-sacrifice, partnership and mutual investment in the marital community. But the new family law system is directed away from the family; it promotes self-sufficiency, self-interest and self-investment. The new system is no longer friendly to the family based upon marriage. It has shifted the legal and economic groundwork against the choice of marriage, childbearing and motherhood. Under the new assumptions, the woman who makes the choice for marriage and motherhood now does so at great risk.

One law school textbook in the United States describes the shift in family law in these terms: "Perceived as neither a sacrament nor a status necessarily assumed for life, the relationship contemplated by parties is not dissimilar from that of other long-term contracts, such as partnership, cotenancy, and sometimes employment." In short, according to the authors, contemporary marriage has become something akin to a speculative joint venture for profit.[13]

The new system has in effect a built-in dynamic for marital instability. Since under the new system the spouses' commitment to mutuality and the marital community is increasingly subordinated to self-interest, the "parties" tend to "invest" less in the marital community and hence derive less from it. The "joint venture" becomes increasingly "speculative" as its "profitability" diminishes.

Underlying this transformation in the legal treatment of marriage is a profound shift in society's attitude toward the purpose of marriage. The procreative end of marriage as constitutive of its mission has been abandoned. This transformation, premised as it is upon the availability of highly reliable contraceptives and abortion as socially and legally acceptable means of birth control, has radically altered the nature of marriage. It is not simply that couples now have for the first time the option to absolutely control their fertility.

Individuals under 40 years of age have lived their entire adult life within a legal and social environment premised upon the assumption that there need be no necessary link between human sexuality and the transmission of human life. To describe this phenomenon as merely a "contraceptive mentality" is simply no longer adequate: it presupposes as a referent a past disposition toward sexuality which views the creation of human life as its object and norm. But for many of childbearing age in our culture today, this attitude is not even a memory; it is completely non-experiential. Just as the change in divorce law changed the structure of marriage, the cultural acceptance of contraception and abortion as normative has changed our attitude regarding the nature of marriage.

These three influences—post-Modern, post-Christian, and post-family—have converged to form a contemporary culture now premised upon the conviction that Christian family life can no longer be lived and ought not to be attempted. This culture today judges that Christianity and its values are no longer normative in regard to the primacy of moral conscience, the integrity of human life and its transmission, and the permanence of married and family life.

It has been more than a decade since John Paul II called for a new evangelization of the Western Hemisphere. During this time, the Holy Father has maintained that the Church's mission to the family is central to its overall mission of evangelization. In order to facilitate this mission, he has implemented initiatives related to the family such as the World Synod of Bishops on the family (1980), the publication of *Familiaris consortio* and the *Charter of the Rights of the Family*, the establishment of the Pontifical Council for the Family and the Pontifical John Paul II Institute for Studies on Marriage and Family. Also, concern for the family can be seen in many of his magisterial pronouncements such as *Laborem exercens*, *Centisimus annus*, and most recently, *Veritatis splendor*, as well as the new *Catechism of the Catholic Church*. It is my thesis that for more than a decade the Holy Father has understood the critical cultural crisis outlined above and has sought to fashion around the call of a new evangelization a realistic response to it. Indeed, in *Redemptoris missio*, the Holy Father maintains "that the moment has come to commit all of the Church's energies to a new evangelization."[14]

As we begin the International Year of the Family, it is well to reflect on how John Paul II has prepared the Church to respond to the present crisis facing the Christian family. Indeed, for many Catholic families not much seems to have changed for the better. Some will suggest the reason must be attributed to the paralysis which has gripped family ministry because of the polarization and bitterness of the debate surrounding *Humanæ vitæ*. They quite reasonably ask how is it possible to heed the Holy Father's call to evangelize the family if one is unwilling or unable to discuss the Church's teaching regarding its principal object: cooperation in the transmission of human life. Another aspect of this problem may well be the failure to adequately confront the profoundly counter-cultural setting of the Catholic family in today's society.

The response of Catholics to this situation must take as its starting point the fact that the Christian vision of the human person is not merely one out of many differing world views or lifestyles. It is not simply another narrative of human existence, but it is the truth. It is a vision of the human person which penetrates his being to its very core and when disregarded in matters of morality, results in a self-contradiction which to varying degrees threatens human existence. Thus, *Familiaris consortio* begins with the recognition that marriage and the family are "willed by God in the very act of creation" and "are interiorly ordained to fulfillment in Christ" (n. 3). And it is for this reason, too, that John Paul II dedicated more than a third of his pontificate to so carefully preparing *Veritatis splendor* with its specific effort of recovering a distinctly Christian vision of the human person and of rebuilding confidence in the moral truth of Christian married love.

It is only by going back to God's creative act in bringing forth the gift of the family that families may attain both self-knowledge and self-realization. And as the husband and wife more fully realize their callings as "an intimate community of life and love" which is "ordained to fulfillment in Christ," they are called to safeguard their responsibility to each other and in the transmission of human life in a Christ-centered fashion.

As Hans Urs von Balthasar reminds us, "God does not show an abstract, theoretical, lifeless and 'dead' faithfulness toward man, concealing his divine truth in mere 'propositions' and 'laws,' but causes his truth to become real, pulsating life and flesh in terms of living history, so he cannot be satisfied with a 'dead' faith as man's response. He is the living God, 'bodily' present with and for man, and so he calls for an 'embodied' response: man, in the entirety of his existence as a hearer and answerer of the word."[15]

The calling to this encounter with the personal God of the Gospel within the heart of the family is central to the new evangelization. In order for the Christian family to become that "domestic Church" envisioned by the fathers of the Second Vatican Council, it must give "pulsating life and flesh" to the saving truths of married life "willed by God in the very act of creation." The new evangelical encounter demands the living witness of Christian families in whose lives the mystery of the Redemption is manifest.

But this task of a new evangelization is today impeded by several obstacles within the Church which are necessary to candidly face. One obstacle is the firestorm of criticism which met *Humanæ vitæ* immediately upon its release and the way in which many in the theological community have marginalized *Humanæ vitæ* since that time. It is not an exaggeration to say that upon its release the encyclical was subjected to the theological equivalent of the "Tet offensive." Like the Americans in Hue and other Vietnamese cities, the encyclical held the high ground and from a tactical standpoint must be considered successful. But from the standpoint of public opinion and the *psychology* of the public discourse, the encyclical, like the Americans, suffered a defeat from which it has been unable to recover. A generation of American leaders continue to be preoccupied with the so-called "Vietnam syndrome" which has made certain forms of foreign intervention virtually impossible.

Similarly, it would appear that many clergy suffer from an analogous type of syndrome regarding *Humanæ vitæ*. They remain simply incapable of returning to a discourse on contraception for fear of encountering again the sort of confrontations which they experienced during the 1960s and 1970s. Certainly there are priests who are committed to the teaching of the encyclical and who preach on it. But for many clergy and laity alike, *Humanæ vitæ* has become a codeword with such high negatives that it may be practically impossible for a majority of Catholics in an entire generation to engage in a fair discourse about it. This is a tragedy of unparalleled proportions for our generation as the prophetic quality of the encyclical is verified virtually each new day by the escalating casualties resulting from the contemporary family pathologies of which we are all too familiar.

Humanæ vitæ accomplished its primary purpose to confirm and preserve the saving teaching of the Church regarding the conjugal life of married persons. But its critics have guaranteed that its effectiveness as a means of evangelization of family life has been limited. The discourse that was possible upon the release of the encyclical but which was prevented by the firestorm fanned by its critics is sadly no longer possible. First, because many of those who initially argued for exceptions to the Church's teaching on contraception now question the existence of virtually all absolute moral norms, including those regarding abortion, sterilization and euthanasia. Second, the cultural setting of the family today is radically altered. Third, the intellectual discourse is radically changed.

Humanæ vitæ may be one of the last great magisterial documents addressed to the intellectual and cultural conditions of Modernity. Certainly every magisterial document engages its own historical context and, at the same time, rises beyond it to each succeeding generation. Yet the discourse of *Humanæ vitæ* presupposes a certain social consensus which no longer exists. That former consensus included a confidence in human reason to find moral truths, an appreciation of procreation as a good of marriage, and of marriage itself as a unique and stable institution. In short, the encyclical presupposed a certain cultural orientation toward marriage, family, and sexual morality which today no longer exists.

Instead of that consensus, there is the skepticism of postmodern philosophy in the capacity of reason, the cultural ascendancy of moral pluralism, and outside of certain Catholic institutions one hardly ever hears discussions of the "goods" of marriage—instead, the question is whether marriage itself is a "good." None of these contentions is entirely new, but what is new is their ascendancy and convergence to form a culture which is radically new and radically different from the culture which existed in 1968. These developments have been responded to in a profound way by John Paul II in *Veritatis splendor* and the new *Catechism*. And why is it that he stated recently that "the importance of *Humanæ vitæ* is grasped in all its breadth in the light of the recent encyclical *Veritatis splendor*."[16]

It is almost as if Western industrialized society listened to the message of *Humanæ vitæ* and chose to move as quickly as possible in the opposite direction. In the United States the marriage and family culture of the 1950s and early 1960s was rapidly dismantled in the 1970s. Gone as well are the specifically Christian moral values of the sanctity and equality of all human life. Today, the task of evangelization can take few cultural values for granted and must instead reach to the very foundation of contemporary culture. It is at this level that the Christian must fashion a response if the Church's mission of evangelization of the family is to be adequate. In a very real sense we are again like St. Paul at the Areopagus: there remain some common threads which permit a philosophical discourse at a certain level, but the encounter with the Gospel message of Jesus Christ must once again reach to the basic premises of our culture.

As *Veritatis splendor* and the *Catechism* make clear, the evangelization of family life must proceed from the understanding that the Christian family is above all a theological reality. The teaching of *Humanæ vitæ* must not be allowed to be marginalized or separated from the Church's response to the present crisis of family life. To be properly understood today, the mission of the Christian family and its service in the transmission of human life must be understood by families themselves as well as by those who are especially entrusted with their pastoral care within the framework of a comprehensive Christian vision of the human person and of personal communion. This is a framework which is constituted by the Christological and Trinitarian teaching of the Church, most recently put forward in *Veritatis splendor* and in the *Catechism*.

Indeed, it is precisely this Trinitarian vision of the human person and of personal communion which has been the focus of John Paul II's call for a new evangelization and it is this new discourse that offers the best hope for dealing with the dissent surrounding *Humanæ vitæ* and with the development of feminism within the Church. Although time does not permit a detailed examination of the question of feminism, several brief observations are nonetheless required.

At the outset, it should be admitted that two common responses to the feminist critique need to be abandoned. The first response finds itself uncomfortable with the conclusions and recommendations of feminists and attempts (unsuccessfully in my view) to counter the feminist agenda by denying the existence of any problem regarding the traditional understanding or treatment of women. The second response, because it finds itself in much agreement with the feminist description of the problem, feels itself obliged (unnecessarily in my view) to concur in the feminist agenda for change.

In beginning to chart a path out of this impasse, I would suggest that the classical view of the female based upon an Aristotelian understanding of "potency" and of the male based upon an Aristotelian understanding of "act" is no longer adequate. Moreover, since "act" is generally associated with "perfection" and "potency" with "imperfection," it becomes too easy to adopt a sort of reductionist view of the female/male relationship as one in which the "imperfect" female is brought to perfection by her association with the action of the "perfecting" male. The weight of this reductionist dynamic is made oppressive by the "technological" way of thinking that is so prevalent in today's culture—a way of thinking which views virtually all relationships as power relationships and which views the assumption of differing roles or tasks as stemming from basic inequalities of power.[17]

Instead, we begin with the Genesis account of the creation of humankind: "God said, 'Let us make man in our own image, in the likeness of ourselves... God created man in the image of himself, in the image of God he created him, male and female he created them" (Gen. 1:26). From this account it should be clear that the *imago Dei* presented here is of a unity of two in one. This unity of Adam as male and female points to "the fact that male and female are equal in their imaging of God. Neither sex is the image of God to the detriment of the other: it is humanity as male and female which embodies something of God in this world."[18]

Moreover, the unity between male and female in this *imago Dei* is an image of the Trinitarian God in whom generativity and receptivity cannot be viewed in terms of act and potency or superiority and inferiority. Thus, if the *imago Dei* is a Trinitarian imaging, then the complementarity of male and female human beings must be somehow analogous to "complementarity" within the Trinity itself. And if this is so then the complementarity of male and female cannot be reduced to categories such as act/potency, superiority/inferiority, and perfection/imperfection. To the contrary, the complementarity of male and female must be viewed as "integral, not fractional."[19] This means as well that the traditional view of complementarity, as one which essentially considers the female as existing in order to complement the male, must also now be abandoned as inadequate. Both male and female must be seen as complementary *of each other*, and it has been in this effort to restore the mutuality of complementarity that John Paul II has developed the term the "nuptial meaning of the body."

Created in the image of the Trinity, female receptivity may never properly be reduced to mere potency or imperfection since it mirrors in the most profound way the receptivity of the Son who emptied himself in order to do the will of the Father. To the contrary, female receptivity must be understood precisely as "act" and as "perfection" when we consider Mary's *fiat*. How is it possible to say that Mary's *fiat*, which is the supreme act of the human race, can in any meaningful sense be considered an imperfection? As John Paul II writes in *Redemptoris mater*: "Mary is totally dependent upon God and completely directed toward him, and, at the side of her Son, she is the most perfect image of freedom and of the liberation of humanity and of the universe."[20]

The effort to lay the foundation of this Trinitarian vision of the human person and communion, of the original unity of man and woman, and of the complementarity of male and female that John Paul II undertook in his weekly audiences between September, 1979, and January, 1983, commonly known as the "Wednesday Catechesis," holds out the possibility of a resolution of the feminist dilemma mentioned at the outset of this brief reflection.[21] Unfortunately, this effort, to which the Holy Father devoted over three years, continues to be virtually ignored in the United States. In a culture which increasingly exposes every person, but especially women, to oppressive, technological forms of manipulation, I would suggest that feminism has arisen as the dominant response to this situation precisely because of the vacuum created by the marginalization of the Church's saving message regarding married love as a communion of persons in mutual giving and receiving found in *Humanæ vitæ* and in the anthropological vision of John Paul II.

I have sought in the foregoing to show that a realistic catechesis on the family demands a realistic assessment of the extent of the cultural crisis confronting today's family. I have also sought to show that in responding to this challenge Pope John Paul II has opened a new theological and pastoral dialogue through his call for a new evangelization. The Holy Father has supported this new evangelical effort through his magisterial pronouncements and also through structural advances such as the World Synod of Bishops on the family, the establishment of the Pontifical Council of the Family and the Pontifical Council for Culture. It is fitting, therefore, that we consider briefly the adequacy of one structural response by the Church within the United States.

In 1990 and 1991, the National Conference of Catholic Bishops collected information regarding family ministry in the United States from over eighty percent of the dioceses in the United States (142 responses). Significant findings of the *1991 Annual Inventory of Diocesan Family Life Services* included: 25 dioceses report no family ministry office (this figure is independent of the 36 dioceses which did not respond to the survey); only 30 percent of family ministry offices report directly to the bishop; offices report an average of 2.8 full-time paid/2.3 part-time paid staff; the average budgets for all diocesan offices report a range from a low of $1,500 to a high of $760,000; one of five offices reporting had a budget of $50,000 or less; marriage preparation is the family life program to which most resources are devoted, and 87 percent of diocesan offices offer such services; while 79 percent of offices report offering services for natural family planning, NFP remains one of several areas to which the least resources are devoted; 31 percent of offices report "No," "Minimal," or only "Occasional" contact with any natural family planning group. As important as such structural indicators are, they are surpassed, of course, by other considerations such as theological competence and education.

In the new evangelization, the Holy Father has provided us two texts that are essential sources, the *Catechism of the Catholic Church* and *Veritatis splendor*. The question may be asked: In what way may these documents escape the difficulties which have affected *Humanæ vitæ*? I would suggest that the answer may be found in the documents' explicit Christocentricism. Both are clearly centered on the living presence of the person of Jesus Christ, and both identify the Christian life as one which flows from an encounter with the person of Christ. They reaffirm that the Christian faith has as its center and point of departure the acknowledgment of the living presence of Christ in the lives of his followers. The Christian life is not primarily a morality; it is not a philosophy; it is not a sociology; it is not a politics. Certainly, this was presupposed in the official teachings of the church prior to these documents; however, in many cases it was not sufficiently explicit. As a result, the Christian proposal has too often been subjected in our culture to a form of reductionism which has attempted to make it primarily a morality or a sociology or a philosophy or a politics. To the extent that this reductionism has succeeded within the Church, the Christian people give the impression of suffering a great absence. In the 1930s, Georges Bernanos already signaled this phenomena in *The Diary of a Country Priest*.

The new evangelization is only secondarily concerned with the repair and rebuilding of structures. Its first concern is making present the inhabitant of those structures. In that connection, we should not accept the view that the first chapter of *Veritatis splendor* is some kind of spiritual meditation in preparation of the substantive, moral analysis which follows. Rather than a pious meditation, the first chapter is profoundly important in that it clearly situates the moral reasoning of the church in the context of the personal encounter with Christ and dialogue with Him. As John Paul II reminds us in the encyclical's opening pages, our disposition must be as that of the rich young man who encounters Jesus and asks what he must do to inherit eternal life (Mt 19:16). It is clearly part of Matthew's theological plan that in his Gospel account this encounter occurs immediately after the discourse of Jesus on marriage and divorce and his admonition to suffer the little children and forbid them not for such is the kingdom of God.

The new *Catechism* exhibits this same characteristic. Because we still await an English translation of the *Catechism*, I can only briefly and in a general way refer to its teaching on the family which is primarily found in two sections: its discussion on the sacrament of matrimony and on the Fourth Commandment.

The *Catechism's* discussion of the sacrament of matrimony realistically acknowledges that in the context of our culture the Church's teaching on the indissolubility of marriage appears as an unrealizable demand. At the very least it is a teaching that causes perplexity and presents many with a seeming contradiction: the demand for marriage is felt to be built into our nature, yet at the same time it appears everywhere as something that cannot be sustained over time. As was mentioned concerning *Humanæ vitæ*, we can no longer take for granted that the appeal to reason or human nature traditionally made by the Church is persuasive in today's culture. That is why I believe the *Catechism* grounds the requirement of indissolubility and the possibility of living it on the following of Jesus Christ: "Having come to reestablish the initial order of creation disturbed by sin, He gives the strength and the grace to live marriage in the new dimension of grace. Following Christ, renouncing oneself, taking upon oneself His cross, the spouses will 'understand' the original sense of marriage and live it with the help of Christ. This grace of Christian marriage is the fruit of the Cross of Christ, source of all Christian life" (Para. 1615).

Family life is more specifically addressed as part of the *Catechism's* discussion of the Fourth Commandment, and here the Christian family is understood fundamentally as domestic church. The *Catechism* states, "The Christian family is a communion of persons, a reflection and image of the communion between the Father and the Son in the Holy Spirit. Its procreative and educative activity is the reflection of the creative work of God. The family is called to participate therefore in the prayer and sacrifice of Jesus Christ...the Christian family is evangelizing and missionizing" (Para. 2205). This evangelical calling of the Christian family pervades all aspects of its daily life. For example, even the parents' concern for teaching the Faith to their children is specifically called an act of evangelization and not merely imparting instruction (Para. 2225).

Finally, it is important that the *Catechism* makes clear that the claim which family bonds have upon us as Christian family is the realization of the life of the Church, which is the family of God in Christ. Outside that context, family bonds are secondary as Our

Lord clearly stated when he put love for Him and fulfilling the will of the Father above all family considerations. The *Catechism* cites Jesus saying, "Anyone who prefers father or mother to me is not worthy of me" (Mt. 1037), and "Anyone who does the will of my Father in heaven, he is my brother and sister and mother" (Mt. 12:50). As the *Catechism* states, "it is necessary to be convinced that the first vocation of the Christian is to follow Jesus Christ" (Para. 2232).

I imagine that there are not many programs of marriage preparation that include reflections on these two Gospel quotes (Mt. 10:37 and 12:49), yet they are both key requirements—especially in our times—for living the life of marriage and family in accordance with the teachings of the Church. These two sayings of Jesus show that any part of married life that is not incorporated into the life of the Church in Christ must be set aside. At all points the following of Jesus Christ has absolute priority. The reason for this, as the *Catechism* makes clear, is that nothing in Christian married life outside of Him makes sense (see Para. 2232, 2233). In today's culture, with its overwhelming bias against family life, nothing less is capable of sustaining the Christian's call to following the Church's teaching on the indissolubility of marriage and on the transmission of human life. The link between marriage and the person of Jesus Christ in the day-to-day reality of family life must be given concrete expression, and in this way the authentic meaning of the Catholic family may be realized through its incorporation into Christ, through whom the Father "has blessed us with all the spiritual blessings of heaven" (Eph. 1:3).

Notes

1. Joseph Ratzinger, *Introduction to Christianity* (San Francisco: Ignatius Press, 1990), p. 15.

2. Quoted in Henry De Lubac, *The Drama of Atheist Humanism* (Cleveland: World Publishing Co., 1950), p. 22.

3. This is a theme I developed more fully in my paper presented at the Ninth Bishops' workshop; see "The Church and Public Policy," in *The Twenty-Fifth Anniversary of Vatican II: A Look Back and A Look Ahead*, R. Smith ed., (Braintree, MA: Pope John XXIII Medical-Moral Research and Education Center, 1990), p. 263.

4. Paul Ricœur, *The Conflict of Interpretations: Essays in Hermeneutics* (1974), p. 148.

5. Jurgen Habermas, *The Philosophical Discourse of Modernity: Twelve Lectures*, trans. by Frederick Lawrence, (Cambridge: MIT Press, 1987) p. 84.

6. Carl Becker, *The Heavenly City of the Eighteenth-Century Philosophers* (New Haven: Yale University Press, 1932), pp. 30-31.

7. Friedrich Nietzsche, *On the Genealogy of Morals/Ecce Homo*, trans. by W. Kaufmann (New York, 1967), pp. 150, 152.

8. Johan Van der Vloet, "Faith and the Postmodern Challenge," *Communio*, (Summer, 1990), p. 133.

9. Gary Madison, "Coping with Nietzsche's Legacy: Rorty, Derrida, Gadamer," *Philosophy Today* (Spring, 1992), pp. 3, 5.

10. George Grant, *English-Speaking Justice*, (Notre Dame: University of Notre Dame Press, 1985), p. 16.

11. 112 S. Ct. 2791, 2807 (1992).

12. See, for example, Carl Anderson, "Symbol of the Eternal Covenant," in *In Search of a National Morality*, William Ball ed. (San Francisco: Ignatius Press, 1992), p. 144.

13. Walter O. Weyrauch and Sanford N. Katz, *American Family Law in Transition,* (Washington, D.C.: Bureau of National Affairs), p. 2.

14. No. 3.

15. Hans Urs von Balthasar, *Prayer,* (San Francisco: Ignatius Press, 1986), p. 36.

16. Address to the 25th Anniversary of *Humanæ vitæ* Congress, *L'Osservatore Romano*, English ed., (December 1, 1993), p. 1.

17. David Schindler, "Catholic Theology, Gender, and the Future of Western Civilization," *Communio* (Summer, 1993), p. 203.

18. Francis Martin, "Male and Female He Created Them: A Summary of the Teaching of Genesis Chapter One," *Communio* (Summer, 193), p. 255.

19. David Schindler, *op. cit.*, p. 223; see also Prudence Allen, "Integral Sex, Complementarity and the Theology of Communion," *Communio* (Winter, 1990), p. 521.

20. No 37.

21. John Paul II, "The Original Unity of Man and Woman: Catechesis on the Book of Genesis," trans. *L'Osservatore Romano*, English ed. (Boston: Daughters of St. Paul, 1931); John Paul II, "Blessed are the Pure in Heart: Catechesis on the Sermon on the Mount," trans. *L'Osservatore Romano*, English ed. (Boston: Daughters of St. Paul, 1983); John Paul II, "The Theology of Marriage and Celibacy: Catechesis on Marriage and Celibacy in the Light of the Resurrection of the Body," trans. *L'Osservatore Romano*, English ed. (Boston: Daughters of St. Paul, 1986).

Chapter 20

CREATIVE REALISM
IN ADULT CATECHESIS

The Reverend Monsignor Daniel N. DiNardo

The very fact of the new *Catechism of the Catholic Church* underscores the following words of the Holy Father in his 1979 Apostolic Exhortation, "Catechesi Tradendæ."

> To continue the series of receivers of catechesis, I cannot fail to emphasize now one of the most constant concerns of the synod fathers, a concern imposed with vigor and urgency by present experiences throughout the world: I am referring to the central problem of the catechesis of adults. This is the principal form of catechesis, because it is addressed to persons who have the greatest responsibilities and

the capacity to live the Christian message in its fully developed form…. Thus, for catechesis to be effective, it must be permanent.[1]

The new *Catechism* is addressed to Church leaders who have direct responsibility for catechetical formation. And the prime analogate for developing full, clear, consistent and integrated catechesis is the adult. At the beginning of Book Three of the *Catechism*, #1697-1698, there is a remarkable schema for summarizing a coherent teaching on the joys and demands of living the Christian life, on the meaning of grace, the Beatitudes, moral action and virtue, sin and forgiveness, and the commandments. This education presumes the presence of adults as both receivers and givers of Christian formation. Catechesis, in its many dimensions, cannot cease at the threshold of adulthood, of maturity.

Still, for many within and without the Church today, adult catechesis seems like an oxymoron. Catechesis is for children. Adults do not need it. Even in places where adult education might flourish, the catechetical dimension of this education is left undeveloped. The publication of the catechism allows us a significant moment in which we can reflect on permeating all forms of adult religious formation with catechetical content.

I am honored to be with you today to speak, in a very practical way, on the meaning of adult formation and catechesis in the faith and to share with you the efforts of one local Church to be both realistic and creative in establishing a forum for the catechesis of its adult members. Last April, at the NCEA convention in New Orleans, a speaker lamented a particular difficulty in the Church; he phrased it bluntly: "To put it simply, we are a church at risk, and a primary reason is that adult Catholics are simply not literate about their religion."[2] Last September, the Diocese of Pittsburgh published an Adult Formation Series, under the direction of Bishop Wuerl. Entitled "Exploring the Teaching of Christ," the program seeks not only to remedy some of that religious illiteracy, but to help adults embrace a way of life that is thoroughly centered on Christ. It is a fundamental formation for adult Catholics.

That there are many kinds of adult formation in the faith can be seen from the plethora of programs and courses listed in Catholic newspapers and publishing houses. Some of the formation deals with certain crucial phases of life such as the time before marriage or the baptism of a child. Some formation deals with preparation for certain ministries in the church such as catechist or family life counselor. Some formation deals with people engaged in special kinds of work or in specialized professions. Finally, some formation is based on a very particularized object of study, e.g., scripture or spirituality or social justice. The sheer multiplication of all these varieties of adult education and formation can be bewildering.

But all of the specialized forms of adult Catholic formation presuppose some basic understanding of the mystery of faith, of those things that Christ taught and entrusted to us all. The Church has repeatedly insisted upon this basic form of adult catechesis which helps adults grasp personally the whole central vision of faith that Christ taught and the whole way of life that teaching makes real.[3]

If adult fundamental formation is seen as a good, even an imperative, for growth in the Catholic faith, the adjective, the modifier, "adult," offers some real challenges. "Adult," first of all, is a positive word. Rather than implying a view of faith that is partial, selective or even cynical, adult implies a certain maturity. An adult Catholic is one who pursues an ever more intelligent insight into the gift of faith that God has given, a more serene desire to live out that insight, and a deepening gratitude for the gift. Adult reflection on faith is more self-conscious than that of children. The world thrusts many more problems at adults; the critical questions of others impel them to think more thoroughly. They have many experiences of life and can thus be more concentrated and alive in their study. In a catechetical context, adults cannot just be "led" to classes where the thoughts of others can drift awhile through their minds. Thoughtful and intelligent participation in class and discussion are essential so that adults can express what weighs on their minds and their own heartfelt convictions can be more and more illuminated by their own personal faith and the faith of the Church. An "adult formation" also implies an ability to seek for assistance where one experiences problems or where one is trying to see through popular rejections or misunderstandings of what the faith teaches.

The faith of an adult does not remain strong if it persists in immature and childish modes. Faith cannot remain simply "what people taught us when we were young." We need to take some deliberate hold of our faith and interiorize it. The role of prayer, the celebration of sacraments in a purposive manner, moral action and practicing social justice, all of these must play an integral and integrating role in fundamental adult formation and catechesis. Faith is always primarily belief in a person, in Jesus as Lord. But faith also believes the message Christ teaches. We believe what He teaches because we have found good and intelligent reasons for believing Him. The words of Peter as recorded in John 6:68-69 still hold true: "Lord, to whom can we go. You have the words of eternal life."

The meaning, then, of fundamental adult formation or catechesis might be summarized in light of the foregoing considerations by emphasizing three elements: an evangelical element, a catechetical element and a mystagogical one.

Under the heading *evangelical*, faith formation seeks to deepen our knowledge of the Gospel. No matter how weak or strong our faith is, we can always interiorize it more deeply and grasp with greater conviction the signs that make us recognize the Lord and the motives that persuade us to bring our "obedience" to the Gospel message. Though it fell on bad days right after Vatican II, and though it does not constitute the totality of what the evangelical element entails, especially personal witness, the role of apologetics in this phase of adult formation should not be overlooked, but integrated into the larger whole.

Under the heading *catechetical*, faith formation seeks to impart a literacy of the content of the faith. As we grow in personal closeness to the Lord, we naturally desire to know what he taught and realize in our lives the ways in which we must walk. This element of adult faith formation is crucial since it makes us mindful of what we believe. As opposed to a series of stunning incoherencies, catechesis is organic and systematic. As opposed to a mere collage of associations, catechesis shows the inner linkage of the mysteries of faith. As opposed to a smorgasbord, catechesis is complete, integral. As opposed to vague and imperceptive judgments, catechesis gives clear direction on moral life. The role that the *Catechism of the Catholic Church* will play in this element of adult faith formation is incalculably important.

Under the heading *mystagogical*, faith formation seeks to do more than simply produce well-informed people. Catechesis leads us deeper into the mystery of faith, into an abiding presence of life with Father, Son and Holy Spirit. This holiness of life leads us into deeper unity with one another. Steeped in this union by prayer and sacramental life, we engage in moral action and in the works of justice.

Since that outlook on fundamental adult formation or catechesis is so comprehensive, it can lead to an inevitable failure of nerve at the prospect of trying to establish such basic catechesis that will be neither uninteresting nor faddish, overly-detailed nor shallow. The key is realism, realism about time schedules, length of sessions, realism about the knowledge level of ordinary Catholics, realism about a growing desire by more and more people today to become closer to the Lord Jesus and be examples for their children, their families, even for acquaintances, indeed for the world.

If basic adult formation in the faith must be really "adult" in its outlook and realistic in its expectations, it must similarly be creative yet faithful in carrying out this work of catechesis. There are a number of adult renewal programs today that are excellent in their process and inventive in approach. They are also frequently one-sided, and the ecclesial dimension of the faith is truncated. Exploring the faith of the Church requires creativity and a freshness in outlook, plus a respect for adult ways of learning, but these cannot compromise or dilute the message of faith.[4]

The local Church of Pittsburgh, as previously mentioned, has recently inaugurated a practical response to these concerns. Our diocese has been going through a rather comprehensive reorganization and revitalization effort. The reorganization dimension is almost completed and has dealt with the restructuring of parishes and their administration. Along with this, the bishop has also seen the great need for revitalization. This dimension deals with everything from a Ministry Institute to Spiritual Life Committees in every parish. Given Bishop Wuerl's keen interest in and dedication to catechesis, already manifest in a weekly Sunday morning program on local television, both broadcast and cable, he became convinced that a fundamental catechetical formation for adult Catholics in the diocese was very necessary as part of Revitalization. Since he was already co-author of a major English catechism, *The Teaching of Christ*, he decided to use the text as a basis for what was to become "Exploring the Teaching of Christ: An Adult Faith Formation Video Series with Bishop Donald W. Wuerl."[5]

The program is a collaborative effort of the Secretariats of Communication and Education of the Diocese of Pittsburgh. As Chief Catechist of the Diocese, the Bishop's role is central in this endeavor. At the core of the program are 30 fifteen-minute videos each dealing with a chapter or chapters from the catechism, *The Teaching of Christ*. Though everyone in the Church shares the task of handing on the faith that Christ gave us, the successors of the apostles, in a primary way, have a responsibility and charism for teaching and witnessing to the faith. The core message is delivered, then, by the bishop, who, with simplicity and directness, gives the essential message. The increasing role and use of electronic media in catechesis is a fact. The real challenge is to use that media in such a way that it enhances and clarifies the message of faith. In the case of this program, the bishop is "present" in every session and provides its focus through his proclamation of Christ's teaching. At the same time, each video segment is short enough that it does not overwhelm participants or make them merely passive receptacles.

Though the program is built on the catechism, *The Teaching of Christ*, which is the basic text for all catechetical endeavors in the diocese, it is also built on the *Catechism of the Catholic Church*. We will look at that aspect in a few moments.

I would like to detail for you now some major aspects of the Exploring Program. It is in the work of each session that the catechetical and theological vision is instantiated along with the outlook of the Program on adult learning. For this reason, I will review and synthesize the process used in each Lesson.

The Table of Contents, enclosed with the packet of materials given to you, is printed at the beginning of both the Participant Book and the Leader Guide of this Program. These two booklets, along with the videos and the catechism, *The Teaching of Christ*, make up the basic materials needed for "Exploring the Teaching of Christ." The Diocese of Pittsburgh is grateful to Our Sunday Visitor Publishing Division for their assistance in realizing this initiative, for sage editorial suggestions, and for publishing and distributing it. As general moderator of the Program, I want to thank them for their great kindness and patience in helping the Diocese of Pittsburgh bring this program to fruition.

In the Table of Contents I just mentioned, you can get a glimpse of the overall structure and vision of the 30 sessions. Beginning with the invitation to faith, the sessions move through the Doctrines of Creation and Redemption, as proclaimed in the Creed, through an understanding of grace, moral life and moral action, the reality of sin, of conscience, i.e., the Commandments, and then to the significance of prayer and the celebration of sacramental life. The final session concerns the last things and the fulfillment of all. It is our hope that the program is clear, systematic and cohesive in exploring our faith, and though very basic, also complete in presenting the salvific teaching of Christ.

One of the major presuppositions of this Program is that the "catechetical moment" is the individual sessions of participants with their catechetical leader. Each session is structured in such a way that this moment will be realized for its importance. Thirty sessions are a long journey, but the program has been put together in such a way that individual sessions can be clustered together and thus allow for periodic breaks, if this is desired. The Introduction to the Leader Guide contains a section of timing and scheduling that should prove helpful to the variety of parishes and groups who participate in this Program.

Each session follows a similar pattern, as provided in the Participant Book, and, in enlarged fashion, in the Leader Guide. Printed at the beginning of each session is the Purpose of the Lesson, the points of the outline of the Lesson that will be discussed in the Video, important Scripture passages germane to the Lesson, and the corresponding pages in the Catechism, *The Teaching of Christ*. (Since the points of the outline of each Lesson are also character-generated on the video itself, the coordination of media is assured.)

Every Lesson, every session begins and ends with prayer. The Opening Prayer is always a formal Prayer Service using Prayer texts from the Roman Sacramentary and Lectionary, the Rites of the Sacraments, the Book of Blessings, and, in a number of cases, prayers from some of the Eastern Rites. It was thought important that the great riches of both East and West be utilized, particularly in Pittsburgh where there are so many Eastern Rite Christians. Further, we thought that music should play a role in the Opening Prayer; as suggestions we have drawn upon five currently available hymnals, including a Spanish Hymnal and the African American Catholic Hymnal, *Lead Me, Guide Me*. The Reading from Scripture plays a prominent role in the Opening Prayer; the text is always chosen from one of the suggested Scripture passages mentioned at the beginning of each Lesson. The exploration of the faith is not simply an intellectual act; it is also a prayerful one. The Leader is asked to allow participants to prepare and adapt the Opening Prayer. The Closing Prayer is purposely left open to spontaneous petition and praise, a spontaneous and creative action of shared prayer.

Scripture is a very important element in "Exploring the Teaching of Christ." It is proclaimed, quoted, and studied. Yet the Catholic view of Scripture is very much in the forefront; the Word of God is interpreted ecclesially, within the Church. The Program does not see personal and individualistic interpretations of the Scripture as final arbiters of faith. Since the purpose of these sessions is catechetical, the meaning of texts is seen within the framework of the whole Church's meditation on them and the authoritative interpretation of the Word through the Magisterium.

After the Prayer Service, the participants and leaders are asked first to reflect on the Scripture from that Service, on God's transcendent Word that addresses us and modifies us. We see this step as most crucial: before we tell our own stories, God's "story," God's Word comes to us. Only then are we to share our own stories relative to the Scripture passage and the purpose of the Lesson. Experiential modes of learning and sharing of personal stories play a significant role in helping us interiorize God's Word, a word that leads to deepening of faith. But since Catholic Christianity is revealed religion, the meaning of experience is itself broadened to include God's self-communication as the first word. It is true that this word tolls, sometimes silently, sometimes more clearly in our own word and stories. But the priority of revelation is the point behind the treatment of the Scripture story first.

The Prayer Service and the sharing of Scripture and personal stories then lead to the video presentation. It is our hope that by this point the minds and attitudes of the participants are focused enough so that the bishop's catechesis can be heard and reflected upon well.

Two movements follow upon the bishops' presentation. First there are a series of Discussion Questions, then a number of Life Experience Questions. The former elements are aimed at understanding the content presented in the video and corresponding chapter(s) of the *Catechism*. The latter are intended to help the participants develop a more personal understanding so as to move faith to action.

Let us first consider the Discussion Questions. Since their purpose is to "unpack" the content of the video and material in *The Teaching of Christ*, it was decided that a summary of each point raised by the bishop in his outline on the video would be provided in the Participant Book. Further, after each point of the outline heading, in brackets, there is provided the relevant paragraph or paragraphs form the *Catechism of the Catholic Church*. This is especially helpful for the Leaders in terms of their preparation for the Discussion Questions. It is also a very concrete way of cross-referencing the *Catechism of the Catholic Church* to the Program and allowing that Catechism to shed further light on the topic or themes being treated in each Lesson.

The Discussion should be assisted by the questions provided in the Participant Book. Leaders are also encouraged to use their judgment as to which questions might be raised. It would not at all be improper for participants to point out difficulties they feel with teaching that is being discussed. Finding help in overcoming problems in accepting the faith wholeheartedly is one of the aims of this Program. But the context is always one of shared faith, not debate or quarreling. The participants gather together so that each can help the other to gain deeper insight and appreciation for the faith. Leaders are reminded not to dominate discussion, but to help keep it on course and avoid triviality. At times it might seem more efficient to just have one person speak or lecture authoritatively. But shared discussion has a salutary effect in building up the Body of Christ.

The Life experience questions are to help both participants and leaders realize that the gift of faith is not only a saving message, but a way of living. Growth in the faith is not just growth in information, but in a maturity where faith penetrates the way we live, even the way we feel and judge—all in the light of Christ and the Gospel. Some of the Life Experience questions are challenging, even pointed. For adults growing in the faith, however, they are a natural development from hearing the message.

Before the final prayer, the Leader then briefly summarizes what has been explored so as to fix more sharply in memory what major points have been discussed. At this point, the participants are also reminded of the preparation and reading they are to do for the next session.

In the samples from Lesson Plans for both Participant Book and Leader Guide that have been provided in the packets you received, you can see how this worked out in print. It is hoped that the material is not only clear, succinct and helpful in discerning the message, but also, to quote the current jargon, "user friendly."

This rapid summary of the movement of each session can allow a glance at the aims and purpose of "Exploring the Teaching of Christ." It is a basic program. It seeks to present the faith in a straightforward way, with attention to orthodoxy of content and involvement by participants. Moments of prayer and reflection are balanced with periods of active engagement and discussion. The teaching role of the bishops is highlighted by the 30 videos of Bishop Wuerl on the content of faith. *The Catechism of the Catholic Church* is cross-referenced throughout the series. The Leader Guide provides some very practical assistance in citing relevant texts: from Bishop Wuerl's Catechism, from *The Catechism of the Catholic Church*, even bibliographical references to the Documents of Vatican II, recent papal encyclicals and liturgical sources. The program, finally, is permeated with the Word of God, with the Scriptures. The Program can be of great help in raising to a more conscious level for adults the ongoing need for basic catechesis.

The real measure of effective catechesis is the integration of faith and life. To know the one true God and the One He sent, Jesus Christ, is ultimately not a human work, but the activity of the Holy Spirit. What the Trinity can achieve in us is no doubt beyond all our methods and plans. Still, human action, particularly human action trying to make known the glory shining on the face of Christ, is very good indeed.

The Bishops of the early Church are still known for their astonishing ability to catechize with astuteness, practicality and love. One of the most famous, St. Augustine, once complained in a letter that the stench and rowdiness of his catechumens drove him out of his Cathedral Church in Hippo during one particularly hot day in August. The following Easter, however, he told the same group, now new Christians, to look upon the altar table to find out who they are: the Body of Christ. He rewarded them by preaching a whole series of homilies on the first Letter of John. Some today may claim that basic catechesis for adults is either unworkable or beside the point. Adults aren't interested. Our initial indications in Pittsburgh are that this point of view is not true. Wherever there are adult Catholics, there is the possibility of gathering them together; where they do share an interest, even a passion, to reflect on the teachings of Christ and the meaning of their Catholic faith, they will come. It is our hope that "Exploring the Teaching of Christ" is a modest contribution towards a greater knowledge and vigor in living out the faith of Jesus in love.

Notes

1. *Catechesi tradendae* (John Paul II), #43 (Boston: Daughters of St. Paul, 1979).

2. Marcel Dumestre, "Toward Effective Adult Religious Education," *Origins*, Vol. 23, No. 2, May 27, 1993, p. 24.

3. "Cat. Trad.," *op. cit.*, #20-21.

4. "Cat. Trad.," *op. cit.*, #46, #51 *Evangelii nuntiandi* (Paul VI), #45 (Boston: Daughters of St. Paul, 1976).

5. "Exploring the Teaching of Christ: An Adult Faith Formation Video Series with Bishop Donald W. Wuerl" (Huntington: Our Sunday Visitor Publishing Division, 1993).